Soviet Space Science

Soviet

Space Science

SECOND REVISED AND EXTENDED EDITION

by ARI SHTERNFELD
winner of the International
Prize for the Promotion of
Astronautics

WITH A FOREWORD AND EPILOGUE
BY WILLY LEY

■

translated by the Technical Doc-
uments Liaison Office, Wright
Patterson Air Force Base, Ohio

BASIC BOOKS, INC., PUBLISHERS, NEW YORK

First Printing, April, 1959
Second Printing, August, 1959

© 1959 Basic Books, Inc.
Manufactured in the United States of America
Library of Congress Catalog Card No. 59-8673
Designed by Alfred Manso

Foreword, by Willy Ley

■
■
■

This book is a survey of U.S.S.R. work, achievements, and plans for the future in the field of space flight. Written by a prominent Soviet space scientist, it was titled in Russian *Iskustvenniye Sputniki* ("Artificial Satellites"); the English translation has been prepared under the auspices of the United States Air Force. The Soviet writer's account carried the story through the launching of Sputniks I and II. I have added a short postscript briefly describing the two subsequent Russian rockets: Sputnik III and Metchta.

American readers of the book will be struck particularly by two things. In the first place, it is singularly free from the propaganda that is so characteristic of Soviet popular writing on practically every subject. The book is suffused, to be sure, with an understandable Soviet pride in the Russian accomplishments. But it avoids politics and confines itself to the science and technology of astronautics, with full recognition of the work being done in other countries, particularly the United States. (The United States satellites are omitted because the Russian book went to press before our first successful rocket, Explorer I, was launched into orbit on January 31, 1958.)

The second striking aspect of the book is the Russian author's easy familiarity with the rocket research and literature of the Western nations. But this should occasion no surprise, for Ari Shternfeld, the author, is no newcomer to the field of rocketry.

More than thirty years ago Robert Esnault-Pelterie of France, then a pioneer in aviation and later a pioneer also in rocketry, persuaded the Parisian banker André Hirsch to establish an annual prize of 5000 francs for the best contribution to the new science of "astronautics"—a word which Esnault-Pelterie himself coined. The first award of the "REP-Hirsch Prize for Astronautics," as it was called, went in 1928 to the German mathematician Hermann Oberth for his book *Wege zur Raumschiffahrt* ("The Road to Space Travel"). In 1930 it was awarded to the French engineer Pierre Montagne. In the years 1929, 1931, and 1932 the Committee found no work done that was deserving of the prize. But in 1933 and 1934 there were contributions which, though not worthy of the full prize, were deemed entitled to a *Prix d'Encouragement*. This award was given in 1933 for a paper by the Frenchman Louis Damblanc. In 1934 it went to a "Monsieur Ary J. Shternfeld" for a voluminous book manuscript entitled *Initiation a la Cosmonautique*. M. Shternfeld's manuscript was never printed in French—the language in which he had written it—but in 1937 it was published in Russian in the U.S.S.R. (to which Shternfeld presumably had transferred his home in the meantime).

Shternfeld's long practice in writing on astronautics in the intervening quarter century explains both his familiarity with the literature and the skill of his exposition in the present book. The fundamentals of astronautics are not easy to explain to uninitiated readers, but Shternfeld here does an excellent job, presenting a lucid account which is readily translatable from Russian to other languages. This no doubt is due to his linguistic versatility: he is completely at home in French as well as Russian and apparently has at least a fluent reading knowledge of German and English.

Shternfeld's book is a valuable contribution to the semi-popular literature of astronautics on several counts. On its own merits it stands as one of the best surveys of the subject published in any country. Besides this, American readers of course will find it especially interesting because it gives a comprehensive and detailed picture of what the Russians are thinking and reading (from the high-school level up) on the subject of space travel.

I have been strongly of the opinion for some time that the Russian people, even those who can read only Russian, have enjoyed, almost by default, a great and unnecessary advantage over Americans in this area of interest and knowledge. They have been given opportunities to be much better informed. Any Russian has been able to read in his own language translations of works by Hermann Oberth, by the Austrian Eugen Sanger, by Esnault-Pelterie and translations of books such as Kooy and Uytenbogaart's *Ballistics of the Future*, R. N. Wimpress' *Internal Ballistics of Solid Fuel Rockets*, George P. Sutton's *Rocket Propulsion Elements*, and the *Mathematical Theory of Rocket Flight* by Rosser, Newton, and Gross. On the other hand, Americans and Englishmen have not had such access to Russian books, simply because there were no translations. Thus while it was easy for the Russians to acquaint themselves with Western ideas and work in this field, the English-speaking peoples almost completely overlooked what the Russians were doing. The Russian rocket literature was largely unknown in the West.

Sputnik I proved not only the validity of Newton's laws but also the dangers of insularity. There is a lesson here for Americans, particularly for publishers. If we acquire the habit of paying more attention to Russian professional literature, future surprises will, at least, not be so surprising.

Preface to the First Soviet Edition

■
■
■

During recent years the term "artificial earth satellite," which had an unaccustomed ring and sounded like a science-fiction title, has been encountered with increasing frequency in the Soviet and foreign press. The artificial satellite, however, is no fantasy or daring dream, but a tangible achievement of the very near future.

Everyone of us is accustomed to see in the sky a natural satellite of the earth, the moon, which constantly revolves around our planet in one and the same orbit. Scientists and engineers of today have set themselves the task of creating a new artificial heavenly body, no matter how small, which, like the moon, will revolve around the earth. The achievements in the field of rocketry, remote radio control, physics, chemistry, and other sciences give the necessary substantiation for asserting that we are on the eve of the realization of this project.

As everyone knows from press reports, plans for launching small artificial satellites of the earth are being developed in the U.S.S.R. and the United States. Such satellites, several tens of centimeters in diameter, will revolve around the earth at an altitude of several hundred kilometers. It is planned to associate the launching of these satellites for scientific purposes with the International Geophysical Year (1957-1958), in which the Soviet Union will participate together with other countries.

The launching of artificial earth satellites will be the first step toward the realization of interplanetary flight.

People in many fields are interested in the subject of the creation of artificial satellites and interplanetary flight. Numerous reports before international congresses on astronautics held in recent years (astronautics, or cosmonautics, is the term applied to the science of flight in cosmic space) have been devoted to these questions. The study of the problems connected with the construction of artificial satellites occupies the center of interest of astronautical societies, which have been founded in more than twenty countries.

At the Academy of Sciences U.S.S.R., an interdepartmental commission has been organized to coordinate the research work in the field of interplanetary communications, in which scientists of widely varying specialties are now engaged. A medal in the name of K. E. Tsiolkovskiy has been created to encourage research in this field. Astronautical groups and circles have been organized at Moscow and other cities of the U.S.S.R. to study and work out questions on whose solution the future development of astronautics depends.

In this booklet we will describe the method of launching artificial satellites, their availability for scientific purposes and as interplanetary stations, and the expected conditions of life on such satellites.

ARI SHTERNFELD

Moscow, November 1956

Preface to the Second Soviet Edition

■
■
■

In the year that has passed since the publication of the first edition of this book, the dream has become reality. On October 4 and November 3, 1957, two artificial earth satellites were launched in the U.S.S.R. These magnificent achievements have cast a new light on our concepts in the field of astronautics and have brought nearer the solution of a number of its problems.

In this connection, the character of this book has been modified. The second edition has been considerably expanded and revised by comparison with the first edition. A chapter on artificial satellites of other bodies of the solar system has been added.

Within the scope of this book it has not been possible to discuss the entire complex of questions connected with artificial satellites. We have given major space to questions of celestial mechanics and rocketry, as the basic elements of the road toward realization of artificial satellites, and have relegated to secondary place questions such as remote control, radio communications, and physiology. This book presents not only a discussion of propositions already known but also results of the author's own research.

ARI SHTERNFELD

Moscow, November 1957

Introduction

■
■
■

Theoretical substantiations for the possibility of creating an artificial heavenly body to revolve around the earth appeared as far back as 1687, when the brilliant work by Isaac Newton, *Mathematical Principles of Natural Philosophy*, was published. In the eighteenth and nineteenth centuries, however, Newton's conclusions were taken merely as abstract arguments to facilitate the understanding of the laws of motion of heavenly bodies.

At the very beginning of the twentieth century, K. E. Tsiolkovskiy (1857-1935) expressed the idea of creating an artificial earth satellite (1895) when he proposed "setting up a permanent observatory, to revolve around the earth beyond the limits of the atmosphere, like its moon," for an indefinitely long time. Tsiolkovskiy's projects could not be realized during his lifetime: Conditions necessary for solving so complex a problem as the creation of an artificial satellite of the earth did not then exist. It has only been in our day, when science and technology have made immense strides forward in their development, that the solution of this problem has proved possible.

The birth in our country of the first artificial moon is not only a forward step in the development of human culture but actually a gigantic jump, a revolution in world science and technology, opening up a new era in the history of world science.

Man has succeeded before this in hurling various missiles over great distances. Despite the high velocities of these missiles, however, they always fell back on the earth. Now that the satellite has attained a velocity of about eight kilometers* a second, however, the range of its flight has suddenly jumped almost to infinity. A structure created by man has begun to revolve around our planet like a heavenly body, and, if it were not for the resistance of the atmospheric envelope of the earth which, despite the existing rarefaction, is still influential, this body would never stop.

With the launching of the second artificial earth satellite, carrying varied scientific instrumentation and an experimental animal, the possibilities of investigating the upper layers of the atmosphere and cosmic rays have been further expanded.

The program of scientific research connected with the receipt of data from the second satellite, laid out for a period of seven days, was successfully concluded. Valuable medico-biological data were obtained on the conditions of existence of living organisms during prolonged flights in space; on the intensity of solar radiation in the short-wave ultraviolet and X-ray regions of the spectrum; on the cosmic rays; on the propagation of radio waves; on the temperature inside the satellite, etc.

The fact that a living organism was able to function for a period of several days under conditions of weightlessness allows us to hope that man will also be able to survive a space journey.

Thus, thanks to the tireless work of Soviet citizens, two stages in the creation of artificial satellites of the earth were covered: the launching of an artificial heavenly body, and confirmation of the possibility of the flight of a living organism in cosmic space. This achievement, however, confronts us squarely with the realization of the next stage, namely, the building of artificial satellites of such dimensions that they can carry not only instruments but human beings as well.

For the construction and utilization of artificial earth satellites, the air envelope of our planet, the atmosphere, is not merely of theoretical but also of great practical interest.

* For the convenience of the reader, a table for the conversion of metric measurements into English units has been added. This can be found on page 350. —PUBLISHER'S NOTE.

The influence of the atmosphere on the motion of the satellite may be either favorable or unfavorable. Thus, during launching and also to a certain extent during motion of the satellite along its orbit, the retarding action of the atmosphere will be an obstacle to motion. On the other hand, on launching flying devices with a satellite, this retardation may be utilized as a favorable factor, not only saving an immense amount of fuel but also considerably simplifying the entire process of re-entry into the atmosphere. The unavoidable heating of a flying device in motion at very high speeds through the air, however, will necessarily lead to hazards. The example of meteoric bodies ("shooting stars"), which become heated to incandescence on penetration into the atmosphere, shows that the landing of a device with an artificial satellite on the earth is a complex problem. The composition and density of the air in the upper layers of the atmosphere is of decisive importance for the degree of heating of the device. For this reason, before discussing the questions relating to the launching and motion of artificial satellites, we will briefly direct the reader's attention to the aerial ocean surrounding us.

The following principal layers of the atmosphere are differentiated today: troposphere, stratosphere, ionosphere, and exosphere. Although the boundaries between these layers are not sharply defined, each of them is characterized by distinct physical features.

In the troposphere—i.e., the lowest layer of the atmosphere where almost all the water vapor is concentrated—all meteorological phenomena take place, especially the formation of clouds. Above the troposphere lies the transparent region of the stratosphere. Near the poles, the stratosphere begins at an altitude as low as 7-10 kilometers, and over the equator, at an altitude of 16-18 kilometers. The stratosphere extends to a height of about 80 kilometers. Beyond that level the ionosphere begins. Its upper boundary lies at about 900 kilometers altitude. The layers of the atmosphere still higher than that are called the exosphere. The exosphere gradually vanishes with increasing altitude. Its upper boundary, located at the approximate altitude of 1200 kilometers, is assumed as the boundary or top of the atmosphere. Beyond the exosphere begins interplanetary space, in which the medium no longer exerts any resistance to the motion of a flying device.

The troposphere and stratosphere show particularly sharp differences with respect to thermal conditions. In the troposphere, the temperature of the air decreases with altitude by about 6° C., on the average, for each kilometer of ascent. In the ascending currents, expansion of the air causes a drop in its temperature, while in the descending currents, compression of the air produces heating.

The stratosphere, in its lowest portion extending to an altitude of about 30 kilometers, has an almost constant temperature which is equal, on the average, to −56° C. Beginning at a height of about 30 kilometers, however, the temperature in the stratosphere gradually rises and, at an altitude of 55 kilometers, somewhat exceeds +30° C. This increase in temperature can obviously be explained by the fact that at these altitudes the oxygen, being converted into ozone, retains the greater portion of the solar rays. At an altitude of 80-85 kilometers, the temperature again drops to about −120° C. (V. V. Mishnevich, U.S.S.R.) and then, already in the ionosphere, again begins to rise. From certain observations which will need further confirmation, the temperature at an altitude of 200 kilometers is about +400° C., at an altitude of 300 kilometers it reaches +800° C. and continues thereafter to increase with altitude.

Systematic soundings of the atmosphere show sharp temperature fluctuations during the course of the day at great altitudes. Thus, at an altitude of 12-16 kilometers the temperature fluctuations may be as much as 30° C. At an altitude of 40 kilometers, air-temperature fluctuation over a range of 40° C. during the course of a day has been recorded in one case. In the uppermost layers of the atmosphere, diurnal temperature fluctuations of the order of several hundred degrees have been recorded. As for the density of the air, at an altitude of 10 kilometers the density is one third of its value at the surface of the earth, at an altitude of 20 kilometers, a fourteenth, and at an altitude of 60 kilometers, a thousandth.

It is considered today that the density of the air at an altitude of about 480 kilometers is 0.000,000,000,000,001 gram per cubic centimeter. Thus, one cubic kilometer of air at this altitude weighs only one gram. If the entire atmosphere of the earth could be compressed to yield a uniform pressure of one kilogram per square centimeter, then the layers of atmosphere now below 208 kilometers would have an altitude of only 8 kilometers, and the entire mass of the air now

■ TABLE 1

Characteristics of the Atmosphere (According to Hagen)

Altitude, in Kilometers	Atmospheric Pressure, in Millibars*	Number of Molecules in a Cubic Centimeter	Altitude, in Kilometers	Atmospheric Pressure, in Millibars*	Number of Molecules in a Cubic Centimeter
0	1,013	2.56×10^{19}	100	3.7×10^{-3}	2.68×10^{13}
10	252	8.53×10^{18}	200	1.06×10^{-5}	1.12×10^{11}
20	56.8	1.84×10^{18}	300	4.84×10^{-7}	3.21×10^{9}
30	12.0	3.75×10^{17}	500	4.06×10^{-8}	1.56×10^{7}
50	1.00	1.92×10^{16}	700	1.16×10^{-8}	3.39×10^{7}
70	0.14	2.22×10^{15}	1000	2.41×10^{-9}	7.03×10^{6}

* One millibar constitutes the pressure of 1.019 grams on one square centimeter. This is a thousandth of the pressure of the atmosphere on one square centimeter of surface at sea level, at the latitude of 45° and a temperature of 0° C.

located above 208 kilometers would be compressed into a layer only 1/400 of a millimeter thick (Hagen, United States).

Table 1 gives a few characteristics of the atmosphere.

Obviously, the number of molecules in one cubic centimeter of space at an altitude of 100 kilometers is about three trillion times smaller than it would be at sea level.

The ratio of the constituents of the air in the lower layers of the atmosphere is generally constant, owing to the continuous mixing of the air. In particular, the troposphere contains, by volume: nitrogen, 78.06 per cent; oxygen, 20.90 percent; argon, 0.94 per cent; other gases, 0.1 per cent. This is the composition of dry air. The lower layers of air contain up to 4 volume per cent of water vapor. In summer, the quantity of water vapor is considerably greater than in winter. With altitude, the humidity decreases gradually and disappears completely at an altitude of 10-11 kilometers. The inert gases, neon, krypton, and xenon, in view of their high atomic weight, do not rise to great heights. At the upper boundaries of the troposphere, even traces of these gases disappear.

In the stratosphere, at an altitude of 17 kilometers, according to the United States Naval Research Laboratory, a strong concentration of ozone is noted which reaches a maximum at an altitude of 25 kilometers. Above 30 kilometers, the concentration of ozone decreases sharply and drops to zero at 48 kilometers altitude.

As for argon, the quantity of argon at an altitude of 85-95 kilometers is smaller than at the surface of the earth (B. A. Mitrov, U.S.S.R.).

Above 60 kilometers, positive and negative ions have been found, and above 70 kilometers, free electrons.

The composition of the ionosphere at greater altitudes apparently differs somewhat from the composition of the lower layers of the atmosphere and varies with altitude.

Besides molecular and atomic oxygen (cf. later in text) and nitrogen, the exosphere probably contains ionized atoms of sodium, calcium, and hydrogen.

Contents

■

■

■

Soviet Space Science

1

The Laws of Motion
of Artificial Satellites

■
■
■

■ Principle of Motion and Speed of an Artificial Satellite

Circular Orbit

We apply the term artificial satellite of the earth to an artificially created heavenly body revolving around the earth only under the action of the earth's gravitation, i.e., without any propulsive unit. The question arises: How does the artificial satellite remain in place? Why does it not fall onto the earth?

The artificial satellite has no support and still does not fall back to the earth, exactly as the moon does not fall on the surface of the earth, despite the fact that the moon, too, is not supported by anything and that it is constantly subject to the earth's gravitation.

Let us define the reason for this phenomenon. Imagine that from the summit of a high mountain a body is hurled at a certain initial velocity, in the horizontal direction. If it were not for the force of gravitation of the earth and the resistance of the air, this body, due to inertia, would move in straight-line and uniform motion and would gradually increase its distance from the surface of the earth. The force of gravity, however, forces the body simultaneously to fall along the arc of an ellipse back toward the earth. As a result, the path of the body is curved. At low initial velocities, the velocity of fall of the body will be greater than the velocity of departure from the earth, as a result of which the body will gradually approach the earth. At a certain entirely definite initial velocity, the body, due to its inertia, will travel away from the surface of the earth, during each minute or second, exactly as much as it approaches the earth as a result of its fall. For this reason, the body on continuing its motion will always remain at one and the same altitude above the earth's surface, i.e., it will move around the earth in a circle whose center coincides with the center of the earth.

The above considerations are illustrated in Figure 1.

■ FIG. 1.—Trajectory of a Body Thrown in a Horizontal Direction.

It will be seen that a horizontally thrown body will move along the arc of an ellipse (E_1, E_2, E_3, E_4) having one focus at the center of the earth (O) and the other (O_1, O_2, O_3, O_4) close to the point from which it is thrown. As the initial velocity increases, the dimensions of the ellipse increase and the second focus of the ellipse aproaches the center of the earth. At some determinate initial velocity, the second focus will likewise coincide with the center of our planet, and the ellipse will be transformed into a circle; motion along this circle will proceed at constant velocity equal to the initial velocity.

The velocity of flight at which the motion of the body along a circle above the surface of the earth begins is called the circular velocity, or first astronautical velocity. At the surface of the earth, at

■ **TABLE 2**

Relation between Circular Velocity and Sidereal Period of Revolution of Artificial Earth Satellites and the Altitude of Flight

Altitude of Flight, in Kilometers	Circular Velocity, in Meters Per Second	Circular Velocity in Per Cent of Circular Velocity of Zero Satellite*	Sidereal Period of Revolution			Sidereal Period, in Per Cent of Period of Revolution of Zero Satellite
			Hrs.	Min.	Sec.	
0	7912	100.00	1	24	25	100.0
200	7791	97.47	1	28	25	104.7
300	7732	97.72	1	30	27	107.1
400	7675	97.00	1	32	29	109.6
500	7619	96.30	1	34	32	112.0
1000	7356	92.97	1	45	2	124.4
2000	6903	87.25	2	7	9	150.6
3000	6525	87.47	2	30	31	178.3
4000	6203	78.40	2	55	17	207.6
5000	5924	74.87	3	21	12	238.3
6000	5679	71.77	3	48	18	270.4
6378	5595	70.71	3	58	47	282.8
7000	5463	69.05	4	16	31	303.8

* In connection with the fact that the earth is oblate, some authors base their calculations of the circular velocity on the mean radius of the earth. This is incorrect since (even if we neglect the resistance of the air) an artificial satellite cannot move in a circle with such a radius. The minimum orbit of a satellite is a circle equal to the equatorial. In this book, therefore, we will usually take the radius of the earth to mean its equatorial radius, which is equal to 6,378 kilometers, and will take the altitude of flight to mean the altitude of flight above the equator.

a height of zero above the equator, this velocity is equal to 7912 meters per second and is called the zero circular velocity. Below, we will denote the corresponding orbit of an artificial satellite as the zero orbit, and a satellite flying at zero altitude above the equator as a zero artificial satellite.[1] With increasing altitude, the circular velocity at first decreases sharply and then continues to decrease more slowly. At an altitude of 200 kilometers, this velocity is 7791 meters per second, and

[1] This case is only of theoretical interest.

at an altitude of 2000 kilometers, it is 6903 meters per second (cf. Table 2).[2]

A different reason why a body does not fall on the earth at circular velocity can also be given.

It is well known that a centrifugal force arises on motion in a circle. This force is the greater, the greater the velocity of motion (it is proportional to the square of the velocity). For a pedestrian moving on a level road along an arc of a great circle,[3] the centrifugal force will amount to one milligram. For a man running, this force increases by a factor of several tens, and for an aircraft flying at a record speed of the order of 2800 kilometers per hour it reaches one per cent of the weight of the aircraft. For the circular velocity of flight, the centrifugal force becomes equal to the force of the earth's attraction and, as it were, eliminates the action of this force from the flying body (by this we do not mean, of course, that the force of gravitation disappears, but that it is completely compensated by the centrifugal force in the opposite direction). A body possessing such a velocity will fly around our planet in a certain orbit and will again travel in its next flight along the same orbit; in airless space its velocity will remain constant. The body will be transformed into an artificial satellite of the earth.

An artificial satellite, in contrast to an aircraft, cannot fly above the earth along a desired route. It is impossible, for instance, to force an artificial satellite to fly along the tropics, or along the polar circles; it is impossible to compel a satellite to fly along a broken line; it is impossible substantially to shorten or lengthen the time of flight of a satellite from one city to another, etc. An artificial satellite can only move on circular or elliptical orbits. Moreover, like a body thrown at an angle to the horizon, it can move only in a plane passing through the center of the earth (Figure 2), i.e., in a plane of a great circle. It is precisely for this reason that an artificial satellite cannot move along any parallel of the earth, the only exception being the equator, or zero parallel of latitude. We emphasize that the plane of the orbit of an artificial satellite remains fixed with respect to the celestial vault (disregarding the perturbations of the orbit). This must be kept in mind in reading the rest of this book.

[2] In this book, all calculation results (in particular the tables), unless otherwise stated, are those of the author.

[3] A great circle is a circle formed on a section of the earth by any plane passing through the center of the earth.

■ FIG. 2.—An Artificial Satellite Can Move Only in a Plane Passing Through the Center of the Earth.

We emphasize a second important peculiarity of the motion of an artificial satellite; an orbit corresponding to the circular velocity at the earth's surface (or to a greater velocity than the circular) can be obtained only in the case where the necessary initial velocity is imparted in a horizontal direction, since, when the satellite is launched at an angle to the horizon, part of its path would necessarily pass within the earth (Figure 3). We note that, owing to the flattening of the earth, a circular orbit passing above the pole will actually be somewhat flattened (but will not be strictly elliptical). Whereas for the earth, however, the value of the oblateness[4] amounts to about 1/300, the flattening of the orbit of an artificial satellite will be less than a tenth of this value. In our further considerations, we will neglect the slight flattening of the orbit of the satellite, due to the oblateness of the earth.

An artificial satellite provided with a rocket engine which can be connected at intervals or which operates continuously will be called an engined artificial satellite. Such a device is capable of flying at any altitude, especially at altitudes where the air is too rarefied for the wings of an aircraft but is too dense for an engineless artificial satellite (for instance, at an altitude of 50-150 kilometers). During motion of such a device (at low altitudes) the engine must be turned on to overcome the resistance of the air. The fuel consumption in this case will be greater, the lower the altitude of flight.[5] In airless space, the engine

[4] The difference of the equatorial radius (a) and the polar radius (b) divided by the equatorial radius is called the oblateness of the earth, i.e., the quantity $\dfrac{a-b}{a}$.

[5] Some authors term such a flying device a satelloid. In our opinion this term is more suitable for an artificial satellite in general.

of such a satellite will not serve to overcome the insignificant resistance of the air but to correct the trajectory of flight.

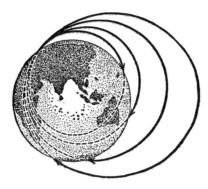

FIG. 3.—Launching of an Artificial Satellite in a Single Impetus from the Surface of the Earth Is Possible Only When This Push Takes Place in the Horizontal Direction.

We note in conclusion that artificial satellites cannot revolve at too great a distance from the earth, since the gravitational fields of the sun, the moon, the planets, and of their own satellites would exert a marked influence on the satellite. It may be considered in practice that a satellite, moving near the earth, is subject only to the force of gravitation of our own planet, while the gravitation of the sun exerts only a negligible influence. In fact, the distance of such a satellite from the sun can be considered as practically equal to the distance of the earth from the sun. For this reason, the sun has almost the same effect on the satellite as it has on the earth, i.e., it imparts to it approximately the same acceleration and velocity or, in other words, hardly interferes in the motion of the satellite around the earth. If the satellite is at a distance from the earth at which all above statements are valid, we can say that the satellite is within the sphere of gravitation of the earth. The radius of the sphere of gravitation of the earth is estimated by astronomers at 0.006 of the distance between earth and sun, i.e., 900,000 kilometers. This is 2.5 times as great as the maximum distance of the moon from the earth (apogee distance). Artificial satellites, however, will not be built for such great distances since, under these conditions, they would prove useless both for studies of the earth and as interplanetary stations.

Elliptical Orbits

The first artificial satellites will fly around the earth on an ellipse differing only slightly from a circular orbit, at an altitude from several hundred to two thousand kilometers.

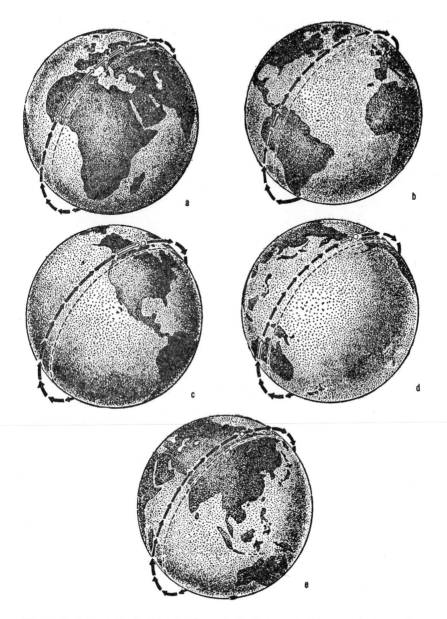

■ FIG. 4.—Orbit of First Artificial Satellite at the Beginning of Its Existence. (a)—the satellite at the instant of flying above Moscow. (b)—the earth with the satellite, after three full revolutions during a period equal to 1/5 of a sidereal day. During this time, the earth rotated easterly about its axis by 72°. Here the satellite crosses the Moscow parallel of latitude, 72° west of our capital (over the Atlantic Ocean). (c), (d), and (e)—the mutual position of the earth and the satellite after the same intervals of time as in the preceding case. After three rotations of the satellite, the position (a) would be repeated.

The launching of artificial satellites on elliptical instead of circular orbits is explained by the following circumstance: A circular orbit can be attained only at a strictly determinate velocity, directed horizontally. Present-day rockets and instruments, however, cannot provide such an ideal accuracy. Owing to unavoidable errors in the velocity and in the direction of launching, it may happen, immediately after take-off, that the satellite begins to approach the earth's surface, which may lead to its destruction. For this reason, preference is given to launching an artificial satellite on an elliptical orbit, giving it an initial horizontal velocity greater than the local circular velocity.

It was with this in mind that the first Soviet artificial satellites were launched. The first artificial satellite had its perigee[6] in the northern hemisphere, and its apogee in the southern hemisphere at an altitude of about 900 kilometers (Figure 4). The second satellite had its apogee at the altitude of about 1700 kilometers.

The orbits of both satellites represent ellipses with an inconsiderable flattening: the difference in the length of the major and minor axis of its orbit amounts only to fractions of one per cent. These orbits form almost circles, with their centers slightly displaced relative to the center of the earth.

In the future, satellites will be given increasingly higher velocities, so that they will move along elliptical orbits that are ever more elongated; however, in each orbit one of the foci will coincide with the center of the earth (Figure 5). The perigee distance of the elliptical orbits will at first remain of the order of several hundred kilometers, while the apogee distance will gradually increase.

Although at first it will be very difficult to raise the "ceiling" (apogee) of an artificial satellite, as the power of the rockets is increased it will become easier to solve this problem. In fact, the increasing initial velocity of the rocket at the earth's surface (for instance, from 7.9 to 10 kilometers per second) will raise the "ceiling" of the satellite by three equatorial earth radii, while the further increase in this velocity by one kilometer a second will mean a raising of the "ceiling" by 25 earth radii (Figure 5). Thus, at a velocity at 11 kilometers per second, the rocket will fly to half the distance between the earth

[6] We recall that the point of the lunar orbit closest to the earth is called perigee (and the corresponding distance, the perigee distance), and the most distant point is the apogee (and the corresponding distance, the apogee distance). Below, we will apply these terms, by analogy, to the orbits of artificial satellites.

■ FIG. 11.—Soviet Rocket (Photographed on Red Square November 7, 1957).

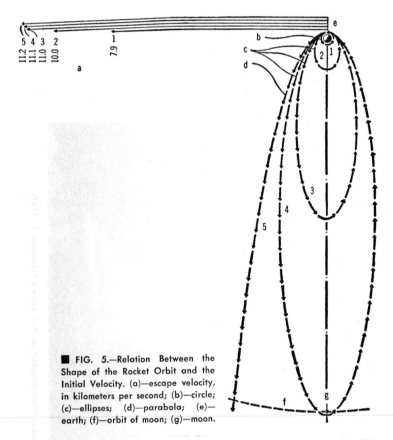

5 4 3 2   1
11.2 11.1 11.0 10.0   7.9
a

b
c
d
e

2 1

3
4
5

f   g

■ FIG. 5.—Relation Between the Shape of the Rocket Orbit and the Initial Velocity. (a)—escape velocity, in kilometers per second; (b)—circle; (c)—ellipses; (d)—parabola; (e)—earth; (f)—orbit of moon; (g)—moon.

and the moon, while still remaining, as before, an artificial satellite of the earth.

Another question is the manner in which the artificial satellites move along their elliptical orbits.

The laws of motion of the planets around the sun, discovered by Johannes Kepler, are applicable to the motion of satellites around the planets. In accordance with the first law of Kepler, one of the foci of the ellipse on which an artificial satellite of the earth moves must coincide with the center of the earth; the second focus, as follows from geometric relationships, will be located at the same distance from the apogee of the satellite orbit as the center of the earth from its perigee.

According to the second law of Kepler, the radius vector[7] of a

---

[7] The radius vector is the segment of a straight line joining the satellite with the center of the earth (or of the other heavenly body about which the satellite revolves).

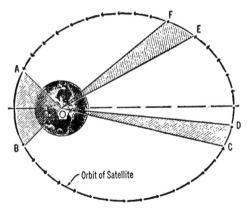

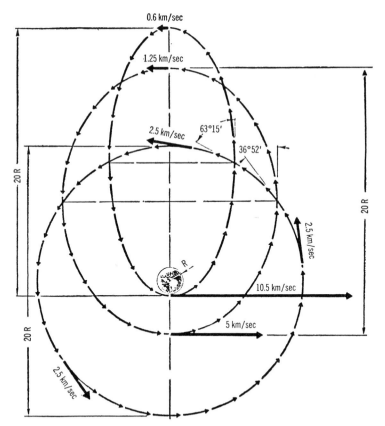

FIG. 6.—The Velocity of Motion of a Satellite along an Ellipse is Determined by the Second Law of Kepler. The hatched areas ABO, CDO, and EFO are equal. The satellite describes the arcs AB, CD, and EF in equal times.

FIG. 7.—The Periods of Revolution of Artificial Satellites along Each of the Orbits Shown Are Equal, since the Major Axes of These Orbits Are Equal, while the Size of the Minor Axis Has No Influence on the Period of Revolution.

satellite will sweep equal areas in equal intervals of time (Figure 6). This law, which is called the law of areas, makes it possible to calculate the variation in the velocity of the satellite over its entire path. At great distances from the attracting body (the earth), the velocity of the satellite will be lower than near the body.

According to the third law of Kepler, the squares of the periods of revolution of satellites around the earth are proportional to the cubes of the major semiaxes of their orbits, i.e., the periods of revolution of satellites along ellipses are determined by the same relations as the periods of revolution along circular orbits, provided the radii of the circles are replaced by the major semiaxes of the elliptical orbits. Consequently, if the major axis of an elliptical satellite orbit is equal to the diameter of the circular orbit of a different satellite, then the period of revolution of the two satellites around the earth will be equal (Figure 7).

The length of the minor axis of the ellipse has no influence on the period of revolution of the satellite and affects only the velocity of motion of the satellite along its orbit. In fact, according to the laws of celestial mechanics, if satellites move at one and the same velocity at a certain distance from the center of a planet, then, regardless of the direction of their motion, the major semiaxes of their orbits must be equal. The shorter the axis of the ellipse, however (at a constant major axis), i.e., the more the ellipse is flattened, the shorter will be its length. Since the period of revolution for equal major axes is equal, it follows that the more flattened the orbit, the smaller will be the mean velocity of orbital motion of the satellite.

It is also interesting to note that the shorter the minor axis (for a given major axis), i.e., the greater the value of the so-called eccentricity of the ellipse,[8] the more rapidly will the satellite move in perigee and the more slowly in apogee. These extreme velocities of the artificial satellite are correlated by a very simple relation. More specifically, it follows from the second law of Kepler that the velocity of the satellite at apogee is as many times smaller than its velocity at perigee as the apogee distance is greater than the perigree distance, i.e., the very same relation is involved here as between the values of the forces and arms in the lever principle, so well known in mechanics (Figure 8).

When a satellite moves in an elliptical orbit, its velocity will some-

[8] The eccentricity of an ellipse is the ratio of the distance between the foci of the ellipse and the length of the major axis.

times be greater than the velocity that it would have if it were moving in a circle with a diameter equal to the major axis of the ellipse, and will some times be smaller than that velocity. If the ellipse is divided into two parts by its minor axis, then the velocity of the satellite will be greater than the corresponding circular velocity when it is moving on the half of the ellipse closest to the earth (the portion of the ellipse inside the circle, cf. Figure 7), and smaller than that corresponding velocity when it is moving on the other half (outside the circle). Finally, the velocity of the satellite at the times of passage through the ends of the minor axis of the ellipse (points of intersection of the ellipse with the circle) is equal to the circular velocity.

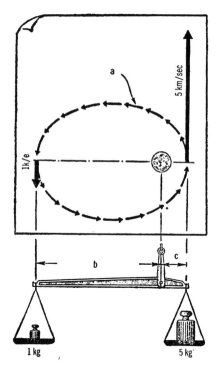

■ FIG. 8.—Analogy Between Laws of Motion of a Satellite in Orbit and the Principle of the Lever. (a)—orbit of artificial satellite; (b)—5 units of length; (c)—1 unit of length.

Table 3 gives certain characteristics of the elliptical orbits of artificial satellites. The perigee of all orbits is assumed to be located directly on the surface of the earth over the equator, and the resistance of the air is assumed to be absent. For comparison, the characteristics of the zero circular orbit are also given.

■ **TABLE 3**

Some Characteristics of Elliptical Orbits of Artificial Satellites with the Perigee at the Earth's Surface

Distance of Apogee from Center of the Earth, in Earth Radii	Length of Major Semiaxis of Ellipse, in Earth Radii	Velocity at Perigee in Kilometers Per Second	Ratio of Velocity at Perigee to Zero Circular Velocity, in Per Cent	Distance of Apogee from Center of the Earth, in Earth Radii	Length of Major Semiaxis of Ellipse, in Earth Radii	Velocity at Perigee in Kilometers Per Second	Ratio of Velocity at Perigee to Zero Circular Velocity, in Per Cent
1.0	1.00	7.912	100.0	20	4.47	10.919	138.0
1.2	1.10	8.264	104.4	25	5.00	10.972	138.7
1.5	1.22	8.667	109.5	30	5.48	11.007	139.1
2	1.41	9.136	115.5	40	6.32	11.052	139.7
3	1.73	9.690	122.5	50	7.07	11.079	140.0
5	2.24	10.214	129.1	60	7.75	11.097	140.3
10	3.16	10.668	134.8	70	8.37	11.110	140.4
15	3.87	10.834	136.9	100	10.00	11.134	140.7

■ **Maximum Velocities of Motion of an Artificial Satellite**

Are any desired velocities of motion possible for artificial satellites?

Imagine an artificial satellite traveling along a zero circular orbit. If, in perigee, the satellite develops a so-called parabolic velocity equal to 11.2 kilometers per second, i.e., 41.42 per cent greater than the zero circular velocity, then it will escape from the earth's gravitational field and will leave it along the branch of a parabola, with a focus at the center of the earth (curve 5, Figure 5), and will consequently cease to be a satellite. For each distance from the center of the earth there is a certain maximum velocity at which a body still remains in the field of the earth's gravitation.

On the other hand, there is also a lower limit to the velocity of a satellite at a given point in space. In fact, if the velocity of a satellite moving along a circular orbit is decreased, then it will begin to move along an ellipse located inside the original orbit. The more we retard the motion of the satellite, i.e., the smaller its velocity at the instant when it passes from a circular orbit into the elliptical orbit, the shorter will be its perigee distance. At a definite initial velocity of motion along its new elliptical orbit, the satellite will touch the earth's surface. It is this velocity (i.e., the velocity of the satellite at the apogee of its elliptical orbit) that may be considered the minimum permissible velocity for an artificial satellite since, at a lower velocity, the satellite will crash into the earth.[9]

■ **TABLE 4**

Extreme Velocities of Artificial Satellites at Different Altitudes

Distance from Center of Earth, in Equatorial Radii of the Earth	Minimum Velocity, in Kilometers Per Second	Ratio of Minimum Velocity to Zero Circular Velocity, in Per Cent	Circular Velocity, in Kilometers Per Second	Maximum Velocity, in Kilometers Per Second	Ratio of Maximum Velocity to Zero Circular Velocity, in Per Cent
1	7.912	100.00	7.912	11.189	100.00
1.5	5.778	73.03	6.460	9.136	81.65
2	4.568	57.73	5.595	7.912	70.71
3	3.230	40.82	4.568	6.460	57.73
4	2.502	31.62	3.956	5.595	50.00
5	2.043	25.82	3.538	5.004	44.72
10	1.067	13.48	2.502	3.538	31.62
15	0.722	9.13	2.043	2.889	25.82
20	0.546	6.90	1.769	2.502	22.36
30	0.367	4.64	1.445	2.043	18.26
40	0.276	3.49	1.251	1.769	15.81
50	0.222	2.80	1.119	1.582	14.14

Table 4 gives the lower and upper limiting velocities of artificial satellites of the earth at various altitudes. For comparison, we also give the values of the corresponding local circular velocities. As indicated in the table, the maximum allowable velocity for an artificial satellite is proportional to the circular velocity (this is always 41.42 per cent greater than that circular velocity), while its minimum velocity drops much more sharply with increasing distance from the center of the earth.

[9] In this discussion, we disregard the earth's atmosphere. In actuality, of course, the minimum velocity will not be the velocity at which the orbit touches the surface of the earth, but a somewhat higher velocity at which the satellite enters more or less dense layers of the atmosphere, which, as a result of the resistance of the air, will lead to destruction of the satellite.

■ Sidereal Time of Revolution of an Artificial Satellite

The altitude of flight of an artificial satellite determines the velocity of its motion and thus the length of the period of its revolution around the earth.

If it were not for the resistance of the air, then an artificial satellite, launched horizontally from the surface of the earth itself at the above-indicated velocity of 7912 meters per second, would make a full revolution with respect to the celestial sphere and would return to its previous position relative to the stars and the center of the earth, after 1 hour 24 minutes 25 seconds. This is what is called the sidereal (or stellar) period of revolution of an artificial satellite.

With increasing launching altitude of an artificial satellite, its orbit becomes longer, and the force of the earth's gravitation weaker. Consequently, the centrifugal force will decrease, the motion of the satellite will slow down, and the period of revolution will lengthen (Table 2).

The revolution of an artificial satellite increases with the distance from the planet, obeying the third law of Kepler, according to which the square of the time of revolution of satellites around the earth is proportional to the cubes of the major semiaxes of their orbits.

At an altitude equal to two earth radii, the sidereal period of revolution amounts to 7 hours 17 minutes and, at altitudes two and three times as great, to 15 hours 44 minutes and 1 day 2 hours 3 minutes respectively. If the satellite was revolving along an orbit a thousand times as long as the circumference of the equator, and the sun (and to some extent the planets) did not perturb this motion, then a full revolution of the satellite about the earth would take 5 years and 4 weeks.

The periods of revolution of the two first Soviet artificial satellites were 1 hour 36.2 minutes and 1 hour 43.7 minutes, respectively, at the beginning of their existence.

Close to the surface of the earth, the sidereal period of revolution of an artificial satellite increases by 1.2 seconds for each kilometer of altitude, and at an altitude of 5-6 earth radii, the increment is already about three seconds for each additional kilometer of altitude; this increment then gradually increases.

When an artificial satellite moves along a circular orbit, it is possible to calculate the sidereal period of its revolution if we know its altitude and velocity. For this purpose, we first determine the length of the circular orbit, i.e., the path traveled by the satellite during the period of a single revolution, and then we divide the obtained result by the circular velocity. For instance, the radius of the orbit of a satellite moving at 6378 kilometers is 12,756 kilometers, while the length of the corresponding circle is 80,152 kilometers. On dividing the latter quantity by the circular velocity, equal to 5.595 kilometers per second, we obtain 14,327 seconds, or 3 hours, 58 minutes, 47 seconds.[10]

■ Angular Velocity of Displacement of a Satellite

To define the concept of the angular velocity of a satellite with respect to the center of the earth, imagine an observer to be located at the center of the earth and to view an arc of the orbit of the satellite as subtending some definite angle. (The vertex of the angle is at the center of the earth, while the sides are directed toward the beginning and end of the apparent arc.) The increase in this angle within one second is called the angular velocity of the satellite relative to the earth (this definition is valid not only for a circular orbit but also for an elliptical orbit). The angular velocity decreases with increasing distance of the satellite from the center of the earth, but naturally not by the same law by which the circular velocity decreases. Thus, at a distance of 100 earth radii, the angular velocity is 1000 times as small as the angular velocity at the surface of the earth, while the circular velocity is only ten times smaller than the zero circular velocity. The angular velocity of a satellite is inversely proportional

[10] The laws by which the altitude of flight of a satellite uniquely determines its velocity and, consequently, the period of its revolution around the earth, are unfortunately not always taken into account by authors of popular science literature. Thus, in one of these books, for instance, contains the following: "The station is located at an altitude of 1000 kilometers above the earth and make a complete revolution around it in 100 hours." If, however, the station were located at an altitude of 1000 kilometers above the earth, then, as will be clear from Table 2, it would make a full revolution around the earth in 1 hour 45 minutes, instead of in 100 hours. If, however, the station did make a full revolution in 100 hours, it would have to be located, not at an altitude of a thousand kilometers above the earth, but a hundred times farther out.

to the period of its revolution. The mean angular velocity is equal to 360°, divided by the sidereal period of revolution of the satellite.

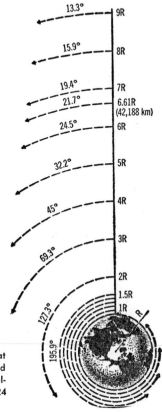

■ FIG. 9.—Path Traveled by Artificial Satellite at Various Distances from the Earth during One and the Same Time (Revolution of an Artificial Satellite Flying Above the Equator Itself, 1 Hour 24 Minutes 25 Seconds).

Figure 9 shows arcs of the orbits traveled during one and the same time by artificial satellites revolving around the earth at various distances from it.

■ Solar and Lunar Periods of Revolution of an Artificial Satellite

The time during which a satellite, moving around the earth in its orbit, returns to its previous position relative to the line earth-sun will be called the solar period of revolution of an artificial satellite. The knowledge of the solar period of revolution of an artificial satellite

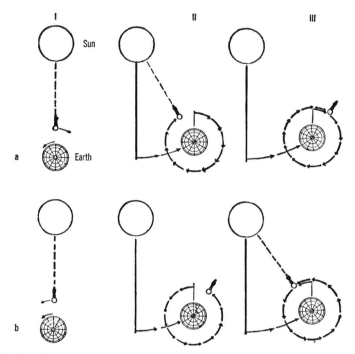

FIG. 10.—The Solar Period of Revolution of a Satellite if Its Motion Is Retrograde (a) Is Shorter than the Solar Period if Its Motion Is Progressive (b). When a "retrograde satellite" has already made a complete revolution relative to the sun (a-II), a "progressive satellite" has not yet completed such a revolution (b-II). When a "progressive satellite" has made a complete revolution relative to the sun (b-III), a "retrograde satellite" will have already completed its second revolution (a-III!).

is very important for an exact determination of the length of the day and night and of the season on a satellite (cf. later in text), for studying the solar radiation, etc.

Let us determine the length of this period.

Together with the earth, the satellite, during the course of a year, makes one revolution around the sun. If the satellite is moving at an altitude equal to one tenth of an earth radius, then, as shown by calculation, it will make 5400 revolutions around the earth relative to the fixed stars during the course of one sidereal year. If its orbit is perpendicular to the plane of the ecliptic,[11] then it will make the same number of revolutions relative to the sun, namely 5400. If, however, the plane of the satellite orbit coincides with the plane of

---

[11] That is, the plane in which the earth moves around the sun.

the ecliptic, then the number of revolutions relative to the sun will differ from this value; more specifically, it will be one revolution less in the case of progressive motion of the satellite, or one revolution more, in the case of retrograde motion.[12]

■ TABLE 5

Comparison of Solar and Sidereal Periods of Revolution of an Artificial Satellite

Sidereal Period of Revolution		Solar Period of Revolution							
		In Progressive Motion				In Retrograde Motion			
Days	Hrs.	Days	Hrs.	Min.	Sec.	Days	Hrs.	Min.	Sec.
—	2	—	1	0	2	—	1	59	58
—	6	—	6	0	15	—	5	59	45
—	12	—	12	1	0	—	11	59	1
1	—	1	0	3	57	—	23	56	4
2	—	2	0	15	51	1	23	44	19
3	—	3	0	35	46	2	23	24	48
5	—	5	1	40	—	4	22	28	—
7	—	7	3	17	—	6	20	50	—
10	—	10	6	45	—	9	17	36	—
15	—	15	15	25	—	14	9	48	—
20	—	21	3	48	—	18	24	5	—
25	—	26	20	5	—	23	9	34	—
30	—	32	16	26	—	27	17	21	—
35	—	38	17	1	—	31	22	33	—
40	—	44	22	4	—	36	1	15	—
50	—	57	22	19	—	43	23	31	—
60	—	71	19	2	—	51	12	50	—

Thus, in the case of the progressive motion of a satellite, the duration of one revolution around the earth relative to the sun will be 1/5399 of a year, whereas in retrograde motion it will be 1/5401 of a year. The difference between these two periods is 2.164 seconds. As the altitude of motion of a satellite increases, this difference also increases; at an altitude of four earth radii, it is about a hundred times as great as in the preceding case and, for an altitude twice this value, the

---

[12] In astronomy and astronautics, the motion of a satellite in the sense of the rotary motion of the earth or of the revolution of the earth around the sun is called progressive motion. The motion of a satellite in the opposite direction is known as retrograde, or backward, motion. The motion of heavenly bodies is shown on the sketches as it would appear if observed from the north pole of the celestial sphere. Thus progressive motion on the sketches will have a direction contrary to that of the motion of the hands of a clock.

difference amounts to almost 20 hours. In comparing each of these solar periods with the corresponding sidereal period, the difference is found to be half as great (the sidereal period is shorter than the solar period for progressive motion, and is longer than it for retrograde motion of the satellite).

Figure 10 clearly shows the reason for the fact that the solar period of revolution of a satellite in retrograde motion (a) is shorter than the solar period in progressive motion (b). In Table 5, the solar and sidereal periods of revolution of satellites are compared for the cases of progressive and retrograde motion; Table 6 gives a comparison of the number of rotations of a satellite and the periods of its revolution relative to the stars and to the observer.

The period of time after which a satellite, moving around the earth in its orbit, returns to its previous position with respect to the line earth-moon will be called the lunar period of revolution of an artificial satellite.

■ TABLE 6

Comparison of the Number of Revolutions of a Satellite and the Periods of its Revolution Relative to the Fixed Stars and to the Sun

Radius of Orbit, in Earth Radii	Number of Revolutions Per Year			Difference between Solar Periods of Revolution in Progressive and Retrograde Motion				Difference between Length of Solar and Sidereal Periods of Revolution Relative to the Sidereal Period, in Per Cent
	Relative to the Fixed Stars	Relative to the Sun		Days	Hrs.	Min.	Sec.	
		In Progressive Motion	In Retrograde Motion					
1.1	5400	5399	5401				2	0.02
1.5	3392	3391	3393				5	0.03
2	2202	2201	2203				13	0.05
3	1199	1198	1200				44	0.08
4	778.8	777.8	779.8			1	44	0.13
6	423.9	422.9	424.9			5	51	0.24
8	275.4	274.4	276.4			13	52	0.36
10	107.0	196.0	198.0			27	6	0.51
15	107.2	106.2	108.2		1	31	32	0.93
20	69.66	68.66	70.66		3	37		1.44
25	49.85	48.85	50.85		7	3		2.01
30	35.44	34.44	36.44		13	57		2.82
40	24.64	23.64	25.64	1	5	43		4.06
50	17.58	16.58	18.58	2	8	43		5.69
60	13.41	12.41	14.41	4	1	30		7.46
70	10.64	9.64	11.64	6	10	52		9.40

The knowledge of the lunar period of revolution of an artificial satellite will be of decisive importance for selecting the moment of departure from a satellite used as an intermediate station in flight to the moon (cf. later in text). For a definite predetermined trajectory of flight, there exists only one such moment during the course of an entire lunar period of revolution.

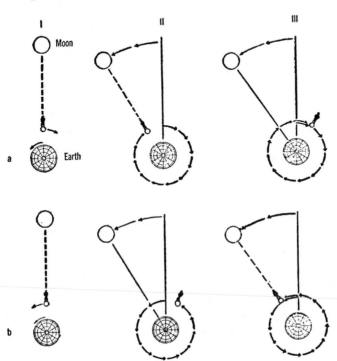

FIG. 11.—Lunar Period of Revolution of a Satellite in Retrograde Motion (a), Which Is Shorter than the Lunar Period in Progressive Motion (b). When a "retrograde satellite" has already made a complete revolution relative to the moon (a-II), the "progressive satellite" has not yet completed such revolution (b-II). When the "progressive satellite" has completed a full revolution relative to the moon (b-III), the "retrograde satellite" will have already completed its second revolution (a-III).

By reasoning analogous to that relating to the solar period of revolution, we obtain the relationship between the lunar and sidereal periods of revolution of artificial satellites (Figure 11). The results of the calculations are given in Table 7, where it has been assumed that the plane of the orbit of the artificial satellite coincides with the plane of the lunar orbit.

In character, the lunar period of revolution differs substantially from the solar period. This is explained by the fact that both these heavenly bodies, the artificial satellite and the moon, are revolving about one and the same heavenly body, namely the earth (cf. Figures 9 and 10).

■ TABLE 7

Comparison of Sidereal and Lunar Periods of Revolution of Artificial Satellite

| Sidereal Period of Revolution | | Lunar Period of Revolution, in Days | | Sidereal Period of Revolution | | Lunar Period of Revolution, in Days | |
Days	Hrs.	In Progressive Motion	In Retrograde Motion	Days	Hrs.	In Progressive Motion	In Retrograde Motion
—	6	0.2523	0.2477	25	—	294.1	13.05
—	12	0.5093	0.4910	26	—	537.3	13.32
1	—	1.038	0.9646	27	—	2293	13.57
2	—	2.157	1.864	27	7.7*	Infinite	13.66
3	—	3.370	2.703	28	—	1128	13.83
5	—	6.120	4.226	29	—	472.1	14.07
7	—	9.411	5.572	30	—	306.0	14.30
10	—	15.77	7.320	35	—	124.5	15.34
15	—	33.26	9.683	40	—	86.19	16.23
20	—	115.5	11.55	50	—	60.23	17.66

* Length of sidereal month.

It is obvious that, in the case of motion of the artificial satellite retrograde relative to the moon, its lunar period of revolution will increase with the sidereal period but will lag more and more behind that period. For a two-hour sidereal revolution, this lag amounts to only 3 minutes, yet for a one-day sidereal period (the case of what is known as a stationary artificial satellite, cf. later in text) it is already equal to 51 minutes. For a sidereal period of one sidereal month, which is 27.32 days (the sidereal period of revolution of the moon around the earth), the lunar period of revolution lags behind the sidereal period by a quantity equal to half of that period, i.e., by $27.32 : 2 = 13.66$ days. The further variation of the length of the lunar period of revolution in retrograde motion of a satellite will likewise proceed smoothly (cf. Table 7).

We obtain an entirely different picture for the progressive motion of an artificial satellite. First of all, the period of revolution with respect to the moon is now greater than the sidereal period. While the latter is equal to 2 hours, the lunar period will be equal to 2 hours 3 minutes. The lunar period then begins to increase more and more sharply. For a 2-week sidereal period it will amount to almost a month, and for a 27-day sidereal period it will amount to over 6 years. If, however, the sidereal period of revolution of an artificial satellite is exactly equal to the period of revolution of our own natural satellite (the moon), then both these satellites will be permanently located at an equal distance from each other on one and the same orbit, i.e., the lunar period of revolution of the artificial satellite in this case will be infinity. On further increase in the sidereal period of revolution of a "progressive" satellite, the lunar period of revolution, as will be clear from Table 7, will first drop sharply and then more slowly, approaching the sidereal period.

■ The Life of an Artificial Satellite

Artificial satellites flying at great heights in airless space will have an unlimited life (if we do not consider such accidents as collision with more or less large meteorites, destruction by cosmic dust, etc.).

The laws of motion we have considered refer to satellites moving in airless space. If, however, the orbit of an artificial satellite, even though only a portion of it, passes through the atmosphere, then the resistance of the air will cause the velocity of the satelite and the altitude of its orbit to decrease gradually with time.

Together with the loss in altitude, the period of revolution of the satellite will grow shorter. Ultimately the satellite will necessarily be destroyed. Entering the denser layers of the atmosphere, it will burn up as a result of friction with the air. It is customarily considered that an artificial satellite must burn up, like most meteoric bodies, which are vaporized and extinguished at altitudes of 90-75 kilometers. In the opinion of some investigators, this takes place as high up as 100 kilometers.

In this connection, artificial satellites may be divided into two categories: permanent and temporary. In the opinion of Tabanera (Argentina) and of other scientists, satellites capable of revolving around the earth for not less than 10 years should be classified as permanent. At perigee, the altitude of such satellites must be at least 800 kilometers, since only in this case will the resistance of the air be entirely unnoticeable.

A number of studies have been made on the life of artificial satellites moving along circular orbits. According to the calculations by I. S. Astapovich and S. A. Kaplan (U.S.S.R.), the rate of descent of an artificial satellite with the characteristics of the first Soviet satellite (diameter of sphere 58 centimeters, weight 83.4 kilograms) would be given in Table 8.

■ TABLE 8

Altitude in km.	100	150	200	300	500	700
Rate of descent, in cm/sec	30,000	120	6	0.3	0.04	0.004

According to calculations by Ketchum (United States) a 0.5-meter spherical satellite weighing 50 kilograms (i.e., a satellite with characteristics very close to those of the first Soviet satellite) could stay in orbit for only a quarter of an hour if it were launched at an altitude of 125 kilometers. If, however, the altitude of flight of the satellite were increased to 500 kilometers, then its life might be extended to one year. For intermediate altitudes, Table 9 gives the corresponding values.

■ TABLE 9

Life of a Spherical Satellite (Diameter 0.5 Meters; Weight 50 Kilograms) at Various Altitudes, According to Calculations by Ketchum (United States)

Altitude of Flight, in Kilometers	Life, in Days	Altitude of Flight, in Kilometers	Life, in Days	Altitude of Flight, in Kilometers	Life, in Days
125	0.01	247	12	399	104
149	1	308	34	449	173
198	4	347	58	500	365

In his calculations, Ketchum assumed that the law used in aviation, according to which the resistance of the air is proportional to the square of the velocity of the body, is also applicable to artificial satellites. However, there are grounds for believing that, at such immense velocities as the circular velocity, this law is no longer applicable.

In calculating the life of an artificial satellite, authors usually consider the satellite to be moving along a circular orbit. In the case of motion in an ellipse, however, it is assumed that the retardation of the satellite takes place only at perigee at a constant altitude, where the resistance of the air reaches its maximum value. In reality, however, the retardation of a low-flying satellite takes place along its entire orbit, as a result of which not only the apogee but also the perigee of the satellite are lowered at each revolution.

■ FIG. 12.—Contraction of the Orbit of an Artificial Satellite Owing to the Resistance of the Air. In the dense layers of the atmosphere, the satellite is transformed into a "shooting star."

The Soviet investigators D. Ye. Okhotsimskiy, T. I. Eneyev, and G. P. Taratynova consider that the lowering of the apogee owing to the resistance of the air is considerably more rapid than the lowering of the perigee (Fig. 12). For instance, if the satellite is moving in orbit with the apogee located at an altitude of 700 kilometers and the perigee at an altitude of 300 kilometers, then a 100-kilometers lowering of the apogee will correspond to only a 6-kilometer lowering of the perigee. For this reason, in a very much elongated orbit, it may in first approximation be considered that only the apogee is lowered, while the perigee remains at practically the same altitude. The raising of the perigee by a certain altitude increases the life of the satellite considerably more than the raising of the apogee by the same distance.

If, for instance, the perigee of a satellite lies at an altitude of 360 kilometers and the apogee at an altitude of 1500 kilometers, then a 20-kilometers raising of the perigee will involve a 40 per cent increase in the life of the satellite, whereas the same change in the apogee can prolong the satellite's life by only 2 per cent.

The raising of the perigee, however (i.e., practically, the raising of the launching point of the satellite), is considerably more difficult than increasing the altitude of the apogee (which is accomplished by increasing the horizontal launching speed of the satellite). For this reason, the latter method of lengthening the life of the satellite must not be neglected, either. For instance, an increase of only 78 meters per second in the velocity of a satellite launched horizontally at an altitude of 360 kilometers is sufficient to raise the altitude of the apogee from 700 to 1000 kilometers. In this case, the life of the satellite would be lengthened by a factor of 2.2.

Table 10 illustrates the length of the life of a satellite as a function of the initial perigee and apogee altitudes of the orbit. (The density of the atmospheric envelope at various altitudes has been taken by the author from the data furnished by the Indian scientist S. K. Mitra. The shape of the satellite is spherical, with a diameter of 0.5 meter and a weight of 10 kilograms.)

■ **TABLE 10**

Life of a 0.5-Meter Spherical Satellite Weighing 10 Kilograms

Perigee, in Kilometers	Apogee, in Kilometers	Maximum Number of Revolutions	Life Years	Life Days
200	400	44	—	2.7
360	800	7,200	1	85
500	1,500	174,000	30	—

The life of a satellite will also depend on a number of other factors. Obviously, the life of the satellite will increase with an increase in its cross-sectional loading[13] and with an improvement in its streamline, etc., and vice versa.

Starting out from these considerations, we can predict that the

[13] The cross-sectional loading is the weight of the body divided by its cross-sectional area.

life of the first artifical satellite will be longer than that of the carrier rocket that ejected it. As will be seen from Table 11, the sidereal period of revolution of the satellite around the earth was 96 minutes, 12 seconds at first and then, owing to the resistance of the atmosphere, began to shorten (although very slightly). During the first three weeks, the period of revolution became shorter by about 2.3 seconds a day, and in 23 days it decreased to 95 minutes, 18 seconds. Thus the diurnal number of revolutions of the satellite during this time increased from 14.97 to 15.11. The period of revolution of the carrier rocket, however, is not only shorter than the corresponding period of revolution of the satellite, but its daily decrease is also greater. Thus, whereas on November 9, 1957 the period of revolution of the satellite decreased, on the average, by 2.94 seconds a day, the corresponding decrement for the carrier rocket was 6.3 seconds, or more than double.

■ **TABLE 11**

Variation of the Periods of Revolution of the First Artificial Satellite and of the Carrier Rocket in October–November 1957

	Period of Revolution, in Minutes		Difference between Periods of Revolution of Satellite and Rocket in Minutes
Date, 1957	First Satellite	Carrier Rocket	
Oct. 6	96.2	—	—
Oct. 12	95.95	—	—
Oct. 21	95.55	95.12	0.43
Oct. 23	95.49	95.01	0.48
Oct. 27	95.31	94.68	0.63
Nov. 9	94.72	93.48	0.76

As we know, however, even in the theoretical case (in the absence of resistance of the medium), the period of revolution of an artificial heavenly body around the earth cannot be shorter than 85 minutes (cf. above), which fact also limits the life of satellites.

The period of revolution of the second satellite was 103.7 minutes on November 4, 1957; 103.6 minutes on November 6; and 103.52 minutes on November 9. It will be clear that its period of revolution decreased only slightly, since it had been raised to altitudes at which the resistance of the air was practically unnoticeable. If the entire orbit of the satellite had been located at the altitude of its apogee

(1700 kilometers), then its life would have been measured in years. The sensible resistance of the air, although slight, is experienced by the satellite only on those parts of its path lying close to perigee. Under the influence of this factor, with time, the velocity of the satellite and its period of revolution will gradually decrease even more. Nevertheless, the second satellite will apparently last longer in space than the first one.

In determining the life of a satellite, one must also take account of the fact that the atmospheric envelope of the earth rotates together with our planet. If we assume that a polar satellite, revolving at an alittude of several hundred kilometers, were to stop for an instant above the equator, then the atmosphere would be carried past it at a velocity of about 0.5 kilometer a second, i.e., there would be a peculiar "cosmic wind" (cross wind) of a velocity 16 times as high as that of a hurricane.

For an equatorial satellite, revolving in the opposite direction, the cosmic wind would increase the resistance to its motion; but for a satellite moving in a progressive direction, such a wind might be a tail wind, and the resistance of the medium would decrease. Thus, an equatorial satellite moving eastward, because of the decrease in the velocity pressure would be able to travel farther than a satellite flying westward. A cross wind blowing against a polar satellite would not change its life.

We note that, in the works we have considered, the structure of the atmosphere at the altitude of the artificial satellite is assumed to be known. Still, the solution of this last question is assumed to have been obtained by observations of the process of retardation of the satellite in the upper layers of the atmosphere!

As for powered artificial satellites, it is natural that, even in flights at a low altitude, the life of such a satellite might be rather long, since the fuel necessary for the correction of the trajectory could be constantly brought up from the earth's surface.

■ Special Features of the Motion of the First Soviet Artificial Satellite

Table 12 gives the principal characteristics of motion of the first Soviet artificial satellite and carrier rocket, compiled from the data of official communiques.

■ TABLE 12

Motion of First Artificial Satellite and Carrier Rocket during the First Month of their Existence (October–November 1957)

| | | Satellite | | Carrier Rocket Ahead of Satellite (+) or behind it (−) | | |
| | | Number of Revo-lutions* | Path Covered, in Thousand Kilometers* | In Time, in Minutes* | In Distance, in Kilometers* | Passes to the East (E) and West (W) of the Satellite, in Degrees of Longitude* |
Date	Time					
Oct. 5	1 hr. 46 min.	0	0	—	—	—
Oct. 6	6 hrs.	18	—	—	—	—
Oct. 7	6 hrs.	32	1,400	—	—	—
Oct. 8	6 hrs.	46	—	—	—	—
	18 min.	—	—	—	−1,000	—
Oct. 9	6 hrs.	63	—	—	—	—
	18 min.	—	—	—	−1,000	—
Oct. 10	6 hrs.	78	3,500	—	0	—
Oct. 11	18 hrs.	100	4,400	+2	+1,000	0.5 E
Oct. 12	—	—	—	+3	+1,500	0.75 E
Oct. 13	6 hrs.	123	5,300	+5	+2,500	1.25 E
Oct. 14	6 hrs.	138	6,000	+6	+3,000	1.5 E
Oct. 15	6 hrs.	153	6,650	—	—	—
	18 min.	—	—	+10	—	2.5 E
Oct. 16	6 hrs.	168	7,200	+11	+5,300	2.75 E
	18 min.	—	—	+13	—	3.25 E
Oct. 17	6 hrs.	183	8,000	+14	+6,700	3.5 E
	18 min.	—	—	+17	+8,000	4.25 E
Oct. 18	6 hrs.	198	8,600	+19.7	+9,000	4.9 E
	18 min.	—	—	+22	+10,000	5.5 E
Oct. 19	6 hrs.	213	9,350	+24	+11,000	—
	18 min.	—	—	+27	+12,400	6.75 E
Oct. 20	6 hrs.	228	10,000	+29	+13,200	7.25 E
	18 min.	—	—	+32	+14,600	8 E
Oct. 21	6 hrs.	243	—	—	—	—
	18 min.	—	—	+39	+18,000	9.75 E
Oct. 22	6 hrs.	258	11,250	—	—	—
	18 min.	—	—	+46	+21,000	11.5 E
Oct. 23	6 hrs.	273	11,900	—	—	—
	18 min.	—	—	+53.2	+24,300	13.3 E
Oct. 24	6 hrs.	288	12,560	—	—	—
	18 min.	—	—	+60	+27,400	15 E
Oct. 25	6 hrs.	303	13,200	—	—	—
	18 min.	—	—	−28.8	−13,200	7.2 W
Oct. 26	6 hrs.	319	13,850	—	−11,700	—
	18 min.	—	—	−21.8	−9,940	5.4 W
Oct. 27	6 hrs.	333	14,452	—	—	—
	18 min.	—	—	−10.5	−4,800	—

■ **TABLE 12** *(Continued)*

| | | Satellite | | | Carrier Rocket Ahead of Satellite (+) or behind it (−) | | |
Date	Time	Number of Revo- lutions*	Path Covered, in Thousand Kilometers*	In Time, in Minutes*	In Distance, in Kilometers*	Passes to the East (E) and West (W) of the Satellite, in Degrees of Longitude*
Oct. 28	6 hrs.	348	15,103	—	—	—
Oct. 29	6 hrs.	363	—	—	—	—
	18 min.	—	—	+12.5	+5,650	—
Oct. 30	6 hrs.	379	—	—	—	—
	18 min.	—	—	+17	—	—
Oct. 31	6 hrs.	393.78	—	—	—	—
	18 min.	—	—	+26.5	+12,000	—
Nov. 1	6 hrs.	408.65	—	—	—	—
	18 min.	—	—	+38	—	—
Nov. 2	6 hrs.	423.54	—	—	—	—
	18 min.	—	—	−45.5	—	—
Nov. 3	18 hrs.	—	—	−30	—	—
Nov. 4	18 hrs.	—	—	−13	—	—
Nov. 7	6 hrs.	500	—	—	—	—
	18 min.	—	—	+34	—	—

* *Approximately.*

It is easy to calculate that the average velocity of the satellite during the first three weeks of its life was 7.58 kilometers per second. The orbital velocity[14] of the satellite, however, is not constant; it is somewhat greater over the northern hemisphere where the satellite flies at a lower height and is somewhat smaller over the southern hemisphere where the altitude reaches its maximum.

Because of the oblateness of the earth, the plane of the orbit of the satellite, without varying its inclination to the plane of the equator, slowly rotates about the axis of the earth. This motion amounts to about a quarter of a degree in longitude for each revolution of the satellite, in a direction opposite to the rotation of the earth.

With the shortening of the period of revolution of the satellite, the size of the orbit also decreases. Thus, on November 9, the apogee of the first satellite lowered to 810 kilometers, and the apogee of the carrier rocket to 695 kilometers. The ceiling of the second satellite on the same day dropped to 1650 kilometers.

[14] The orbital velocity is the velocity of motion of the satellite along its orbit.

The carrier rocket that put the first satellite into orbit at first trailed behind the satellite. Subsequently, however, the carrier rocket overtook and even led the satellite.

Imagine that a satellite and a carrier rocket are moving side by side parallel to the earth's surface at almost the same velocity, high above the North Pole (Fig. 13-I). So long as they do not encounter resistance of the air, the two bodies will continue to move around the earth along one and the same path. At this time, however, dropping constantly lower under the influence of the earth's gravitation and making a half-revolution on an ellipse, they will enter the more or less dense layers of the atmosphere at a relatively low altitude above the South Pole, continuing to move parallel to the surface of the earth. After flying a certain distance, they will again break out into extra-atmospheric space, piercing the atmospheric envelope of the earth in about the same way as a needle goes through the skin of an orange. (Fig. 13-II). However, the velocities of the satellite and the carrier rocket, because of the resistance of the air encountered in the atmosphere, will no longer be at their previous value and, which is the main point, they will now differ. If we throw with one hand a metal ball and a lump of foil of the same size, the ball will fly further than the lump of foil, in spite of the fact that their velocities were the same at first. The reason for this is that the air retards the foil more sharply than the metal ball. In the same way, in our case, the air retards the spherical satellite less than it does the carrier rocket which had dropped its streamlined cap (in the sketch, the carrier rocket has a streamlined shape only by convention). Owing to this, the carrier rocket, which on leaving the atmosphere had a lower velocity than the satellite, no longer rises as high as the latter. According to the laws of celestial mechanics, the rocket will (for example) make a polar revolution along a shorter ellipse, while the satellite describes the considerably smaller angle $\propto$ around the earth. Figure 13-II which has not been drawn arbitrarily but in accordance with the second and third laws of Kepler shows that at the time when the carrier rocket is already over the North Pole, the satellite will be still considerably behind it. An observer on the earth will note the fact that the carrier rocket is ahead of the satellite because the rocket started over the Southern Hemisphere . . . at a lower velocity than the satellite. In this example, the satellite will be over the North Pole

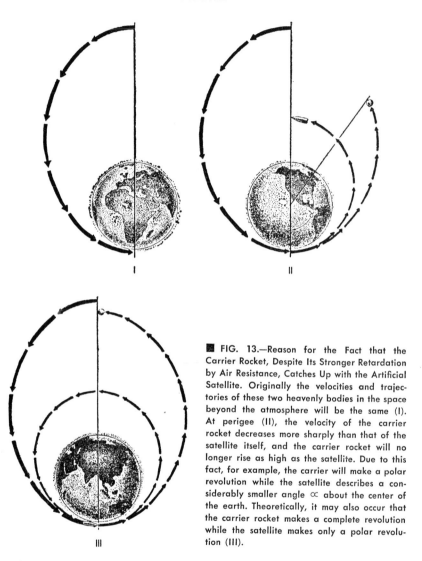

■ FIG. 13.—Reason for the Fact that the Carrier Rocket, Despite Its Stronger Retardation by Air Resistance, Catches Up with the Artificial Satellite. Originally the velocities and trajectories of these two heavenly bodies in the space beyond the atmosphere will be the same (I). At perigee (II), the velocity of the carrier rocket decreases more sharply than that of the satellite itself, and the carrier rocket will no longer rise as high as the satellite. Due to this fact, for example, the carrier will make a polar revolution while the satellite describes a considerably smaller angle $\propto$ about the center of the earth. Theoretically, it may also occur that the carrier rocket makes a complete revolution while the satellite makes only a polar revolution (III).

only when the carrier rocket has made a full circuit around the earth (Fig. 13-III).

For greater clarity, we have exaggerated the difference in the degree of retardation of the satellite and carrier rocket by the atmosphere; however, in principle, this actually happened with the first Soviet satellite of the earth and its carrier rocket. We have assumed the period of revolution of the satellite in our example to be double the period of revolution of the carrier rocket. In reality, however, the period of revolution of the first satellite was only slightly longer than the corresponding period of the carrier rocket. At the same time, the arc by which the carrier rocket gains over the satellite at each revolution is small: on October 21 this lead was 1.63°; on November 9 it increased to 2.93°; and at the beginning of November* 1957 the carrier rocket had already made two revolutions more than the satellite (502 and 500 revolutions, respectively).

On October 10, 1957, the carrier rocket was moving almost together with the satellite but then began to cross the parallels of latitude to the east of the satellite. It might therefore seem, on first glance, that the orbit of the carrier rocket was constantly deviating easterly from the orbit of the satellite. In reality, however, the two orbits lie in one and the same plane. The passage of the carrier rocket to the east of the satellite is explained by the earth's rotation and by the lead of the carrier rocket over the satellite. For example, on October 24, 1957, at 1800 hours, the carrier rocket crossed a certain parallel of latitude and proceeded beyond it, moving all the time in a plane fixed relative to the fixed stars. The satellite, following it, arrived at the same parallel one hour later. However, during this time the earth had rotated about its axis to the west by 360°:24 (hours) = 15°. Consequently, the satellite crossed this parallel of latitude 15° to the west of the rocket. In other words, the carrier rocket passed 15° of longitude to the east of the satellite, despite the fact that the two artificial heavenly bodies were revolving in one and the same plane. We note that since the satellite crossed any parallel at intervals of about 24° of longitude, the crossing of that parallel by the carrier rocket (for example, 15° to the east of the satellite in longitude) is equivalent to a crossing by $24° - 15° = 9°$ to the west of it in longitude. Conversely, on October 25, the carrier rocket passed 7.2° of longitude to the west of the satellite, which is equivalent to $24° - 7.2° = 16.8°$ of longitude to the east of the satellite.

* Translator's note: As in text.

2

Motion of the Satellite
Relative to the Observer on Earth

■
■
■

■ Period of Revolution of an Artificial Satellite Relative to an Observer on Earth (Synodic Period)

As stated above, the sidereal period of a revolution of a satellite flying around the surface of the earth is 1 hour 24 minutes 25 seconds. This is the period of revolution of the satellite with respect to the celestial vault or with respect to an observer at one of the poles of the earth. Imagine, however, that the orbit of the satellite is located in the plane of the equator and that the satellite, like the earth, revolves from west to east. By the time the satellite has made one full revolution relative to the celestial vault, the observer at the equator will have revolved together with the earth through a rather large angle relative to the celestial vault and, as a result, will be far ahead of the satellite. Only after 5 minutes 16 seconds will the satellite overtake the observer.

Thus, the time of revolution of a zero artificial satellite relative to the observer will be 1 hour 29 minutes 41 seconds. This is what is known as the synodic time (or synodic period) of revolution of the satellite relative to the earth.[1] After this interval of time the satellite will return to its previous position relative to the observer. In other words, after 1 hour 29 minutes 41 seconds, the observer will see the artificial satellite in the sky in its previous position relative to him, for instance, in the zenith.

With increasing altitude of flight, the synodic period of revolution will also increase but to a considerably greater degree than the sidereal period. Thus, at the surface of the earth the synodic period is only 6.24 per cent longer than the sidereal period; at an altitude of 8000 kilometers it will be 25 per cent longer; at an altitude of 13,900 kilometers, 50 per cent longer; and at an altitude of 28,400 kilometers, four times as long, etc.

At an altitude of 27,800 kilometers, the synodic period of revolution is 10 years and at an altitude of 34,800 kilometers, 100 years. Finally, at an altitude of 35,810 kilometers, the synodic period of revolution is infinite, i.e., the satellite will remain motionless relative to an observer on the earth. Such a satellite is called a stationary artificial satellite (cf. later in text).

Let us now discuss satellites whose orbits are located still higher. It is found that, for these, the synodic period will decrease with increasing radius of the orbit. If the radius of the orbit of a satellite exceeds the radius of the orbit of a stationary satellite by 2.29 per cent, then its synodic period will be equal to 30 days, while at a radius 7.27 per cent longer, the synodic period will be shortened to ten days. However, no matter how far away the artificial satellite may be moved, its synodic period of revolution will naturally never become shorter than a day.

Could the synodic period of revolution of an artificial satellite become equal to the sidereal period, i.e., to the period of revolution relative to the celestial vault? For a satellite lying inside the stationary

[1] In astronomy, the synodic period of revolution is the time after which a planet returns to its position of conjunction or opposition relative to the sun. By analogy with this concept (not with the concept of the synodic month, which is the interval of time between two successive similar phases of the moon), we have taken, as the synodic period of revolution of an equatorial artificial satellite, the interval of time between two identical positions of the satellite relative to an observer on the equator.

orbit, the synodic period is always longer than the sidereal period of revolution. However, an artificial satellite moving outside the stationary orbit will have, for orbits close to stationary, a synodic period of revolution that is longer than the sidereal period, while, for more distant orbits, that period will be shorter.

Indeed, the sidereal period of revolution of a stationary satellite is equal to one day, while the synodic period is infinite. If the radius of the orbit of a satellite only slightly exceeds the radius of the stationary orbit, then its sidereal period of revolution will be only slightly longer than a day while its synodic period will extend over many years. For a very distant satellite, however, the situation is exactly the opposite: Relative to the celestial vault, such a satellite will move very slowly so that the observer on the earth will see it, after a day, at almost the same position as on the day before. In other words, in this case, the synodic period of revolution is shorter than the sidereal period.

Consequently, there is a distance at which the synodic period is equal to the sidereal period. Calculation shows this distance to be 58.74 per cent longer than the distance of the stationary orbit and to be equal to 66,970 kilometers, while the time of revolution of a satellite on such an orbit is two days.

In all cases discussed above, the artificial satellite was moving from west to east. If the satellite were revolving in the plane of the equator in a circular orbit from east to west, then the observer on the equator would apparently be moving in the opposite direction. For an artificial satellite moving from east to west at the very surface of the ground, the synodic period of revolution would be 4 minutes 41 seconds shorter than the sidereal period of revolution and would amount to 1 hour 19 minutes 44 seconds. This is the shortest synodic period of revolution of an artificial earth satellite. In general, however, as shown in Figure 14, the period of revolution of a "retrograde" equatorial satellite (Fig. 14a) relative to an observer (synodic period) is shorter than the corresponding period of a "progressive" equatorial satellite (Fig. 14b). When the former satellite has already made a complete revolution relative to the observer (a-II), the latter satellite will not yet have completed such a revolution (b-III). But by the time the "progressive satellite" has made a complete revolution relative to the observer (b-III), the "retrograde satellite" will already have completed its second revolution (a-III).

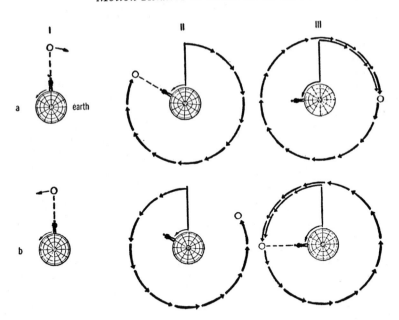

■ FIG. 14.—The Period of Revolution of a "Retrograde" Equatorial Satellite (a) Relative to an Observer (the Synodic Period) Is Shorter than the Corresponding Period of a "Progressive" Equatorial Satellite (b). By the time the first satellite has already made a complete revolution relative to the observer (a-II), the latter satellite has not yet completed such a revolution (b-II). By the time the "progressive satellite" has made a complete revolution relative to the observer (b-III), the "retrograde satellite" will have already completed its second revolution (a-III).

Under certain conditions the synodic period of a "retrograde" equatorial satellite may lengthen with increasing altitude of flight. In contrast, however, to the synodic period of a satellite revolving in the progressive sense, i.e., from west to east, this period cannot exceed one day. In the special case where an artificial satellite is moving in the plane of the equator along the same orbit as a stationary satellite but in the opposite sense (from east to west), it will pass any point on the equator twice a day.

As shown by calculations, for each synodic period of revolution exceeding 1 hour 29 minutes 41 seconds, two satellites moving at different altitudes can be indicated. If the sidereal period is shorter than a day, then satellites having the same synodic period of revolution will move in opposite directions, but in all other cases they will move in the same direction, i.e., only in the progressive direction from west to east.

With an eight-hour sidereal period of revolution, a satellite will appear in the field of vision of an observer every 12 hours, provided it is moving from west to east. If the satellite is moving in the retrograde sense, however, it will be visible to an observer on the earth every 6 hours. If the sidereal period is lengthened to 12 hours, then the synodic period of revolution of a satellite moving in the progressive direction will increase to one day, and of one moving in the retrograde direction, to 8 hours.

On the basis of the above it will be possible, by the aid of simple reasoning, to predict a number of phenomena connected with the observation of artificial satellites.

In some cases, it will be possible to judge the direction of motion of a satellite from the length of its synodic period of revolution alone. Assume that an observer on the equator has noted that 1 hour 28 minutes have passed between two successive culminations (passages across the zenith) of an artificial satellite. He will be able to conclude from this that the satellite will rise in the east. The point is that if the synodic period of revolution is shorter than 1 hour 29 minutes 41 seconds, then the satellite can move in its orbit only in a direction opposite to the motion of the earth (cf. above). Only due to the fact that the observer, because of the earth's rotation about its axis, is moving in a direction opposite to that of the satellite does the interval between successive encounters seem so short. If the artificial satellite were flying in the retrograde sense, even at the maximum velocity possible for an earth satellite, it would still not have time to reappear after 1 hour 28 minutes at the point where the observer is located. Consequently, both relative to the celestial vault and relative to the observer, the satellite will revolve from east to west, i.e., it will rise in the east.

Sometimes the apparent direction of motion of a satellite in the heavenly vault alone will be sufficient to determine the true sense of its motion relative to the fixed stars as well as the approximate altitude of its orbit. For instance, if an observer on the equator notes that an artificial satellite is moving in a direction opposite to that of the motion of all other heavenly bodies, then he will be able to conclude that the satellite must be at least 10.5 times closer to the earth than the moon. As readily demonstrated, the point is that such a satellite must be lower than the stationary orbit. If its orbit were higher than this, then, regardless of the direction of its true motion, the motion of the satellite would still seem, to an observer on the earth, to take place in the direction of rotation of the entire celestial sphere.

An astronomer, after determining the speed with which an artificial satellite rises, could calculate the altitude at which it is flying, which could not be done, for instance, by observing the motion of an aircraft. The altitude of flight of an artificial satellite could also be judged from the time interval between its rising and its setting.

◼ Projections of the Motions of an Artificial Satellite onto the Earth

As emphasized above, the orbit of an artificial satellite represents an ellipse which is almost[2] motionless relative to the fixed stars. Relative to an observer on the earth, however, this motion will be highly complex, because of the earth's rotation about its axis. For example, an artificial satellite, flying above the poles, will not move along the meridians, even at a low altitude of flight. The projection of the motion of such a satellite on the earth's surface will describe a line resembling the Latin letter S, and at high velocity (at low altitude) a line resembling the mathematical sign of the integral $\int$, with its upper and lower ends at the poles of the earth.

If an artificial satellite flies over the poles of the earth, while making a complete revolution in a sidereal day, then the projection of its path onto the surface of the earth will represent a great "figure-eight," with the loops intersecting at the equator (crossed ordinary and "left-hand" letters S). This figure-eight will have its greatest width, equal to one quarter the length of a parallel of latitude, on the parallels corresponding to 45° N. and S. Lat. Figure 15 shows the trajectories of the projections of three such artificial satellites, moving in planes dividing the equator into equal arcs. These projections will trace three figure-eights on the earth's surface.

Figure 16 shows the variation of the projection, onto the earth's surface, of the motion of a polar satellite during lengthening of its period of revolution from 2 to 12 days. If viewed from a point in the plane of the equator and very far from the surface of the earth, then, with increasing period of revolution of a polar satellite, this projection will more and more approach a straight line. If this same

[2] Here, the perturbations of motion of the satellite are not taken into account.

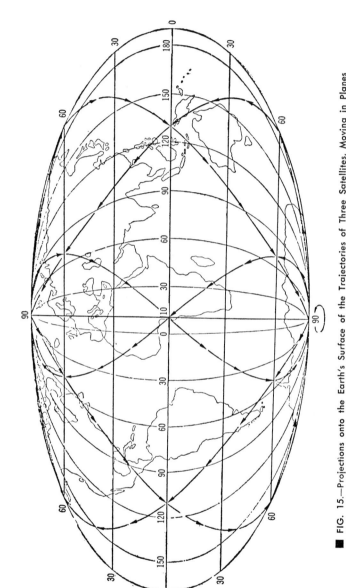

■ FIG. 15.—Projections onto the Earth's Surface of the Trajectories of Three Satellites, Moving in Planes Dividing the Equator into Equal Arcs (of 60° Each). The satellites will encircle the earth's poles, making one complete revolution in a sidereal day.

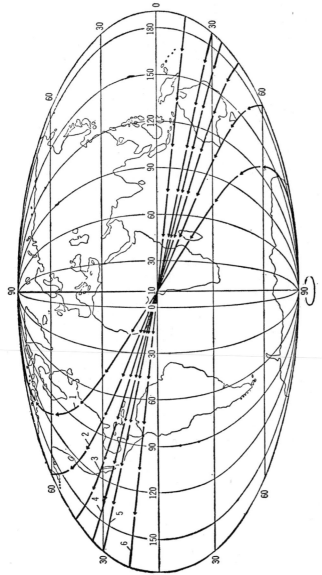

■ FIG. 16.—Projections onto the Earth's Surface of the Motion (in One Day) of Polar Satellites Making a Complete Revolution around the Earth in Two (1), Three (2), Four (3), Five (4), Six (5), and Twelve (6) Sidereal Days.

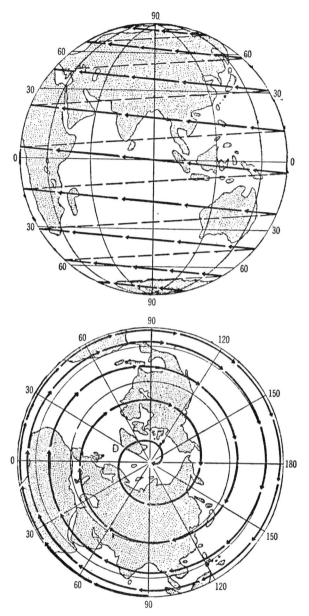

FIG. 17.—Projection into the Earth's Surface of the Motion of a Polar Satellite with a 20-Day Period of Revolution. The upper sketch shows a projection onto the earth's surface of the motion for the 10 days during which the satellite is moving from the South Pole to the North Pole. At the bottom, the projection of this motion onto the northern hemisphere during the 5 days when the satellite is passing from the equatorial plane to the North Pole.

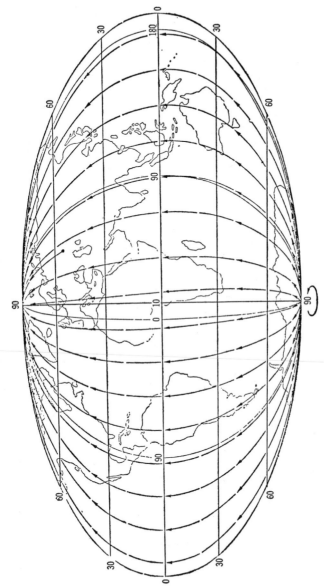

■ FIG. 18.—During the First Day, an Artificial Satellite Flying Over the Pole at Altitude 210 Kilometers Will Circle the Earth over Sixteen Times. Here we show, in projection onto the earth's surface, the portion of its path covered in daylight, when an observer on the satellite will be able to see the earth well.

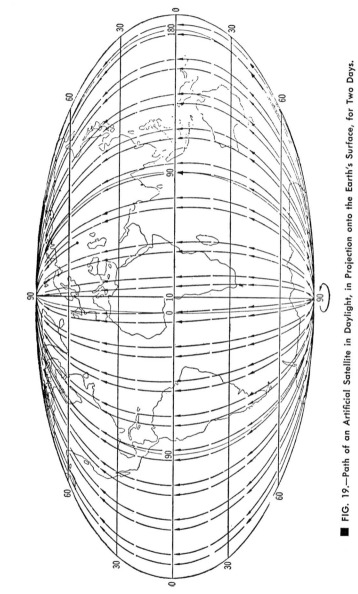

■ FIG. 19.—Path of an Artificial Satellite in Daylight, in Projection onto the Earth's Surface, for Two Days.

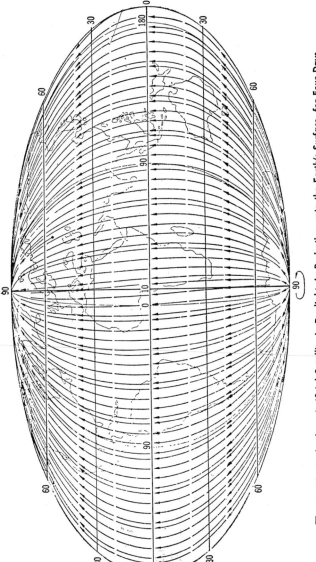

■ FIG. 20.—Path of an Artificial Satellite in Daylight, in Projection onto the Earth's Surface, for Four Days.

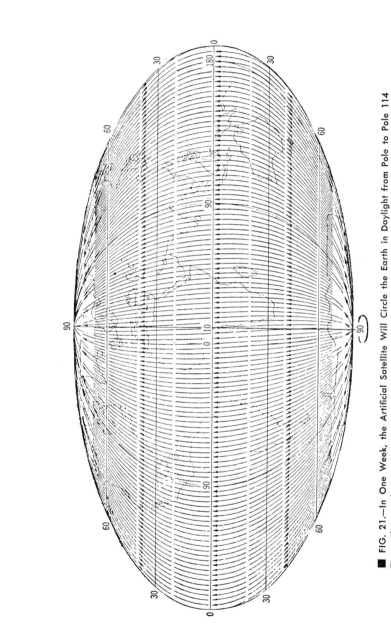

■ FIG. 21.—In One Week, the Artificial Satellite Will Circle the Earth in Daylight from Pole to Pole 114 Times. The net of routes is so dense that the interval between adjacent lines is only 3°9′.

projection, however, is viewed from a point located high above a pole, it will appear as a spiral (Fig. 17).

To make observations on artificial satellites from different points of the earth's surface, there is no need for launching several satellites in different directions. For instance, if observations must be made from the north and south poles, then it is sufficient to launch a satellite in such a manner that it will appear at once over the North Pole. Naturally it will also make a pass above the South Pole. The path of such a satellite will always go over the poles also in the future.

Imagine an artificial satellite circling the earth 16 times a day at an altitude of 287 kilometers above the poles (265 kilometers above the equator). From such an altitude, the earth will appear to the observer as an immense disk occupying the greater part of the celestial vault: one will see what will look like a "cap" of our planet, 3700 kilometers in diameter. This "cap" will be moving constantly. During one revolution of the satellite, the earth will make one sixteenth of a revolution about its axis, and the "cap" will be shifted on the equator by 40,000 : 16 = 2500 kilometers. In this way, after 16 revolutions of the satellite in the course of a single day, the entire surface of the earth will have passed before the eyes of the observers both in daylight illumination and under cover of the night.

We note that the range of vision from an aircraft, even one flying at an altitude of 25 kilometers, will only be 565 kilometers. If the area of the entire surface of the earth (510 million kilometers^2) is divided lengthwise into belts of the earth's surface visible from an altitude of 25 kilometers (565 × 2 = 1130 kilometers), then we will get a value of 452,000 kilometers. This is approximately the stretch that an aircraft would have to fly in order to view the entire surface of the earth. Flying at a speed of 1000 kilometers per hour, this would take 19 days. Thus the artificial satellite, thanks to its considerable altitude and its high speed of flight, will allow all the earth to be viewed about 20 times as rapidly as from an aircraft.

If an artificial satellite flies above the poles at an altitude of 210 kilometers, then, after making 114 revolutions around the earth, it will return after a week to the spot over which it had previously passed. Such a satellite would cross the equator 114 × 2 = 228 times per week. In that case, the maximum distance between adjacent places crossed by the satellite, i.e., between such places located on the equator, would not exceed 180 kilometers ($40,076 : 228 = 175.6$ kilometers). This would permit a study of the surface of our planet with great accuracy. Figures 18-21 shows the route of such a satellite for a week (see below).

If it is desired to have an artificial satellite make a second pass across the zenith, for a certain place, after (for instance) 4 sidereal days, with the altitude of the satellite being only slightly higher than in the preceding case, it would have to make 65 complete revolutions relative to the fixed stars during this period. During one revolution of the satellite, the earth would rotate about its axis through 22°9'23". Therefore, the projection of the trajectory of the satellite onto the earth's surface would be shifted, after each of its revolutions, through the same angle, regardless of the latitude.

The same artificial satellite might be seen at intervals of about 1.5 hours over Tokyo, Peiping, Lhasa, Srinagar (Kashmir, India), Teheran, Istanbul, and other cities in the twilight, sinking after each such pass into the umbra of the earth. During the time of passage of the satellite over these places, which have just passed into the shadow, the conditions for observation of the satellite, still illuminated by the sun, would be the most favorable.

It is somewhat more difficult than in the case of a polar or equatorial satellite to obtain the projection onto the surface of the earth of the motion of a satellite whose orbit is inclined at some angle to the plane of the equator. This did take place for the first two Soviet artificial satellites, whose orbits were inclined to the plane of the equator at an angle of about 65°.

Let us discuss the method of making such a projection, permitting a determination of the points over which the artificial satellite would appear and of the time of such passes. In practice, it is easiest to proceed as follows:

On a globe, place a ring inclined at an angle of 65° to the equator and attach that ring to the spindle of the globe. At a definite instant, for instance when the satellite is flying over Moscow, turn the globe so that Moscow is in the plane of the ring schematically representing the orbit of the satellite. Now, a simple calculation will be sufficient to determine the location of the satellite at any instant of time. Let us find, for instance, the location of the satellite 12 minutes after its pass over Moscow. In one minute the satellite flies 360° divided by 96.2 (the period of revolution around the earth in minutes of time), i.e., 3.74°, and in 12 minutes about 45°. Place a corresponding mark on the ring. During this time the earth has rotated about its axis through an angle of 3°. Turn the globe 3° to the east, so that the mark on the ring will indicate the required point on the earth's surface.

The inverse problem, namely to find the time of passage of the satellite over some definite place, is solved in a similar manner. We may also calculate whether or not the satellite will pass at all over a given area.

If by this method one loop (or more) is placed on a globe and then transferred to a map in cylindrical projections, the sinuous line shown in Figure 22 will be obtained. If, by means of this device, the consecutive projections of the satellite along its orbit are traced on the globe, we will find that the sixteenth loop of such a projection almost exactly coincides with the first loop, the seventeenth with the second, and so on. Figure 23 shows the scheme of motion of the first artificial satellite for a day, in cylindrical projection.

As already stated, the first Soviet satellite makes about 15 revolutions per day. For this reason, if we assume (as we have done up to now) that the plane of the orbit of the satellite remains fixed relative to the stars, then after each revolution the satellite would cross a parallel of latitude of the earth displaced by 24° toward the west. As we know, however, the plane of the orbit of the satellite actually rotates relative to the stars about the axis of the earth (known as precession). For this reason, the distance between the points of consecutive crossing by the satellite of a parallel of latitude on the earth is somewhat greater and amounts to about 24.5°.

The inclination of the orbit of the second satellite to the plane of the equator is the same as that of the first satellite (65°), and the projections of the two orbits onto the surface of the earth, at a given moment, are one and the same. It might therefore seem, on first glance, that the scheme of motion of the two satellites would also be one and the same. These schemes actually differ, however, since the periods of revolution of the satellites are different (cf. above); therefore, the earth, in rotating about its axis, occupies a different position relative

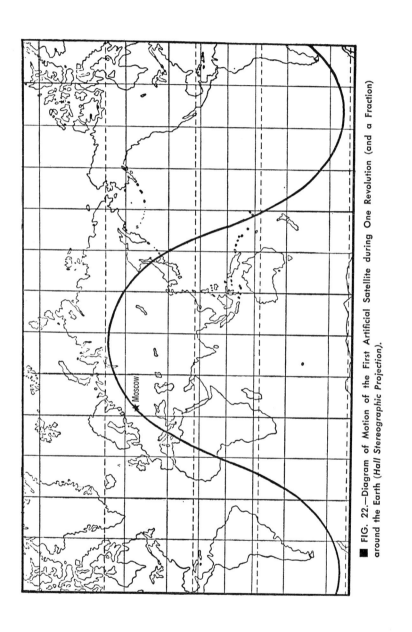

■ FIG. 22.—Diagram of Motion of the First Artificial Satellite during One Revolution (and a Fraction) around the Earth (Hall Stereographic Projection).

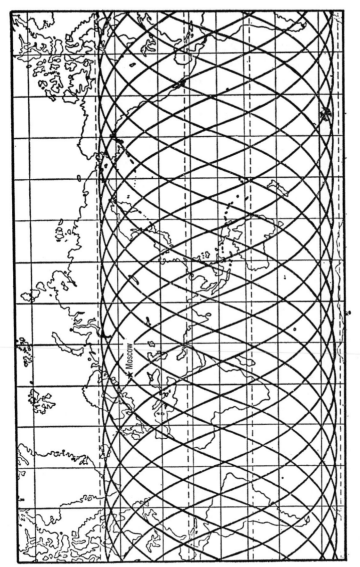

■ FIG. 23.—Diagram of Motion of the First Artificial Satellite for One Day (*Hall Stereographic Projection*).

to them. The distance between the points of consecutive crossing of a parallel of latitude by the second satellite is 1.8° greater than in the case of the first satellite, and amounts to 26.3°.

A satellite can be launched in such a manner that it will fly only once over any point of the earth's surface, and will never appear again over that point. For this purpose, the artificial satellite must have a period of revolution incommensurable with the period of one revolution of the earth about its axis or, in other words, it must make an irrational number of revolutions (for instance, $11\sqrt{2} - 15.566 \ldots$, or $5\pi = 15.707 \ldots$) in a sidereal day.

For a satellite to be able to reappear over a given area, its orbit (as easily understood) must be inclined to the plane of the equator at an angle equal to, or greater than, the geographic latitude of the place. In this case, the satellite will be visible from all countries of the earth located between a certain parallel of north latitude and the corresponding parallel of south latitude. Consequently, the nature of the artificial satellite is such that, if launched from Moscow, it must necessarily encircle almost all of western Europe (except countries located to the north), whereas if launched from Kushki, the southernmost city of the U.S.S.R., the selected orbit may be such that the satellite does not pass above Europe at all, except for the southernmost part of the Pyrennean Peninsula.

It is well known that other artificial satellites will also be launched from the territory of the U.S.S.R. during the International Geophysical Year. All these satellites will necessarily have to fly over part of Europe and North America, over almost all of South America and Australia, and over all of Africa.

■ Angular Velocity of Displacement of a Satellite Relative to the Earth's Surface[3]

In contrast to the angular velocity of displacement of a satellite relative to the center of the earth (cf. above), the angular velocity relative to an observer is the term we will apply to the increment of the corresponding angle in the case where the observer (the vertex of the angle) is on the surface of the earth.

For a ground observer, an artificial satellite moving at an altitude

[3] Only circular orbits will be considered here.

of 200 kilometers will be displaced in the sky, when it passes over the zenith, at the same angular (apparent) velocity as an aircraft flying at an altitude of 7130 meters at a speed of 1000 kilometers per hour or an aircraft flying at an altitude of 3065 meters at a velocity of 500 kilometers per hour. It is clear from this that it will be easy to hold the moving artificial satellite in the field of vision. The apparent velocity of motion of artificial satellites flying higher than 200 kilometers will be still smaller. As a rule, however, satellites will fly at exactly these greater altitudes.

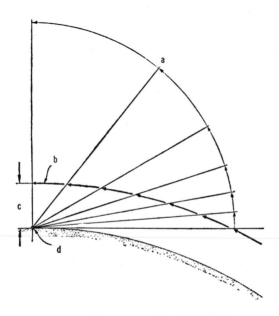

■ FIG. 24.—At the Moment of Rising, an Artificial Satellite Will Have Its Minimum Apparent Velocity. As the satellite rises, its angular velocity relative to an observer (the velocity of apparent motion of the satellite in the celestial sphere) will rapidly increase. (a)—apparent motion of satellite in the celestial vault; (b)—orbit of satellite; (c)—0.1 earth radius; (d)—point of observation.

If an artificial satellite is not at the zenith, but lower in the sky close to the horizon, then its speed of motion along the heavenly vault will make it still easier to follow. In fact, it follows from geometric considerations that, at the instant of rising (or setting), an artificial satellite will be displaced, relative to an observer in the plane of its orbit, at the same apparent angular velocity at which it actually

is in motion about the center of the earth. As the satellite rises, however, its angular velocity relative to the observer (velocity of the
apparent motion of the satellite on the celestial sphere) will rapidly
increase, and the rate of increase in velocity will be higher, the lower
the orbit of the satellite (Fig. 24). For example, if the altitude of the
satellite orbit is equal to the earth's radius, then the rate of its angular
motion relative to the observer at zenith will be twice as high as on
the horizon. But for a satellite moving at an altitude of 300 kilometers,
its angular velocity at the zenith will already be 22 times as great as
its angular velocity on the horizon. If the actual velocity of the satellite
relative to the center of the earth had the magnitude as it appears to
an observer, at the moment of its passage through the zenith, then the
satellite would make a complete revolution around the earth in four
minutes.

After passing over the observer at zenith, an artificial satellite
begins to decelerate its motion relative to the observer and, at the
moment of setting, its angular velocity will drop to the value it had
on rising.

We note, incidentally, that the angular velocity of the moon
relative to the observer likewise varies with the motion of the moon
in the celestial vault. Because of the great distance of the moon from
the earth, however, the variation in this angular velocity is impercep-
tible: At the zenith, it is only 1.7 per cent greater than on the horizon.

■ TABLE 13

Angular Velocity of Polar Satellite at the Zenith, Relative to Observer

Altitude of Flight, in Kilometers	Angle of Advance at Zenith Relative to Observer, per Second	Ratio of Angular Velocity of Satellite at Zenith to Angular Velocity at Horizon	Altitude of Flight, in Kilometers	Angle of Advance at Zenith Relative to Observer, per Second	Ratio of Angular Velocity of Satellite at Zenith to Angular Velocity at Horizon
100	4°29'53"	64.8	500	0°34'56"	13.8
150	2°59'13"	43.5	1,000	0°25'17"	7.4
200	2°13'55"	32.9	2,000	0°18'37"	4.2
250	1°46'43"	26.5	3,000	0°07'29"	3.1
300	1°28'36"	22.3	6,378	0°03'21"	2.0
400	1°05'57"	16.9			

Table 13 gives the values of the angular velocities of artificial satellites at the zenith, relative to an observer, for various altitudes of flight (the corresponding values for altitudes of 100-150 kilometers, at which only powered satellites can fly, are also given). The last column indicates the values of the ratio of the angular velocity of an artificial satellite at the zenith to its angular velocity on the horizon. It follows from the above statements that the same values also indicate the number of times that the angular velocity of the satellite relative to the observer at the zenith exceeds its angular velocity with respect to the center of the earth. Thus, after determining the apparent velocities of the satellite on the horizon and at the zenith from observations, we can use the table to find its altitude of flight as well.

■ **TABLE 14**

Angular Velocity of Polar Satellite at the Zenith, Relative to Observer

Altitude of Passage over Equator, in Kilometers	Percentage by which the Angular Velocity of Satellite for an Observer at the Pole Is Smaller than for an Observer at the Equator	Altitude of Passage over Equator, in Kilometers	Percentage by which the Angular Velocity of Satellite for an Observer at the Pole Is Smaller than for an Observer at the Equator
100	17.61	400	5.07
150	12.47	500	4.10
200	9.66	600	3.44
250	7.88	1,000	2.09
300	6.65	2,000	1.06

If we neglect the rotation of the earth about its axis, then the angular velocity relative to the center of the earth for an artificial satellite having a circular orbit will be a constant, regardless of the position of the plane of its orbit in space. Relative to an observer on the ground, however, the angular velocity, even at the zenith, will differ for observers at different latitudes, which will be a result of the oblateness of the earth. The closer to the pole, the higher will be the height above the ground of passage of the satellite at the zenith, owing to the oblateness of the earth, and the smaller, consequently, will be its angular velocity. For various velocities, Table 14 gives the percentage by which the angular velocity of a polar artificial satellite at the zenith, relative to an observer at the pole, will drop below the angular velocity for an observer at the equator (the latter velocity being taken as 100 per cent). As indicated in the table, this quantity decreases sharply with the altitude of the satellite. The altitudes of 100 and 150 kilometers shown in the table are of interest only for the fall of artificial satellites toward the earth, or for powered satellites.

The process of increase in angular velocity of a satellite relative to an observer, from the time it rises until culmination, i.e., to the point of highest ascent in the celestial vault, will take a different course for satellites moving at different altitudes. As an example, Table 15 shows the variation in angular velocity of a satellite relative to an observer at the equator, as an equatorial satellite rises in the celestial vault from the horizon to the zenith. The influence of the earth's rotation has not been taken into account.

■ TABLE 15

Variation in the Angular Velocity of an Equatorial Satellite at Orbit Altitude of 0.1 Earth Radius, during the Time of Advance from the Horizon to the Zenith (for an Observer on the Equator)

Altitude of Artificial Satellite above the Horizon	Angle by which the Satellite Advances Per Second, Relative to the Observer	Ratio of Angular Velocity Relative to Observer and Angular Velocity Relative to Center of Earth	Altitude of Artificial Satellite above the Horizon	Angle by which the Satellite Advances Per Second, Relative to the Observer	Ratio of Angular Velocity Relative to Observer and Angular Velocity Relative to Center of Earth
0°	4' 6"	1.00	50°	28'58"	7.05
10°	6'22"	1.55	60°	35'23"	8.61
20°	10'13"	2.49	70°	40'35"	9.88
30°	15'37"	3.80	80°	43'59"	10.71
40°	22' 7"	5.38	90°	45'11"	11.00

■ Apparent Motion of a Satellite in the Celestial Vault (Taking the Earth's Rotation into Account)

The first artificial satellites will be easily recognized among the other bodies shining in the sky, since, in contrast to the latter, the satellite will move in the sky in northerly, northeasterly, easterly, southeasterly, and southerly directions, but never in a westerly direction (nor in a northwesterly or southwesterly one). This is attributed to the fact that the first artificial satellites will not be launched in a direction opposite to the direction of rotation of the earth and, in addition, will be launched into low altitudes.

Since, as soon as more powerful rockets are available, it will be possible to launch satellites in a retrograde direction as well, this specific feature of artificial satellites will disappear. Later, satellites will be launched into greater altitudes, into tens of thousands and hundreds of thousands of kilometers. In the latter case, their relative velocity of motion in orbit will be so small that even if their motion with respect to the fixed stars takes place in the direction of the earth's rotation (i.e., from west to east), they will still lag markedly behind the ground observer who, together with the earth, will rotate about its axis at a higher angular velocity than the satellites; therefore, it may appear to an observer that the satellites move westward. Strictly speaking, this will be true only for equatorial satellites. All others will, as a rule, move southwest or northwest, so that the nonequatorial satellites, traveling at very great altitudes, will also have a distinctive feature by comparison with the motion of other heavenly bodies.

If an artificial satellite is launched in the plane of the equator in a direction opposite to the rotation of our planet, then, relative to an observer on the earth, the satellite will move from east to west, at a velocity which will be lower the higher the altitude of flight. If, however, a satellite is launched in the direction of rotation of the earth, then, depending on the altitude of flight, it will move relative to the observer in two possible directions. Figure 25 indicates that, at low altitudes of flight, its angular velocity will be greater than the angular velocity of the earth, and relative to an observer on the earth the satellite will move in a direction opposite to that of the motion of the heavenly bodies.[4] With increasing altitude of flight, the relative angular velocity of the satellite will decrease, but only so long as it does not become equal to zero for a stationary satellite. With further increase in altitude of flight, an artificial satellite will seem to the

[4] It is interesting to note that a similar phenomenon is observed on Mars with respect to the motion of its own satellite Phobos (of course, relative to a hypothetical observer).

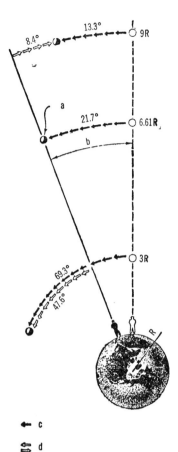

■ FIG. 25.—The Direction of Motion of Artificial Satellites, Relative to an Observer on the Earth, Depends on the Altitude of Their Flight. Satellites located below the stationary orbit will appear to move in an easterly direction; those located above that level will appear to move in a westerly direction, although both of them are, in reality, moving eastward. (a)—Stationary satellite; (b)—angle of rotation of earth; (c)—true motion of satellite; (d)—apparent motion of satellite.

observer on earth to move in a westerly direction, although actually, relative to the fixed stars, it will be moving eastward. The farther away the artificial satellite is, the more closely will the value of its relative angular velocity approach the angular velocity of the earth, which becomes equal to it at infinity (theoretical case).

Thus it will appear to the observer on earth that artificial satellites move in opposite directions, while in fact their revolutions are in the same sense.

Consider in particular two artificial satellites moving in the direction of rotation of the earth, i.e., from west to east in the equatorial plane, on circular orbits with radii of 33,800 and 59,400 kilometers, respectively (Fig. 26a). Assume that at a certain instant of time the two satellites are over the head of an observer, at a single point in the sky, the zenith. The lower satellite, with a period of revolution of 17.1 hours, describes an arc of 360°:17.1 = 21° in an hour, while the upper satellite, with a 40-hour period of revolution, describes an arc of 360°:40 = 9° in the same period. During this same hour, however, the observer, participating in the diurnal rotation of the earth, describes an arc of 360°:24 = 15° in an easterly direction. Thus, in an hour, the lower satellite passes beyond the observer by 21° − 15° = 6°, while the upper satellite lags behind him by 15° −

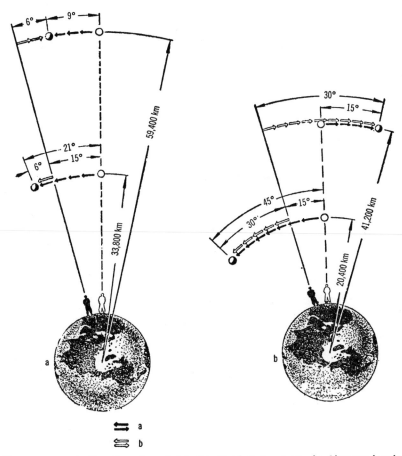

◘ FIG. 26.—In the Two Cases Presented in This Sketch it Appears to the Observer that the Satellites Are Moving in Opposite Directions at the Same Velocity, although in Reality the Directions of Their Motion in One Case Coincide (a) and in the Other Case Are Opposite (b). (a)—true motion of satellite; (b)—apparent motion of satellite.

$9° = 6°$. It will seem to the observer, however, that the satellites move in the heavenly sphere in opposite directions (lower, easterly; higher, westerly), covering $1°$ in 10 minutes ($6°$ per hour).

The synodic periods of revolution of the satellites under consideration (relative to the observer) coincide and amount to $360:6 = 60$ hours.

It should not be taken for granted, however, that, if two satellites seem to the observer to be moving in opposite directions at the same angular velocities (i.e., if the synodic periods coincide), this necessarily implies that both satellites are revolving in one and the same direction in their orbits. It is not difficult to visualize an example where, under the above conditions, the motion of an earth satellite will actually take place in opposite directions.

Consider two equatorial artificial satellites whose circular orbits have respective radii of 20,400 kilometers and 41,200 kilometers (Fig. 26b). The period of revolution of the lower satellite is 8 hours, that of the upper satellite 24 hours. In one hour, the lower satellite will describe an arc of $360°:8 = 45°$ and the upper an arc of $360°:24 = 15°$. If the satellites are moving in opposite directions in Fig. 26b (the lower, eastward; the upper, westward), then during this hour the lower satellite will gain by $45° - 15° = 30°$ on the observer, while the upper will lag behind him by $15° + 15° = 30°$. Thus the satellites will appear to the observer to be moving on the celestial vault in opposite directions, at the same angular velocities and, consequently, with the same synodical period, equal to $360:30 = 12$ hours.

An equatorial artificial satellite moving easterly can be seen up to seventeen times a day, and one moving westward up to nineteen times a day. An "easterly" equatorial satellite, revolving in a circle close to the stationary orbit, however, will have so long a synodic period of revolution that, during the course of a human lifetime, only one revolution of the satellite can be noted from the equator, although in reality (relative to the celestial vault) it will have made many thousands of revolutions during this time. The reason for this is the fact that the angular velocity of such an artificial satellite is almost equal to that of the earth itself.

One and the same artificial satellite may pass over a given place, once from the south to the north and then from the north to the south, but not because of the fact that the satellite suddenly changes the direction of its motion in orbit—this would be impossible—but because of the fact that, during the time separating one observation from another, the earth has made half a rotation about its axis, thus causing the direction of passage of the satellite in the celestial vault to change to the opposite.

■ Stationary Artificial Satellites

In view of the fact that all heavenly bodies exert a mutual attraction, it is impossible to construct a satellite that would remain motionless in interplanetary space. Such a satellite would be doomed to destruction. A satellite can be created, however, which, while moving relative to the fixed stars, is motionless relative to an observer on the earth.

Indeed, as mentioned above, the period of revolution of a satellite around the earth increases with the distance of the satellite from the earth. Whereas a satellite moving at an altitude of 265 kilometers will make one revolution around the earth in 1.5 hours, the moon, which is about 400,000 kilometers from the earth, takes about four weeks for this. There obviously is also a distance in existence at which one revolution of an artificial satellite would be accomplished in exactly one day.

If, in addition to this, such a satellite was moving in the plane of the equator from west to east, then its angular velocity would be equal to the angular velocity of rotation of the earth about its axis and would thus remain motionless with respect to a terrestrial observer. Such a satellite—we will call this a stationary artificial satellite—must, as already mentioned, be located at an altitude of 35,810 kilometers above the equator. It is true that the attraction of the moon would cause certain perturbations of the satellite orbit which, in time, would impair its state of being "motionless"; but these perturbations could be eliminated by a suitable correction of the orbit (cf. later in text).

In order to obtain a clearer concept of the possibility of creating a "motionless" artificial satellite, imagine a tower 35,810 kilometers high to be erected on the equator. With increasing height of this tower, the linear velocity of rotation would increase (in connection with the increase in the radius of rotation about the earth's axis) and, consequently, the centrifugal force would also gradually increase, while the earth's gravitational attraction would, on the other hand, decrease. At the very top, these two forces are in balance. Imagine that there is a gondola at the summit of the tower. If the tower is removed, the gondola, as is obvious from the above statements, will not fall. Rather, it will rotate together with the earth, remaining at the same distance from it. To an observer on the earth, the gondola will seem to be motionless; it has become a stationary artificial satellite.

A stationary artificial satellite has a number of advantages over

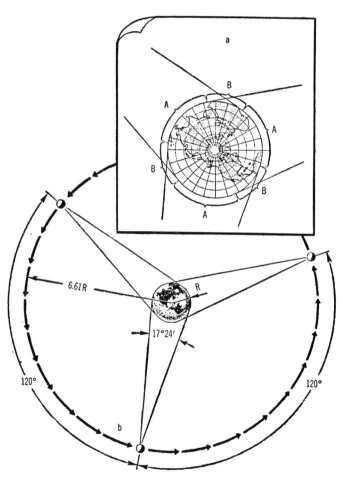

■ FIG. 27.—For Simultaneous Observations of the Entire Circumference of the Earth by the Aid of Artificial Satellites, at Least Three Such Satellites Are Necessary. (a)—A(77°21′) one satellite visible, B(42°39′) two satellites visible; (b)—stationary orbit 3076 meters per second.

other satellites. In fact, from such a satellite the earth will appear motionless; the apparent diameter of our planet will be about forty times as great as the apparent diameter of the moon from the earth, and the area of the visible disk will be 1600 times as large. The crew of a stationary satellite will more easily communicate with the earth by means of directional radio waves or light signals. Flight to a stationary satellite may be accomplished at any time, without waiting for the necessary position of the satellite relative to the launching pad.

As will be clear from Figure 27, at least three stationary satellites are required to cover the entire earth by observations. But since the orbit of a stationary satellite can lie only in the plane of the equator, the polar zones will not be visible from such stations.

Table 16 gives the principal characteristics of a stationary artificial satellite.

■ TABLE 16

Principal Characteristics of a Stationary Artificial Satellite

Period of rotation relative to the sun (solar period)	24 hours
Period of revolution with respect to the celestial sphere (sidereal period)	23 hours 45 minutes 4 seconds
Distance from center of earth	42,188 kilometers
Altitude above equator	35,810 kilometers
Circular velocity	3076 meters per second
Length of arc of equator from which artificial satellite is visible and which is visible from artificial satellite	162°36′30″
The same arc in units of length	18,102 kilometers
Arc of equator not covered by two stationary satellites	34°47′
The same arc in units of length	3872 kilometers
Total length of arc on equator from which two of three equidistant artificial satellites will be visible	14,232 kilometers
The same length in per cent of total length of equator	26.21

If the orbit of an artificial satellite is at the same distance from the center of the earth as the orbit of a stationary satellite (42,188 kilometers) but, in contrast to it, does not lie in the plane of the equator, then the period of revolution will remain as before, except that the satellite will not be constantly visible from one and the same point of the earth's surface in a definite direction, but at various times will be visible at a different angular altitude above the horizon.

At one and the same time of the sidereal day, however, it will be observed at one and the same point of the celestial vault.

■ "Rocking" Artificial Satellites

In the case of an equatorial artificial satellite following an elliptical orbit, its motion in the celestial vault as seen by an observer on earth may be oscillatory: from west to east, from east to west, and again from west to east. We will denote such satellites as rocking types.

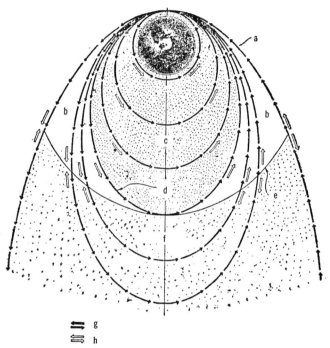

■ FIG. 28.—The Apparent Motion, for an Observer on Earth, of an Equatorial Artificial Satellite on an Elliptic Orbit May Be Oscillatory: from West to East, from East to West, and again from West to East. For artificial satellites revolving in the first zone, the apparent direction of motion will coincide with the actual direction, since here the angular motion of the satellite is more rapid than the diurnal rotation of the earth about its axis. For other satellites, passing partly through the second and third zones, the apparent and actual motions will coincide only on part of the path: when the satellite is near the earth, its angular velocity is higher, and it will appear to be moving eastward (second zone). As the interzonal boundary shown in the sketch is approached, it will gradually slow its motion so that, on reaching that boundary, it will stop for an instant and then begin to move in the opposite direction, from east to west (third zone). (a)—Parabolic orbit; (b)—second zone; (c)—first zone; (d)—interzonal orbit; (e)—interzonal boundary; (f)—third zone; (g)—true motion of satellite; (h)—apparent motion of satellite.

Figure 28 shows the elliptic orbits of equatorial artificial satellites. For artificial satellites revolving in the first zone, the apparent direction of motion will coincide with the actual direction, since their angular velocity is greater than the angular velocity of rotation of the earth about its axis. For other satellites passing partly in the second and third zones, the apparent and actual directions will coincide only for part of the path. So long as the satellite is close to the earth, its angular velocity is relatively high and it will appear to be moving eastward (second zone). As the satellite approaches the interzonal boundary shown in the sketch, its apparent motion in the celestial sphere will gradually slow down. At the instant the satellite reaches this boundary, it will appear to stop for an instant (the angular velocity drops to zero) and will then appear to move in the opposite direction, from east to west (third zone). The latter motion will last until the satellite again reaches the interzonal boundary and the apparent direction of motion again changes.

■ Periodic Artificial Satellites

An artificial satellite may be launched in such a way as to appear periodically at definite intervals over one and the same place. In this case, during the time interval in which the earth executes one revolution relative to the fixed stars (the sidereal day), the artificial satellite will make a complete (whole) number of revolutions and will pass over the place above which it already had passed one sidereal day earlier. We will call such a satellite a periodic artificial satellite.

We note that sidereal days are shorter than "solar" days, since, relative to the fixed stars, the earth makes one rotation about its axis not in 24 mean (solar) hours, but in 23 hours 56 minutes 4 seconds. The difference between sidereal and mean (solar) time is due to the fact that the earth executes rotation about its axis less during a year relative to the sun than it does relative to the stars. For this reason, the sidereal year is one day longer than the solar year, and the sidereal day is 24 hours: 365.25 (days), i.e., 3 minutes 56 seconds, shorter than an ordinary day. Satellites can fly over approximately one and the same locality at one and the same time of the solar day by which we live (not of the sidereal day!) only after a whole year has passed, when the earth has made an integral number of rotations both with respect to the sun (365) and with respect to the stars (366).

If a satellite makes 16 revolutions around the earth in a sidereal day, then each complete revolution will last 90 sidereal minutes. This number of sidereal minutes corresponds to 1 hour 29 minutes 45 seconds of ordinary (solar) time. Such a satellite will move on a circle passing at an altitude of 265 kilometers above the earth's equator, and will appear over its initial point on the surface of the earth at intervals of one sidereal day.

Table 17 gives some of the characteristics of orbits of periodic "daily" artificial satellites, revolving in circular and elliptic orbits. In the latter case, it is assumed that the perigee distance remains constant and equal to 200 kilometers. If, however, the perigee is a definite number of kilometers higher than this, then, for the same period of revolution of the artificial satellite as before, its apogee will be by this definite number of kilometers lower (since the major axis of the orbit must remain as before).

■ **TABLE 17**

Some Characteristics of Circular and Elliptical Orbits of Periodic "Daily" Artificial Satellites

Number of Revolutions in a Sidereal Day	Period of Revolution			Relative Radius of Orbit (Relative Major Semiaxis)*	Altitude of Flight over the Equator in Kilometers		
	Hrs.	Min.	Sec.		For a Circular Orbit	For Elliptical Orbits	
						Minimum	Maximum
17	1	24	28	1.003	2	—	—
16	1	29	45	1.042	265	200	330
15	1	35	44	1.087	558	200	916
14	1	42	35	1.139	884	200	1,568
13	1	50	38	1.196	1,252	200	2,304
12	1	59	40	1.262	1,670	200	3,140
11	2	10	33	1.337	2,150	200	4,100
10	2	23	36	1.424	2,700	200	5,200
9	2	39	34	1.528	3,370	200	6,520
8	2	59	30	1.653	4,170	200	8,140
7	3	25	9	1.807	5,150	200	10,100
6	3	59	21	2.007	6,420	200	12,640
5	4	47	13	2.261	8,040	200	15,880
4	5	59	1	2.624	10,360	200	20,520
3	7	58	41	3.179	13,900	200	27,600
2	11	58	2	4.165	20,190	200	41,800
1	23	56	4	6.611	35,810	200	71,420

* The equatorial radius of the earth is taken as the unit.

The first column in Table 17 shows the number of revolutions of the periodic satellite around the earth during the course of one day. The maximum number of revolutions around the earth made by any artificial satellite in a day cannot exceed 17. Indeed, the shortest period of revolution, namely the period for a zero artificial satellite, amounts to 5065 seconds. During the course of a sidereal day, however (lasting 86,164 seconds), such a satellite will have time to make only 86,164 : 5065 = 17.01 revolutions. An artificial satellite making exactly 17 revolutions a day would have to cross the equator flying at an altitude of 2 kilometers. Of course, in view of the high density of the air, an artificial satellite at such a low altitude cannot be realized.

An artificial satellite may be forced to follow an orbit such that it will fly (for example) once a week or once a day at one and the same time over Berlin and from there travel (let us say) directly to Moscow. At low altitudes (several hundred kilometers), the flight from one capital to the other would take less than 4 minutes. We note that, because of the earth's rotation, a satellite flying west would cover the distance Moscow-Berlin about 15 per cent faster than a satellite flying the same course at the same velocity relative to the sun and stars, but traveling eastward. It is impossible, however, to force an artificial satellite to fly daily over Berlin and Moscow at exactly the same time of day. Every day, the satellite would appear over each of these capitals earlier than on the preceding day, by the same period of 3 minutes 56 seconds as was mentioned above; in this way, during the course of a year, the satellite would have flown over these cities at widely varying times of the day.

The orbit of an artificial satellite can be so designed as to make the satellite periodically fly over several assigned cities, for instance, these same cities, Moscow and Berlin. After flying over Moscow, the satellite would first proceed to the North Pole and then to the South Pole, and finally to the sky of Berlin. Such an almost-round-the-world flight from Moscow to Berlin ("almost," since Berlin is somewhat south of Moscow) will take 1 hour 34 minutes 34 seconds. After the lapse of one sidereal day, the entire cycle of flight to these two capitals will recommence. In a sidereal day the satellite will make exactly 15 revolutions around the earth. To be very exact, the satellite will actually fly over Moscow slightly west of center and over Berlin slightly east of center; it is obvious, however, that this will have no effect at all on the excellent conditions of visibility of the satellite, not only in these capitals but also in the neighboring cities.

One may also "plot the route" of artificial satellites in such a way that the satellite will not appear at all over certain cities and regions, even though their orbits will intersect all parallels of latitude of the earth.

3

The Rocket Starter
of the Artificial Satellite

■
■
■

As everyone knows, the device that escaped from the earth and, ascending for hundreds of kilometers, was transformed into an artificial satellite of our planet was a rocket.

Why did an aircraft or an artillery shell prove unsuitable for this purpose?

As a man can walk on the earth only by planting his feet on the ground, as a locomotive can move only by pushing itself with its wheels away from the rails, so an aircraft can fly above the earth only deriving its support from its wings. No matter how powerful the aircraft engines may be, no matter how perfect their design, it cannot rise more than 50-60 kilometers. It must, however, be noted that an aircraft may be used for the initial acceleration of a rocket, as has been proposed by several specialists (cf. later in text).

Artillery shells also proved unsuitable. Assume that we have a cannon capable of firing a shell at a velocity of 8 kilometers per second or more.

If the shell is fired horizontally, it would have to move through the dense layers of the atmosphere and, consequently, would experience an immense air resistance, which would lead to its gradual loss of speed. If, however, the shell is fired at a certain angle to the horizon, then, even if we neglect the resistance of the air, the shell, obeying the laws of gravitation, would either, as we have seen above (Fig. 3), fall back on the earth (at velocities of less than 11.2 kilometers per second) or would leave the surface of the earth forever. The shell, once fired, would need at least one more push to convert it into an artificial satellite, but it is impossible to do this by means of a cannon.

The only means for obtaining the desired result has proved to be the rocket, which is able to change its direction of motion both in air and in airless space. Another peculiarity of the rocket is its ability to move at very low accelerations, i.e., its ability to pick up the necessary velocity gradually. In time, this will make it possible to transport human beings on an artificial satellite without endangering their lives.

Moreover, because of the low acceleration, the velocity of the rocket in the dense layers of the atmosphere is still relatively low, which means that the resistance of the air will also not be too great, so that no great expenditure of fuel is required to overcome this resistance. Incidentally, even the shell of the rocket does not have time to become excessively heated by the resistance of the air.

A rocket capable of developing an adequate velocity for transition to a circular or elliptical orbit, i.e., inherently able to transform itself into an artificial earth satellite or of placing a satellite in definite orbit is called an orbital rocket.

An engine whose action is based on the force of reaction (counteraction) of a substance ejected from it is called a rocket engine. This substance is the gas formed on combustion of the fuel carried by the rocket.[1] The gases, on issuing from the rocket at high velocities through a special opening (nozzle), propel the rocket in a direction opposite to that of the exhaust.

Reactive motion can be observed in the animal world. The

[1] The combustible and oxidant, taken together, are called the fuel.

denizens of the sea include an invertebrate animal, the octopus. The octopus propels itself forward by its tentacles but does not use them in moving backward, making use instead of a jet of water ejected from its body cavity. According to recent observations, marine molluscs, the abalones, also make use of the reactive principle, enabling them to jump from the water and sail as much as 45-55 meters through the air.[2]

The principle of the rocket engine may be demonstrated by a very simple experiment which is easy to stage in the home. Place a rubber tube on a faucet. Fit the free end with an elbow, bent at a right angle. As soon as the faucet is opened and the water begins to flow from the opening of the elbow, the rubber tube immediately bends away from its former vertical position toward the side opposite the motion of the emerging stream. The stronger the stream, the further the tube will be bent.

■ Speed of the Rocket

In free space,[3] a rocket would move faster, the more fuel it consumed and the higher the exhaust velocity of the issuing gas. This velocity, i.e., the velocity that a rocket will develop in free space, is called the ideal velocity.

In practice, rockets do not move in free space. A rocket is always subject to the action of a certain gravitational field which exerts an influence on its velocity, sometimes increasing it but more often decreasing it in comparison with the ideal velocity. On motion of a rocket in air, its velocity is always lower than the ideal velocity. Consequently, in order to obtain the desired design velocity, it must be designed with a certain "reserve." Only in this case will the rocket be able to reach its planned objective, despite the loss of velocity on the way. And since, in each specific case, the rocket is constructed for a definite ideal velocity which determines all of its technical characteristics, the ideal velocity is sometimes called the characteristic velocity.

The ideal velocity does not depend on the ignition sequence of the fuel: after a certain fuel supply has been consumed in the rocket,

[2] T. Heyerdahl, *Kon-Tiki* (Chicago: Rand McNally, 1950), Chap. 5.

[3] By free space we mean space without a resistant medium and far enough from heavenly bodies to be able to neglect all forces of gravitation.

this velocity will remain one and the same, no matter in what portions the fuel has been consumed, at what rate it has been burned, and what intervals of time have been required by the consecutive periods of combustion. (In this case, the exhaust of gas remains constant, since the quality of the fuel does not change.)

The higher the exhaust velocity of the gases, the easier will it be to build a rocket, since the ratio of the initial mass of the rocket to its final mass will then be correspondingly smaller. The value of this ratio characterizing the fuel consumption is of great importance. It enters into the Tsiolkovskiy formula which establishes the relation between the ideal velocity of the rocket and the fuel consumption.

Assume that a rocket must develop an ideal velocity of 4 kilometers per second. If the exhaust velocity is equal to one kilometer a second, such a rocket cannot be constructed since, according to Tsiolkovskiy's formula, the ratio of the initial mass of the rocket to the final mass in this case would have to be 55, i.e., the weight of the "dry" rocket would have to be only 2 per cent of the weight of the fuel! However, if the exhaust velocity is increased to 3 kilometers per second, then, according to the same formula, this ratio is decreased to 3.8, and the construction of the rocket involves no major difficulty.

■ TABLE 18

Relation between Ideal Velocity of a Rocket and Fuel Consumption at an Exhaust Velocity of 1000 Meters per Second

Ratio of Fuel Consumed to Initial Mass of the Rocket, in Per Cent	Ratio of Initial Mass of Rocket to Final Mass	Ideal Velocity of Rocket in Meters Per Second	Ratio of Fuel Consumed to Initial Mass of the Rocket, in Per Cent	Ratio of Initial Mass of Rocket to Final Mass	Ideal Velocity of Rocket in Meters Per Second
50.0	2	693	87.5	8	2,079
60.0	2.5	916	88.9	9	2,197
66.7	3	1,099	90.0	10	2,303
71.4	3.5	1,253	95.0	20	2,996
75.0	4	1,386	96.7	30	3,401
77.8	4.5	1,504	97.5	40	3,689
80.0	5	1,609	98.0	50	3,912
83.3	6	1,792	98.7	75	4,317
85.7	7	1,946	99.0	100	4,605

The relation between the ideal velocity of the rocket and the fuel consumption is shown in Table 18. The ideal velocity of a

■ FIG. III.—Two-Stage Rocket Bumper, Which Reached an Altitude of 390 Kilometers.

■ FIG. IV.—Start of the Rocket Viking No. 5, Which Reached an Altitude of 172 Kilometers. The ceiling of *Viking* No. 11 was 254 kilometers.

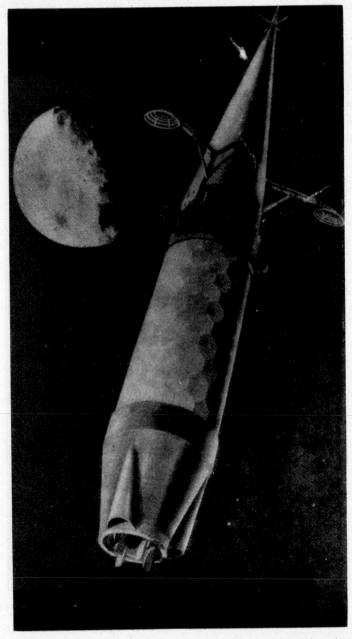

■ FIG. V.—Step Orbital Rocket (According to Design of Gatland, Kunesch, and Dixon).

■ FIG. VI.—Head Stage of Rocket of Preceding Photograph, Designed To Serve as Artificial Satellite.

rocket, according to Tsiolkovskiy's formula, is directly proportional to the exhaust velocity. For this reason, if the exhaust velocity is two, three, etc., times as great as in the case for which the table has been prepared (1000 meters per second), then the ideal velocity of the rocket will also be the same number of times greater than the value shown in the table.

In general, the velocity of a rocket can exceed the velocity of the gases ejected from it. At the instant when, in free space, the mass of the gases ejected from a rocket amounts to 63.2 per cent of the initial weight of the rocket, the velocity of the rocket will be comparable to the exhaust velocity and, on further operation of the engine, will exceed it. This is one of the advantages of a rocket over an artillery shell whose velocity can never be greater than the velocity of the gases that have ejected it from the muzzle of the gun.

It follows from the law deduced by Tsiolkovskiy that, if the ratio of the velocity of the rocket to the exhaust velocity of the gases increases in arithmetical progression, the ratio of the initial mass of the rocket to its final mass will increase in geometrical progression. In other words, the supply of fuel necessary to reach a given velocity increases considerably faster than the velocity of the rocket itself. This is where the difficulty of obtaining cosmic velocities lies.

Theoretically, a rocket is capable of rising to a considerably higher altitude than the maximum altitude to which the combustion products could have risen if the energy of the fuel had been completely utilized to lift them. This is one of the principal advantages of the rocket.

■ The Step Rocket

Theoretically the ordinary (single-stage) rocket, provided with a sufficient quantity of fuel, would permit reaching any desired velocity. In practice, however, the velocity of such a rocket is limited since the amount of fuel that it can carry aloft is limited. It is unfeasible to build an apparatus whose weight would be negligibly small by comparison with the weight of the fuel it contains.

In the opinion of specialists, a lightening of the rocket structure and an increase in exhaust velocity could, at best, increase the maximum velocity developed by modern rockets by 40-50 per cent.

In the ordinary (single-stage) rocket, during the time of operation of the engine, the mass of the fuel tanks remains constant and
only the mass of the fuel itself decreases. The empty portion of the
tank system, continuing in accelerated motion together with the rocket,
requires an unproductive consumption of energy for its acceleration.
For this reason, the rocket must be freed as soon as possible from the
empty tanks.

This leads to the idea of an apparatus of more complex design,
in which the acceleration of the main rocket takes place by the aid of
another auxiliary rocket. As the auxiliary rocket burns out, it is automatically detached and descends, for instance, by parachute. It is only
then that the main rocket is started. In this way, at the instant of
starting, the main rocket is already at a certain altitude and possesses
a certain velocity, which allows it to rise higher than the ordinary
(single-stage) rocket. Such a compound rocket is called a two-stage
rocket.

A compound rocket may also be of the multistage type; since the
velocities attained by the aid of each stage are additive, this method,
with a sufficient number of stages, is able to yield the desired terminal
velocity. The ceiling of a compound or step rocket, as a rule, is higher
than the sum of the ceilings that could be obtained by the individual
stages.

There is an erroneous opinion that a compound rocket is heavier
than a single-stage rocket carrying the same payload and that, therefore, when the number of stages of a rocket is increased, its take-off
weight is also increased while the relative amount of payload is decreased. In reality, the situation is precisely the opposite. For one and
the same payload, a step rocket is always of lesser initial weight than
the corresponding nonstep rocket, and this weight decreases with increasing number of stages.

Assume that we are to impart a velocity of 6 kilometers per second
to one ton of payload. If we assume an exhaust velocity of 3500
meters per second and consider that the structural weight of the
rocket is one fifth the weight of the fuel being carried, then the initial
weight of the rocket will be equal to 60 tons, as will be shown by
calculations. If, however, the same velocity is given to the same payload by means of a two-stage rocket with similar characteristics, then
the take-off weight of the rocket is decreased more than fivefold, while

a three-stage rocket will weigh less than a sixth as much. This is explained by the fact that the passive part of the rocket, which no longer participates in the accelerated motion, is dropped more often with increasing number of stages so that the fuel supply can be reduced.

In most modern compound rockets, not only the used tanks and piping but even the engines themselves are jettisoned. In this case, the engine of each stage of the rocket operates for a considerably shorter time than the engine of the corresponding single-stage rocket would have to operate. It is therefore easier to build such engines. Moreover, the power of the engine of each succeeding stage may be considerably less than the power of the engine of the preceding stage, since the mass of the entire system is constantly decreasing.

It is considered today that for rockets of different tonnage and also for different stages of compound rockets, engines of one or two standard types, installed in varying numbers, will be used.

It would be easiest to drop the passive mass of a rocket continuously, as it becomes expendable. It is entirely understandable, however, that a tank can be jettisoned only after it has been completely emptied, i.e., only after a more or less prolonged interval of time. A rocket in which the passive mass could be continuously jettisoned is not yet realizable, although it is not impossible that such a continuous rocket may be built in the future. Under the assumptions adopted here, its weight would be 15 per cent less than the weight of the three-stage rocket discussed above.

The method of simple separation of the burned-out stages of a rocket is not the most economical method. By means of a certain additional design complication, it will be possible to eject these stages backward, like an artillery shell, and thus to utilize the recoil effect for increasing the velocity of the rocket and decreasing the fuel consumption.

To avoid the hazards caused on the ground by the impact of jettisoned parts of a space rocket, such dropping must take place over uninhabited areas (oceans or deserts), or the fall of these parts must be retarded by utilizing the resistance of the air. The second method is preferable over the first one, since it permits recovery of the ejected stage of the rocket and its re-use, after repair.

In conclusion, we note that the invention of the compound rocket dates back several centuries. The Belgian Jean Beauvie has left descriptions and sketches of such rockets, dated 1591. Considerably more detailed description and drawings were made by a Pole, Casimir Semenovicz, in 1650.

■ Powder and Liquid Rockets

Depending on the fuel on which they operate, rockets are divided into powder rockets and liquid rockets.

Powder rockets are unsuitable for launching an orbital rocket. In these rockets, the consumption of fuel (powder) during flight cannot be regulated, just as the flame of a candle cannot be regulated. The burning of powder can also not be stopped and, consequently, the engine cannot be stopped if necessary. Scientific thought has been working for several decades already on the question of a gradual introduction of powder (or other solid fuels) into the combustion chamber, for instance in the form of pellets or cartridges. But the results attained in this field are still unsatisfactory.

Powder rockets were used up to the end of the Twenties. As long ago as thirty years, however, most experimenters on jet motion had finally changed over to work with liquid-fuel rockets. This problem, because of its complete novelty and technical complexity, was incomparably more difficult than the development of powder rockets but, at the same time, also opened up wider prospects. It is true that numerous experiments to launch liquid rockets into the stratosphere have long remained unsuccessful; not one of the rockets launched went beyond the boundaries of the troposphere. Nevertheless, the theoretical and practical work in this direction has continued, and gradually the immense possibilities and advantages of the use of liquid rockets have become increasingly obvious.

Efforts are today being directed primarily toward the improvement of rockets operating on liquid fuel. Most liquid fuels have a higher heat value than solid fuels; the fuel intake can be regulated, while the fuel and oxidant can be stored separately and come into contact only in the combustion chamber, which is safer. The weight of an engine operating on liquid fuel, by comparison with the weight of the fuel, can be less than in powder rockets since, in the former case, only the small combustion chamber is subjected to high pressures but not the container with the fuel, as is the case in the shell of a powder rocket. In a liquid rocket, it is only the combustion chamber that is particularly strong, and consequently also particularly heavy.

Because of all these properties, liquid rockets are widely used in modern technique.

On the other hand, powder rockets are considerably simpler in design than liquid rockets, and their thrust is very high compared to their own weight. This makes them useful as auxiliary engines for accelerating an orbital rocket at the start. Thanks to the simplicity of storage of such rockets and their equipment they also find another use, namely, that of vehicles for astronauts outside an artificial satellite in extra-atmospheric space and also that of a reserve motive force for correcting the orbit of an artificial satellite.

There are also rockets of mixed type, operating on solid-liquid fuel. In this case, powdered coal, compressed into cylinders with drilled circular orifices, is most often used as the fuel. Liquid oxygen or nitrous oxide is used as the oxidant. The coal pellets are first inserted in the combustion chamber, while the liquid oxidant is supplied by pump as needed. The thrust of the engine is regulated in this way. The combustion can be stopped at any instant. In this case, the total volume of the fuel is smaller than that of liquid fuel.

Rockets of mixed type are still only imperfectly developed, and for the time being it is hard to draw any conclusion as to their suitability for launching an artificial satellite.

World War II was a turning point in the development of rocketry. It is deplorable that this development proceeded along the lines of tactical use. Various military rockets appeared. Stages on the path in the development of foreign rocketry were the creation of rockets of the types V-2, Bumper, Viking, and Aerobee. These will therefore be described briefly, and their principal technical characteristics will be presented.

In 1944 the Germans were the first to use, for the barbarous bombardment of the civilian population of London and the Southern region of England, the "flying missiles," V-1, and then the long-range rockets, V-2. The latter had a radius of action far greater than the range of artillery shells; they covered 270-300 kilometers, rising to an altitude of over 100 kilometers along their trajectory. The V-2 missile was about 14 meters high and up to 1.65 meters in diameter. With its initial weight of 12 tons, of which 8.9 tons were fuel and one ton the high-explosive warhead, the V-2 missile developed a thrust of about 25 tons for 65 seconds.

In the postwar years, intensive work was done in the United States to improve the captured V-2 German rockets. Such rockets were used for studying the upper layers of the atmosphere, for photographing spherical segments of the earth, and for other research work. On vertical launching, the missiles rose to an altitude of 218 kilometers. After the rocket had reached the ceiling, the instruments with the observation records were dropped by parachute. Frequently, the rocket itself, for reasons of safety, was blown up before entering the dense layers of the atmosphere. Thus individual nonstreamlined parts of the rocket encountered high air resistance and therefore fell to the ground at a relatively low velocity.

In one of the experiments conducted in the United States in 1949, one of eight compound two-stage rockets of the Bumper type rose to an altitude of 390 kilometers (Fig. III). The bottom stage of the rocket was a modification of the V-2 rocket, weighing 12 tons, while the head, of the type of the Wac-Corporal, weighed 300 kilograms, of which 11 kilograms was payload (instruments). The height of the rocket head was about 5 meters and its diameter 30 centimeters. The engine of this rocket used a fuel consisting of aniline and nitric acid which, on contact in the combustion chamber, entered into chemical reaction without ignition. The fuel components were fed by means of compressed nitrogen. The rocket tail was launched from the earth's surface, while the head engine of the rocket was connected at an altitude of 34 kilometers, when a flight velocity of 1.7 kilometers per second had already been acquired. The maximum velocity attained was 2250 meters per second, and the flight lasted 12 minutes.

The V-2 rockets had a number of disadvantages; in particular, it was necessary to balance the rocket shell by the aid of ballast (burdening the rocket, which, even without that, was extremely overloaded), the fragility of the gas-turbine blades, etc., and for this reason, Aerobee and Viking rockets subsequently began to replace the V-2.

The rocket of the Aerobee type is able to lift a payload of 60-70 kilograms on vertical take-off, to an altitude of over 120 kilometers. The records of the instruments are dropped by parachute or transmitted by radio. Such a rocket consists primarily of a welded stainless steel structure, 38 centimeters in diameter and 6 meters in height. The rocket engine operates on nitric acid and aniline fed into the combustion chamber under the pressure of compressed helium. In the most advanced versions of the Aerobee, the ratio of the initial mass of the rocket to its final mass was reduced to 4.62 (in other modern rockets, this characteristic quantity has been considerably exceeded).

The Viking rocket is about the same length as the V-2 but has only half the diameter of that rocket. The two rockets operate on one and the some fuel (alcohol with liquid oxygen), but the Viking rocket is considerably more compact. At a dry body weight of 903 kilograms, it is able to lift 3360 kilograms of fuel. At the end of 1952, such a rocket rose to an altitude of 217 kilometers, and in May 1954 the eleventh modification of this rocket, of an initial weight of 7.5 tons, lifted over 300 kilograms of instruments to an altitude of 254 kilometers (Fig. IV).

■ Design of the Engine

The most important part of a rocket engine is the combustion chamber and the nozzle for the exhaust of the gaseous combustion products of the fuel. The combustion chamber and its auxiliary mechanisms, during operation of the engine, are subjected both to the action of the very low temperature of the fuel components (for instance liquid oxygen) and to the very strong heating from the extremely hot combustion products under high pressure. These circumstances make particularly strenuous demands on the choice of the material for the combustion chamber and on its cooling system.

The design and dimensions of an orbital rocket depend on the characteristics of the orbit selected for the artificial satellite and on the amount of payload to be carried, but these parameters may fluctuate within wide limits.

A large part of the volume of the rocket is necessarily occupied by the fuel tanks, so that their shape and arrangement largely determine the form of the entire flying device.

The ratio of the tank weight to the weight of the fuel carried, under assigned pressure inside the tanks, remains constant for any desired tank size. If, for instance, a certain amount of liquid oxygen requires ellipsoidal tanks weighing 100 kilograms with an internal pressure of 15 atmospheres, then an amount of liquid oxygen ten times as great, under the same pressure and with the same material stresses, such tanks would have to weigh ten times as much, i.e., one ton.

But, other conditions being equal, the weight of tanks depends on their shape. Thus, elongated cylindrical tanks, for the same volume and pressure of the contained liquid oxygen, would weigh a third more than ellipsoidal tanks. Spherical tanks are the lightest of all, but they produce excessive resistance in traveling through the atmosphere.

In general, the materials for building such a flying device must be particularly strong and at the same time sufficiently light. The following striking example will give an idea of the suitability of a given material. Assume that cables, made of various materials, are trailed from a stratosphere balloon. At a certain length, which is entirely definite for each material, the cables will break under the action of their own weight. A lead cable will break at a length of only 0.1 kilometers, a tin cable at 0.5 kilometers, a zinc cable at 1.7 kilometers, a red-copper cable at 2.6 kilometers, a cast-iron cable at 3 kilometers, a forged-steel cable at 13 kilometers, a Dural cable at 19 kilometers, and one of special steels, at 20-24 kilometers. The longer the maximum length of the cable before rupture, the more suitable will the material of the cable be for building many rocket satellite parts.

Certain materials become stronger at low temperatures; for instance, at the temperature of liquid oxygen ($-182°$ C.), the strength of duralumin increases by 26 per cent and that of forged steel by 34 per cent.

As an example for the selection of structural materials for orbital rockets, the tanks of the first stage of the American Vanguard rocket are made of aluminum, and those of the second stage of stainless steel. The frame of the engine compartment, as well as that of the middle stage of the rocket, are made of aluminum trusses and are covered with a riveted magnesium skin. A special type of plastic ("Kel-F"), possessing low thermal conductivity, is also used.

The question of the selection of material for the combustion chamber is more difficult. The combustion chamber and the nozzle, as already mentioned, are subjected simultaneously to the action of pressure and high temperature. Thus, in modern rockets, the gas pressure in the combustion chamber reaches 100 atmospheres and more, and the temperature goes up to 3000-3500° C.

The higher the pressure in the combustion chamber of an orbital rocket, the greater will be the exhaust velocity of the gas. This, however, does not mean that it is always advantageous to increase this pressure. The point is that, with increasing pressure, the engine weight must also be increased, while the gas temperature is also raised, which makes it difficult to find refractory materials for the combustion chamber and nozzle. For this reason, designers are compelled to determine the range of optimum (most advantageous) pressure.[4]

Of the known materials, the most heat-resistant types are alloys of nickel, of cobalt, and of titanium, chromium-molybdenum steel, fire-resistant ceramics, and refractories. In a high-altitude rocket of the Skylark type (Great Britain), the nozzle is considerably lightened by the use of bakelite asbestos. There are also prospects of using such refractory metals as molybdenum and tungsten (whose melting points are, respectively, about 2600 and 3400° C.).

By regulating the fuel feed, the pressure is held within the range of values that are safe for the strength of the combustion chamber. To protect the chamber from the destructive influence of high temperature, liquid cooling by one of the fuel components is used. The heat absorbed by it is again liberated in the combustion chamber.

Despite the high temperatures in the combustion chamber, it is entirely possible to protect it from destruction, the more so since the time of operation of the engine before the artificial satellite goes into orbit will amount to only a few minutes.

In feeding the fuel components into the combustion chamber it is necessary to assure the most complete mixing and the most rapid combustion. The mixing occurs either in a special space (the prechamber), or directly in the combustion chamber itself. Electricity (a sparkplug) or some chemical catalyst, is used for igniting the mixture.

The fuel is usually fed to the combustion chamber by pumps driven by steam produced in a vapor-gas generator by mixing hydrogen peroxide and potassium permanganate or sodium permanganate.

[4] A. Shternfeld, *Introduction to Astronautics* (Moscow-Leningrad, 1937), pp. 220-223.

The pumps may also be driven by a gas turbine operated by the main fuel components. With the fuel fed by pumps, the gas pressure in the combustion chamber amounts to 50-60 atmospheres.

Besides engines with a pump fuel feed, there are also liquid rocket engines with gas-cylinder feed. In these cases, the combustible and oxidant are fed to the combustion chamber under pressure produced in the fuel tanks by a compressed inert gas (helium, nitrogen).[5]

At a pressure of the order of 20 atmospheres in the combustion chamber, the original pressure of the inert gas (in a separate cylinder) amounts to about 250-300 atmospheres; in the fuel tanks it is reduced to a constant level of 30-40 atmospheres.

Sometimes, even though the fuel is supplied by turbopumps, an inert gas (for instance, helium) is still introduced under pressure into the combustible and oxidant tanks. This precaution has the object of ensuring the initial flow of fuel into the combustion chamber, and also of avoiding the possible interruption of the flow of the fuel components to the pumps. Gas under pressure also gives the tanks the necessary rigidity. For this reason, the rocket need not necessarily have a special shell for the fuel tanks, and the tanks themselves are used as structural members in this case.

On launching a rocket, which is effected, for instance, by means of a detonator exploded by an electric contact, the oxidant at first enters the tanks under the action of its own weight and under pressure of the inert gas, and is then followed by the combustible. A pickup is actuated by the ignition of the fuel mixture and opens the valve of the hydrogen peroxide line. Vapor then begins to enter the turbine, thus starting up the fuel pumps. A silver screen may be used as a catalyst to decompose the hydrogen peroxide in the vapor-gas generator.

To reduce the speed of the turbine and increase the moment on the pump shafts, a reduction gear may be used. Liquid oxygen under pressure of several atmospheres is admitted to the centrifugal pump. The stoichiometric[6] metering of the fuel components (or the planned deviation from such proportion) is regulated by means of a control

[5] Gases which do not enter into chemical reactions with the fuel components are here termed inert gases.

[6] Stoichiometry is the study of the weight relationships between the combustible and oxidant at which complete combustion of the fuel, without leaving any of its components, takes place.

valve installed on the liquid oxygen lines, while the combustible, after passage through a worm pipe, cooling the walls of the engine, passes freely to the orifices of the combustion chamber. If the engine must be shut off, the combustible, oxidant, and vapor-gas lines are simultaneously closed.

What shape must be given to the rocket jet so that the gases exhausted through it will have the maximum possible velocity? This question might seem to be of secondary importance, but its solution involves one of the most interesting episodes in the history of the development of rocketry.

For decades, engineers and technologists unsuccessfully attempted to increase the exhaust velocity of the vapors and gases. Often, however, calculations gave one value while experiment yielded an entirely different value of much lower magnitude. The experimenters made various attempts in their search for a solution. For example, they provided an orifice in the wall of the steam boiler, with a highly polished endpiece rounded on the inside; increased the temperature and pressure of the vapor; reduced the pressure in the vessel into which the vapor was fed; and reduced this pressure to a practical vacuum. All this was in vain: in the most narrow cross section of the jet at a given pressure and density, the exhaust velocity of the vapor never exceeded the velocity of propagation of sound. Practically, this meant that it was impossible to build a turbine operating with sufficient economy and that it was impossible to build rockets developing high speed. For a long time, technology could find no way out of this blind alley, until the Swedish engineer de Laval used a nozzle that was constricted at first and then flared into the form of a horn (1889). On passing the most narrow spot, the neck of the nozzle where the exhaust velocity reached the velocity of sound, the vapor and gas began to move in the bell mouth at a greater and greater velocity. The invention of this nozzle made it possible to construct powerful turbines. But the engineers of that time hardly realized the importance of this nozzle for the development of rocket engineering. It was precisely this nozzle that made it possible to obtain a manifold increase in the efficiency of the rocket and to answer the question "to be or not to be" for the high-altitude and space rockets.

Although, however, an expanding nozzle is necessary to accelerate the motion of the molecules on emerging from the combustion chamber, it is not absolutely essential to have an initial constriction of the nozzle. A distinctive feature of the combustion chamber, for example, of the British engine of the Screamer type is its cylindrical form. The chamber is directly connected with an expanding bell mouth (nozzle) (without an intermediate constricting cross section as is the case in all other rocket engines known today). The choice of this shape for the combustion chamber was dictated mainly by the simplicity of the cooling system. The coolant water passes at first through the jacket of the combustion chamber, and is then sprayed into the combustion chamber itself. This reduces the combustion temperature slightly, but it ordinarily does not fall below 3200° C. It is true that, other conditions being equal, the exhaust velocity of the gases decreases with decreasing temperature. On the other hand, the water also has the advantage of decreasing the mean molecular weight of the combustion products; in addition, the lower the molecular weight of the gases, the higher will be their exhaust velocity, other conditions remaining equal.

At first glance a rocket engine, in view of the absence of any moving parts, reciprocating mechanism, flywheels, transmission mechanisms, might seem to be a very simple machine, but this is not so. A rocket does have: a complex fuel supply system (turbine pumps for supplying combustible and oxidant); a vapor-gas generator to feed the pump drives; fuel distributors; internal and external cooling systems for the engine head, the combustion chamber and the jet; gas rudders, working in the extremely hot jet of the exhaust gases; servomotors serving these rudders or other control units of the rocket; an ignition system, etc.

■ Rocket Propellants[7]

As already stated, rockets operate on solid or liquid propellant, the liquid forms of fuel being preferred. Let us consider the principal forms of liquid propellants.

Modern engineering is concerned mainly with questions of the combustible, since the oxidizer (oxygen) for ordinary engines can be taken in unlimited amount from the atmosphere. For rockets, however, both fuel components are of equal importance.

[7] Rocket propellant is often termed propergol in the special literature.

As everyone knows, hydrogen on combining with oxygen liberates more heat than most known fuels. But hydrogen, even in the liquid state, has a very low specific gravity (it is only a fourteenth as heavy as water) and, consequently, demands considerably larger tanks than any other fuel. Besides this, it is rather difficult to prepare liquid hydrogen in large amounts, owing to its low boiling point (−253° C.). Liquid acetylene and liquid methane are more suitable as combustibles.

It is considered today that the best results can be obtained with a combustible that is liquid at room temperatures. For such combustibles, the design of the tanks is simplified and no special measures need be taken to protect the combustible from the influence of the temperature of the outside air; moreover, such combustibles have a high specific gravity, being at least ten times as heavy as liquid oxygen. Starting out from these considerations, the following propellants are used for rocket engines burning liquid fuel: liquid hydrocarbons, for instance, kerosene, gas oil, gasoline, turpentine, alcohol, as well as hydrazine (a compound of nitrogen and hydrogen) aniline (an organic compound), and others.

Attempts are also being made to increase the exhaust velocity of the gases by using liquid fuels containing metals in the form of a metal additive or a chemical compound ("metallic fuel").

It is well known that atomic hydrogen[8] liberates an immense amount of energy per unit weight in forming ordinary molecular hydrogen, which even exceeds the liberation of energy in combustion reactions (one kilogram of atomic hydrogen is sufficient to heat half a ton of ice water to the boiling point). Atomic hydrogen, however, is very unstable (the time spent by a hydrogen atom in the free state is only a fraction of a second) and no method for preparing it in large quantities has yet been developed.

Attempts have recently been made to utilize atomic fuel (cf. below) for flying devices, rockets, and aircraft. However, these attempts have not yet been successful.

The oxidizer used may be nitric acid (with a small amount of sulfuric acid added to reduce its corrosive action), chloric acid, tetranitromethane, 80-85 per cent hydrogen peroxide, and other substances which are liquids under normal conditions. Some of the components

---

[8] Particles of atomic hydrogen in the free state occur in the form of atoms, while in ordinary hydrogen the atoms are combined pairwise into molecules.

of the oxidizers do not participate in combustion. The oxygen content of chloric and nitric acids, for example, is respectively only 64 per cent and 76 per cent, and in other oxidants such as potassium chlorate and nitrate, it is even less than 50 per cent.

As far as complete oxidation is concerned, oxygen is obviously the most advantageous oxidant. This oxidant, the most widely distributed on earth, condenses at a temperature of $-183°$ C. to a light-blue liquid. Liquid oxygen is 13 per cent heavier than water and freezes at $-219°$ C.

Ozone would be still more advantageous as an oxidant, since its reaction of decomposition into oxygen is accompanied by the liberation of heat (710 kilocalories per kilogram) which would substantially increase the heat value of the propellant and, consequently, would make it possible to increase the exhaust velocity of the gases. Moreover, the boiling point of ozone ($-112°$ C.) is not as low as that of oxygen while its specific gravity is considerably higher (1.45 grams per cubic centimeter in the liquid state), which would permit a reduction in the weight of the tanks. But ozone also has its shortcomings: its strongly oxidizing action on metals and the ease with which it explodes. It has not yet been possible to use ozone in the pure form as an oxidizer in rocket engines. In view of this fact, attempts are being made to use a mixture of liquid ozone and liquid oxygen. Such a mixture is rather stable, i.e., it will not decompose if its ozone content is less than 25 per cent.

Recently fluorine is coming into wider use as oxidizer. Fluorine, however, is highly toxic and retains its toxic properties even after entering into chemical reaction. The exhaust gases of fluorine fuels, on mixing with the atmospheric air, may therefore poison living beings in the area near the rocket launching pad. From this point of view, oxygen fluorides, which are the most powerful oxidants next to ozone, are less dangerous.

The opinion is frequently expressed that powder yields the highest exhaust velocity. This is not the case. The exhaust velocity does not depend on the velocity of the chemical reaction (combustion) of a given mixture (which, for powder, is in fact very high) but on its heat value. The heat value of powder mixtures is relatively low.

In exactly the same way as powder, which already contains the oxygen necessary for combustion, there are also liquid fuels which in themselves contain both the combustible and the oxidizer (single-component fuel). These include mixtures of methyl nitrate with methyl alcohol, ammonia with ammonium nitrate or with nitrous oxides, etc. Naturally, such types of fuel need only a single tank and a single pump. During the operation of an engine burning such fuel, however, the flame from the combustion chamber may backfire into the tank through the pipes and the pump. Although it is possible to take precautionary measures against this, designers would hardly rely on such an engine for a passenger rocket.

Of the two-component liquid propellants (i.e., fuels consisting of a combustible and an oxidizer), hydrazine in combination with nitric acid is preferred. Hydrazine is a colorless viscous liquid, considerably heavier than most other fuels, for example, hydrocarbons (its specific gravity is slightly higher than that of water). Nitric acid also has a number of advantages over other oxidizers; its specific gravity is 1.52 grams per cubic centimeter (for concentrated nitric acid); the vapor pressure is low; it is chemically stable and has a low freezing point. Therefore, tanks for both hydrazine and nitric acid may be small and have rather thin walls.

The ordinary fuels today yield an exhaust velocity of about 2.5 kilometers per second for the gases issuing from the rocket. If the combustion involved no losses, then the exhaust velocity would reach 6 kilometers per second and even a slightly higher value if the best fuels were used. In practice, this velocity may be expected to be increased to 4 kilometers per second.

A rocket propellant, in general, is more valuable, the higher the exhaust velocity of its combustion products and the greater its density. The former requirement results directly from the fundamental law of rocket motion, according to which the velocity of a rocket is proportional to the velocity of the gases ejected; the second requirement is explained by the fact that, at greater fuel density, the required volume and weight of the tanks become smaller, which permits a rocket design with a smaller drag.

The value of a propellant is also determined by its technology, by the availability of raw material, and by the difficulty of its extraction, as well as by the conditions of storage and transportation. These questions in turn are related to the stability of the fuel, its explosion safety and corrosive action, i.e., the degree of corroding the tank walls. To retard this process, an additive is sometimes used in a fuel as a corrosion inhibitor (an additive being a substance added in small quantities to a fuel to improve its properties). The toxicity of a given fuel and the possibility of its harmful action on the human organism must also be taken into account. The group of rocket propellants, especially of synthetic liquid propellants, is rapidly increasing because of the continuous search for the most perfect fuel.

■ The Atomic Rocket

In order to accelerate the efflux of gases from a rocket still further, it is necessary to replace ordinary fuel by nuclear fuel. What is nuclear fuel and what are its advantages?

Physics today has successfully solved the problem of the transmutation of some chemical elements into others. These transformations are, in some cases, accompanied by the liberation of atomic energy. A substance liberating such energy is called a nuclear fuel. A peculiarity of such fuel is the fact that a small quantity of it contains an immense amount of energy. A nuclear fuel, together with a liquid or gas, is called an atomic fuel.[9]

Although the process of liberation of atomic energy takes place at very high speed, it can be controlled.

An atomic rocket will presumably operate on the following principle: A small vessel, resembling the combustion chamber of a liquid rocket, will be charged with liquid hydrogen or some other fluid. The atomic energy, liberated in the form of heat, will instantaneously heat the hydrogen to a very high temperature; the hydrogen will then change into the gaseous state and will rush out under immense pressure. The jet of gas will be ejected at a velocity of some tens of kilometers a second. The higher the exhaust velocity, the less fuel will be needed to realize orbital flight. This is the great advantage of the atomic rocket.

In principle, the atomic rocket will not differ substantially from ordinary rockets. A number of technical difficulties, however, stand in the way of its creation. For instance it will be necessary to "subdue"

[9] The terms "nuclear fuel" and "atomic fuel" are merely figurative, since the liberation of atomic energy and its transmission to an inert body are not processes of ordinary combustion.

the superhigh temperatures and pressures that will arise in the atomic rocket, otherwise not a single metal will be able to withstand them. It is also necessary to take measures to protect personnel from the radioactive radiations that accompany the liberation of atomic energy.

Work on the realization of the atomic rocket is today underway in various countries.

4

Launching of an Artificial Satellite

■
■
■

■ Energy Necessary to Place an Artificial Satellite in Orbit

Although in practice the launching of an orbital rocket should take place only on an optimum trajectory (cf. later in text), it is nevertheless advisable to consider the various possible versions of launching, even under the conditions of absence of air resistance. These theoretical versions are of interest since they permit a better definition of the features of launching an artificial satellite.

In order to launch an artificial satellite, the following two necessary conditions must be satisfied: the flying device must be lifted a certain vertical distance, and a definite velocity must be imparted to it.

To lift a load two meters requires twice as much work as to lift it one meter, but lifting a load (for instance, an artificial satellite) a hundred million meters does not necessarily require a hundred million times as much work. In view of the fact that the force of gravity decreases with altitude in inverse proportion to the square of the distance from the center of the planet, there is an immense saving of energy: to lift a load this distance would take only 1/16.7 times as much as the value obtained by ordinary calculation, if the force of gravity is assumed to remain constant with altitude.

Thus the energy that must be expended in placing an artificial satellite in orbit is not proportional to the altitude.

Assume that we have lifted an artificial satellite a distance equal to the radius of the earth and have expended a definite amount of energy for this purpose. If we continue the lifting, then, to raise the artificial satellite two earth radii, we will not need twice as much energy but, as will be shown by calculation, only 1/3 more. However, for each successive lift by the same increment of height of one earth radius, we will expend only 1/6, 1/10, 1/15, respectively, of the work that was performed in lifting the satellite by one radius. To raise a body to infinity, 100 earth radii from the center of the earth, takes only 1 per cent of the energy that would be necessary to raise it to infinity from the surface of the earth.

Mathematical calculations show that the work necessary to lift a body from the surface of a planet to infinity is equal to the work that would have to be expended to lift it a distance equal to the radius of the planet, if the intensity of gravity did not vary with the distance of the body from the center of the planet. For this reason, for example, to remove a pebble weighing one gram from the earth's gravitational field, the same work would have to be performed as would be required

■ **TABLE 19**

Altitudes Reached with Vertical Take-off from the Earth's Surface at Various Velocities

Take-off Velocity, in Meters Per Second	Reached, Altitude in Earth Radii	Velocity Increment, in Comparison with Preceding Velocity, in Meters Per Second	Altitude Increment in Comparison with Preceding Altitude in Earth Radii	Ratio of Energy Expended to Energy Necessary to Remove Body to Infinity, in Per Cent
7,912	1	0	0	50
9,136	2	1,224	1	67
10,008	4	872	2	80
10,639	9	631	5	90
11,133	99	494	90	99
11,189	Infinity	56	Infinity	100

to lift a load of 6.4 tons one meter. Half of this work will be enough to lift the same pebble a distance equal to the earth's radius.

A body, to lift a certain distance, however, need not be continuously pulled upward. An initial velocity may be imparted to the body at the surface of the earth, all at once, to make its kinetic energy equal to the work required for lifting it the assigned distance.

Assume that, at the earth's surface, a body is given an ever increasing vertical velocity.[1] In this case, the altitudes reached will increase still more rapidly than that initial velocity. As shown by Table 19, the range of velocities can be so selected that the increment of altitude will increase despite the increasingly smaller velocity increment.

Theoretically, with any method of launching an artificial satellite and for any trajectory, to place it in orbit, the amount of energy expended on the lift must be one and the same.

■ Launching Altitude of an Artificial Satellite

To what altitude should artificial satellites be launched? There is a sharp difference of opinion among scientists on this question. Some have proposed an altitude of 200 kilometers above the earth's surface or even less, while others, fearing the resistance of the earth's atmosphere, suggest an altitude of several thousand kilometers.

What circumstances must be taken into account in selecting the altitude to which an artificial satellite is launched?

If an artificial satellite were designed to fly at a low altitude, its launching would be considerably easier, since the rockets would have to develop only a relatively low velocity. The realization of such a satellite, however, encounters a number of obstacles. First of all, even if we neglect the resistance of the air, the presence of mountains would not allow an artificial satellite to fly lower than 9 kilometers (the altitude of Mt. Everest). Moreover, a satellite with a strictly circular orbit could in no case fly lower than 21.5 kilometers above the poles. At lower latitudes, it would inevitably land in the ocean or smash against the surface of the continents, because of the oblateness of the earth (we recall that the polar radius of the earth is 21.5 kilometers shorter than the equatorial radius). Even if this altitude of flight of the satellite above the poles were doubled, it would still not ensure

[1] We assume that the velocity is imparted instantaneously to the rocket, instead of gradually, as is done in reality.

its safety. Indeed, in this case it would be sufficient for the velocity of the rocket, at the instant of combustion cutoff, to be—within the limits of error—0.08 per cent less than the required value, for the satellite to strike the ground. Even an accurately adjusted velocity would not completely guarantee safety. At so low an altitude, the slightest deviation of flight from a horizontal direction would imply catastrophe.

We have, however, completely disregarded the resistance of the air. If the satellite were launched to an altitude of as much as several tens of kilometers, the atmosphere would still impede its motion and would cause the satellite to fall back to earth. Therefore, an artificial satellite must be launched to beyond the dense layers of the atmospheric envelope of the earth. At altitudes above 200 kilometers, the air is so rarefied that it no longer exerts a sensible resistance, even at cosmic speeds of the order of 8 kilometers per second. Consequently, the orbit to be described by the satellite would retain its original shape for some time.

The slight changes in the shape of the orbit that would still take place, even in this case, as a result of the retardation of the satellite's motion could be corrected at long intervals of time by the aid of a rocket engine, at negligible fuel consumption. If this is not done, even insignificant perturbations would involve increasingly serious deviatons from the original orbit. If, for instance, an artificial satellite were moving in an elliptical orbit, then the resistance of the air would be most sensible during its passage through perigee; under the influence of this resistance, the eccentricity would gradually decrease (cf. above and later in text). We note that even in the case of the highest vacuum that can be obtained under laboratory conditions, where the pressure of the air is 0.1 millibar (this corresponds to the air pressure at an altitude of about 75 kilometers), one cubic millimeter of air still contains about 3 million molecules. This circumstance should be borne in mind in studying the resistance of the air that would be encountered by a flying device in the uppermost layers of the atmosphere. Theoretically, even meteoric dust and the pressure of the solar rays should to some extent modify the orbit of a satellite, but it is doubtful that such modification would be noticeable in practice.

In selecting the altitude of flight of an artificial satellite, the basic premises must be, on the one hand, the creation of an energy reserve of the orbital rocket and, on the other hand, the intended life of the satellite. The launching of the first Soviet artificial satellite was scheduled to attain an altitude of several hundred kilometers (like the plans for American satellites now being worked out), although only a little more energy would be necessary to reach greater altitudes. The decision, during the first period, to dispense with high-flying artificial satellites is explained by the fact that the launching of a satellite, even to a minimum altitude of several hundred kilometers, with the necessary accuracy in speed and direction, is already a very difficult problem for modern rocket engineering.

There is still another argument in favor of the lower position of the orbit of an artificial satellite: the danger from meteors is less, the lower the altitude at which the satellite moves.

As already mentioned, the altitude of flight of a polar satellite in a circular orbit is continuously varying, because of the oblateness of the earth. Such a satellite would have to overfly the poles at an altitude about twenty odd kilometers higher than the equator. But a polar satellite can be created that would move, in a certain segment of its path, at constant altitude. For this purpose, the altitude at which the satellite would fly over one of the poles, for instance over the North Pole, would have to be equal to the altitude of its flight above the equator. On the portion of the path—equator-North Pole-equator —the altitude of the satellite would then remain almost constant. From the moment of crossing the equator, during the flight of the satellite over the southern hemisphere, the altitude of the satellite would gradually increase, so as to reach its "ceiling" above the South Pole, where the altitude is over 40 kilometers greater than over the North Pole. Theoretically the orbit would be an ellipse, but practically, because of its very small eccentricity (equal to 0.003), the orbit of the satellite could be considered a circle with its center, like the center of the ellipse, on the earth's axis, 21.5 kilometers south of the center of the earth (the second focus of the ellipse would be twice as many kilometers south of the center).

■ Influence of the Earth's Rotation

Let us see whether the geographical position of the launching site and the direction of take-off are of significance for the launching of a rocket designed to become an artificial satellite of the earth.

An aircraft making a flight around the world needs the same amount of fuel to fly around the earth from east to west as it does for the flight from west to east. For this purpose, it makes no difference whether it is to fly around the earth, around the equator, or along the meridian, and from what point the flight is to start (if, of course, we disregard the meteorological conditions, etc.).

The situation is different for space flights. An orbital rocket will need less fuel for the launching of a satellite moving from east to west than for the launching of a satellite moving from west to east; and less for a launching along the equator in an easterly direction than for a launching along a meridian.

On the other hand, the launching site is of considerable importance for an orbital rocket. Let us consider two completely identical rockets, capable of developing one and the same velocity in free space.

Let the first of these rockets be launched at a definite velocity in Ecuador to meet the rising sun, and then, at an altitude of several hundred kilometers, after combustion cutoff, begin to revolve around the earth in a circular orbit. The second rocket is launched at the same velocity in Iceland and will have its combustion cutoff at the same altitude as the first rocket. Will this rocket, like the first one, revolve around the earth in a circular orbit? The answer is no: after combustion cutoff, it will approach the surface of the earth.

What, then, is the cause of this failure? The point is that, on launching the rocket, the peripheral velocity of rotation of the earth at the point of launching is added to the velocity of the orbital rocket. On the territory of Ecuador, the peripheral velocity of the earth is 465 meters per second (on the equator), while in Iceland it does not exceed 207 meters per second (this is its value at the southernmost tip of that island, located on the parallel 63°23′N.Lat.).

The above-mentioned null circular velocity, equal to 7912 meters per second, was calculated under the assumption that the earth does not rotate about its axis. In other words, this velocity holds only for take-off from a pole. On take-off from any other point of the earth's surface, however, the peripheral velocity of this point must be taken into account.

On the equator where, as already noted, the peripheral velocity is 465 meters per second, on take-off in an easterly direction, i.e., in the direction of rotation of the earth, it is sufficient to develop a velocity of $7912 - 465 = 7447$ meters per second, while on take-off toward the west (opposite to the earth's rotation) a velocity of $7912 + 465 = 8377$ meters per second would be necessary. If, however, a rocket, which on take-off in a westerly direction is able to become a zero artificial satellite, is launched in an easterly direction, then it will move along an elliptical orbit with the apogee at an altitude of over 4000 kilometers.

Thus, for maximum utilization of the rotary motion of the earth, the rocket launching pad must be located as close as possible to the equator. In this way, an equatorial artificial satellite has the advantage that, on launching, the peripheral velocity of rotation of the earth about its axis can be fully utilized. The launching of an artificial satellite in the progressive direction (i.e., in the direction of the earth's rotaton) is, as it were, a "cosmic swimming with the current."

■ TABLE 20

Velocity To Be Imparted to a Rocket on Horizontal Take-off at an Angle to the Equator, To Transform It into a Zero Artificial Satellite

Angle of Inclination of Direction of Take-off to Easterly Direction	Take-off Velocity, in Meters Per Second	Ratio of Take-off Velocity to Null Circular Velocity, in Per Cent	Angle of Inclination of Direction of Take-off to Easterly Direction	Take-off Velocity, in Meters Per Second	Ratio of Take-off Velocity to Null Circular Velocity, in Per Cent
0°	7,447	94.1	90°	7,926	100.2
30°	7,513	95.0	120°	8,154	103.1
60°	7,690	97.2	150°	8,318	105.1
88°19′	7,912	100.0	180°	8,377	105.9

For launching an artificial satellite whose orbit passes over the poles, the minimum velocity is needed on take-off from a pole, since the influence of the earth's rotation has no effect at a pole. On the equator, however, in order to force a satellite to overfly the poles, it would be necessary to make a take-off at a velocity 14 meters per second greater than at the pole and in a direction somewhat inclined to the west of meridional. Table 20 indicates the velocities that must be imparted to a rocket on horizontal take-off at sea level, at various angles to the line of the equator, to transform it into a zero artificial satellite.

The lowest velocity would be required on launching an equatorial artificial satellite from the summit of Mt. Kenya in equatorial East Africa or from the summit of Mt. Chimborazo in equatorial America (Ecuador). The former of these summits is 5194 meters high and its peripheral velocity is 465.50 meters per second. Mt. Chimborazo is somewhat higher (6272 meters), but the peripheral velocity of its summit is somewhat less and is 465.45 meters per second (the summit of Mt. Chimborazo is nearer the earth's axis than the summit of Mt. Kenya).

In practice, it is inadvisable to place a launching pad for an orbital rocket on a mountain peak for optimum utilization of the rotational motion of the earth, since, in the best case, the advantage in velocity could not be over 38 centimeters per second. Such a start, however, would have certain practical advantages.

Polar satellites enjoy advantages over others. They can be observed frequently from one and the same point in the polar zone and, in addition, they circle the entire globe. These advantages, however, are not gained cheaply, since the launching of an artificial satellite along a meridian demands a somewhat higher velocity to obtain one and the same orbit than launching in a plane inclined at an acute angle to the plane of the equator. On the fortieth parallel of latitude, for example, which crosses the territory of both the U.S.S.R. and the United States, the velocity of a point on the earth's surface amounts to 350 meters per second. Assume that, from some point on this parallel, two identical satellites are launched by the aid of two identical rockets. One satellite is launched so as to fly over the poles at an altitude of several hundred kilometers and the other one exactly in an easterly direction. Calculations show that the second satellite will reach its ceiling at an altitude more than a thousand kilometers higher than the first satellite. Consequently, the second satellite would already move beyond the limits of the atmosphere and its life would be almost unlimited, while the former satellite would be destroyed by the resistance of the air.

If an artificial satellite is to serve as an interplanetary station, the rotational velocity of the earth would naturally have to be utilized to its maximum extent (cf. later in text), i.e., the satellite would have to be launched in the direction of the earth's motion and, if possible, from a pad located close to the equator. For general geophysical research, a satellite revolving around the earth in an orbit making an angle of several tens of degrees with the plane of the equator, such as, for instance, the second artificial satellite, is of greater interest.

As will be seen from Table 20, even in this case the rotation of the earth can to some extent be utilized, provided that this angle is less than $88°19'$.

■ Circular Launching of Artificial Satellites

In all cases considered above it has been assumed that, on launching an artificial satellite, the necessary velocity is imparted to it instantaneously and that the flight is then accomplished after combustion cutoff. In reality, however, this increase in velocity must take place gradually; consequently, the launching must take a certain time. It is this case that we will consider below.

Assume that an artificial satellite is launched on a circular orbit at sea level, and that the take-off is along the local horizontal, i.e., that the satellite is launched directly into its orbit. Here and below we will assume (except where specifically stated otherwise) that there is no resistance from the air. If the velocity increment is 40 meters per second squared, then it will take $7912 : 40 = 197.8$ seconds to reach circular velocity, and during this time the rocket designed to become an artificial satellite will have traveled 782.5 kilometers.

How much fuel will be expended on this? This depends on the methods of navigation.

For instance, let the orbital rocket be equipped with two rocket engines. By means of one of these, which ejects its gases in the direction of the center of the earth, the rocket is maintained at constant altitude (i.e., it moves in a circle) until, owing to the simultaneous operation of the other or pusher rocket in the horizontal direction, the circular velocity is reached. Under the action of the earth's attraction during the first second, the rocket will acquire a vertical velocity of fall equal to 9.814 meters per second which, by the end of the launching, will have increased by a factor of 197.8, i.e., it will have reached 1941 meters per second. The operation of one of the engines must "neutralize" this vertical velocity, in order to maintain the satellite at the proper altitude, i.e., to prevent it from falling back on the earth. But after five seconds, the rocket, owing to the operation of the other engine, would already have acquired a horizontal velocity of $40 \times 50 = 200$ meters per second (if the increment of velocity is 40 meters per second squared); therefore, if it were not for the earth's gravitation, the rocket, owing to the curvature of the earth's surface, would travel 6 millimeters away from the earth during the first second alone. As a result, after this first second the rocket would acquire a vertical velocity of fall of 9808 millimeters per second instead of 9814 millimeters per second.

After one hundred and five seconds, the horizontal velocity of the rocket would already be 4200 meters per second. Because of the curvature of the earth's surface, the rocket would be traveling away from the earth at a velocity of 2.766 meters per second, so that its vertical velocity of fall would already be only $9.814 - 2.766 = 7.048$ meters per second.

Further calculations show that, during the launching of the artificial rocket, a total velocity of 1294 meters per second would have to be neutralized. These are the socalled gravitational losses of velocity. With respect to the actually acquired velocity of 7912 meters per second, the gravitational losses would amount to 16.4 per cent.

But are there no methods to reduce these losses? It turns out that there are. In the case under consideration, one rocket engine was operating the entire time in a vertical direction, supporting the rocket at a definite altitude, while the other was operating in a horizontal direction, accelerating it to the circular velocity. Using the principle of the parallelogram of forces, the two engines may be replaced by a single one, producing a thrust at a definite angle to the horizon. The thrust of this engine will obviously be less than the sum of the thrust of the two previous engines (the diagonal of a parallelogram is always shorter than the sum of two of its sides), and thus, ultimately, the same velocity will be attained.

Calculations show that in this case the gravitational losses will be decreased to 1.6 per cent. Thus, if at an exhaust velocity of 4 kilometers per second there were no losses, Tsiolkovskiy's formula (see above) would indicate that the fuel weight would have to be 6.23 times as great as the final weight of the rocket and, taking account of the gravitational losses, 6.46 times as great.

Obviously, with the above-described navigational method of circular launching of an artificial satellite, the gravitational losses will be very low.

■ Launching of an Artificial Satellite on a Rectangular Trajectory

Because of the existence of the atmosphere, the above-mentioned method of launching naturally cannot be realized. In practice, the first stage of the launching of a satellite must be a take-off to a great height, where the resistance of the air is no longer noticeable.

From the point of view of control of the rocket, the following method of launching is the simplest: The rocket at first takes off vertically. At the moment of reaching its ceiling and stopping for an instant (its velocity drops to zero), it is given the circular velocity. In this case, the trajectory of take-off will have a right-angled inflection.

The higher we desire to send a satellite in launching by this method, the greater must be the velocity required for the vertical acceleration. But the greater the altitude, the smaller will be the corresponding circular velocity. In order to hurl a body (rocket or artificial satellite(to an altitude of 1, 1.5 or 2 earth radii, initial velocities of 7912, 8667, or 9136 meters per second are required respectively. The circular velocities at these altitudes, however, are equal to 5595, 5004, and 4568 meters per second, respectively. If all these velocities are assumed to be imparted instantaneously to the rocket, we obtain the result that, to launch an artificial satellite to these altitudes, the following total velocities[2] are required: 7912 + 5595 = 13,507; 8667 + 5004 = 13,671 and 9136 + 4568 = 13,704 meters per second, respectively,

The launching on such a trajectory, which may be termed rectangular, is advantageous not only because it permits the simplest control of the rocket but also with such a method of take-off, it would be easiest to overcome the resistance of the atmospheric envelope of the earth. From the point of view of total fuel consumption, however, rectangular launching is highly disadvantageous by comparison with the other methods of launching, which will be considered later.

It is interesting to note that with increasing altitude to which an artificial satellite is launched, the gravitational losses can be reduced

---

[2] We apply the term total velocity to the arithmetic sum of the velocities imparted to a rocket at the moment of launching and at various moments of its flight.

to such an extent that the total velocity may even be less on launching to a higher altitude. Here we encounter one of the characteristic paradoxes of astronautics. For instance, when the radius of a circular orbit increases from 3 to 10 earth radii, the necessary total velocity gradually falls from 13,704 to 13,141 meters per second (Fig. 29).

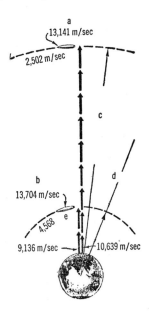

■ FIG. 29.—Launching of an Artificial Satellite along a Rectilinear Trajectory: an Orbital Rocket at Take-off Is Given a Velocity in the Vertical Direction and, at the Ceiling, a Velocity in the Horizontal Direction. Sometimes, as shown in the sketch, the result may be that, on launching by such a method to a greater height, less fuel will be consumed. (a)—Total velocity 13,141 meters per second; (b)—total velocity 13,704 meters per second; (c)—10 earth radii; (d)—3 earth radii.

In Table 21 this paradox is confirmed by several cases, corresponding to various altitudes.

■ TABLE 21

Launching of Circular Artificial Satellite on Rectangular Trajectory

Radius of Circular Orbit, in Earth Radii	Velocity of Vertical Take-off from Surface of the Earth, in Meters Per Second	Circular Velocity, in Meters Per Second	Total Velocity, in Meters Per Second	Radius of Circular Orbit, in Earth Radii	Velocity of Vertical Take-off from Surface of the Earth, in Meters Per Second	Circular Velocity, in Meters Per Second	Total Velocity, in Meters Per Second
1.1	3,374	7,544	10,918	7	10,359	2,990	13,349
1.3	5,375	6,939	12,324	10	10,615	2,502	13,117
1.5	6,460	6,460	12,920	15	10,808	2,043	12,851
2	7,912	5,595	13,570	20	10,906	1,769	12,675
3	9,136	4,568	13,704	30	11,001	1,445	12,446
5	10,008	3,538	13,546	70	11,109	946	12,055

■ Launching of an Artificial Satellite on a Semi-elliptical Trajectory

It is considered to be generally recognized in the literature on astronautics (Hohmann, Oberth, Pirquet, Esnault-Peltier, Loden, etc.) that in the absence of a resisting medium, the total velocity necessary for passage into a circular orbit will be minimum if this transition is accomplished on a semi-elliptical trajectory tangent to the orbit. In the launching of an artificial satellite, one end of the semi-ellipse must be tangent to the earth's surface and the other end, to the

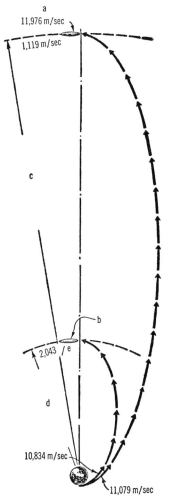

■ FIG. 30.—Launching of an Artificial Satellite on a Semi-Elliptical Trajectory. The orbital rocket is twice given a horizontal velocity, once at take-off from the ground and once at apogee. Sometimes, as shown on the sketch, the result may be that on launching by such a method to a higher altitude, less fuel will be required. (a)—Total velocity, 11,976 meters per second; (b)—total velocity, 12,155 meters per second; (c)—50 earth radii; (d)—10 earth radii.

circular orbit (Fig. 30). In a flight from one artificial satellite to another, however, each end of the semi-ellipse must be tangent to one of the two circular orbits.

With a method of launching as in the latter case, it may sometimes prove easier to raise a satellite to a higher altitude than to a lower.

Assume that we have launched two rockets horizontally at the earth's surface, with respective initial velocities of 10,834 and 11,079 meters per second (Fig. 30). If we neglect the resistance of the air, then the rockets will take off on semi-ellipses and, as indicated by calculations, will reach maximum altitudes of 15 and 50 earth radii respectively, measured from the center of the earth. As the rockets rise, their velocities will drop and will be 722 and 222 meters per second respectively at the ceiling. In order to go into the circular orbit, the former rocket would have to increase its velocity by 1321 meters per second and the latter by 897 meters per second.

Thus, the first rocket would have to develop a total velocity of 12,155 meters per second and the second one, a total velocity of 11,976 meters per second. Again we encounter the paradoxical phenomenon that the launching of a satellite to a greater altitude demands a smaller total velocity.

■ **TABLE 22**

Launching of a Circular Artificial Satellite on a Semi-elliptical Trajectory

Radius of Circular Orbit, in Earth Radii	Take-off Velocity from Earth's Surface, in Meters Per Second	Velocity of Arrival in Circular Orbit, in Meters Per Second	Circular Velocity, in Meters Per Second	Total Velocity, in Meters Per Second
1.1	8,098	7,362	7,544	8,280
1.3	8,412	6,471	6,939	8,881
1.5	8,667	5,778	6,460	9,349
2	9,136	4,568	5,595	10,163
3	9,690	3,230	4,568	11,028
5	10,214	2,043	3,538	11,710
7	10,467	1,495	2,990	11,962
10	10,668	1,067	2,502	12,104
15	10,834	722	2,043	12,155
20	10,919	546	1,769	12,142
30	11,007	367	1,445	12,085
70	11,110	159	946	11,897

If, however, an artificial satellite is launched by this method to lower altitudes, for instance, to an altitude of 10, 6, etc., earth radii, the fuel consumption will decrease constantly.

All this can be conveniently checked in Table 22.

Launching on a semi-elliptical trajectory from the very surface of the earth is practically impossible since, on horizontal take-off the rocket would have to overcome the resistance of the external medium in the dense layers of the atmosphere, which would require immense fuel expenditure. For this reason, on launching by such a method, the perigee of the semi-elliptical orbit would have to be placed into the ionosphere where the resistance of the air is already unnoticeable.

The launching of an artificial satellite on a semi-elliptical trajectory into a circular orbit might likewise be accomplished with a "stop" on one or several artificial satellites revolving in circular orbits of smaller dimensions (cf. later in text). In this case, a smaller amount of fuel could be expended on starting from the earth, but the duration of the flight into orbit would have to be considerably lengthened. The necessary total velocity to be imparted to the rocket would likewise be somewhat greater, although in practice it would only be slightly greater than on direct transition into final orbit. If for instance, the radius of the final orbit were twice the radius of the earth, then the corresponding losses would be expressed in fractions of a percent. With increasing dimensions of the final circular orbit, for the case of a stop on an intermediate satellite, the losses would also increase and might go as high as 8 per cent.

The method of intermediate circular orbits is useful not only for launching a satellite from the earth but also for flight from one satellite to another. In this case, the relative losses increase three- or fourfold.

■ Launching of an Artificial Satellite on a Ballistic Elliptical Arc

In one of the cases considered above, the take-off of an orbital rocket is vertical (see above), in another case, horizontal (see above). As has been shown, each of these methods of launching has its advantages and disadvantages. Naturally a compromise solution, i.e., an inclined take-off, may be successful in practice. In this case, it is

■ FIG. VII.—Gantry Test of Second Stage of Vanguard Orbital Rocket *(United States).*

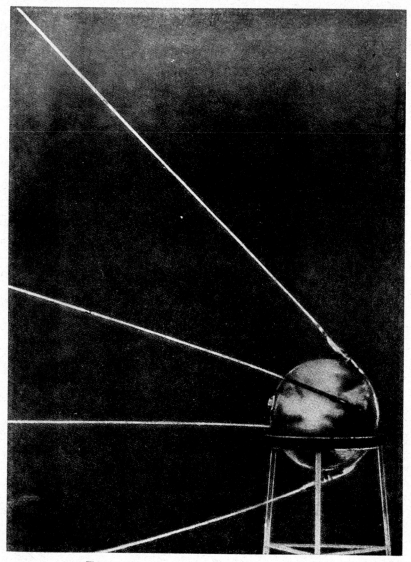

■ FIG. VIII.—First Soviet Artificial Satellite on Stand.

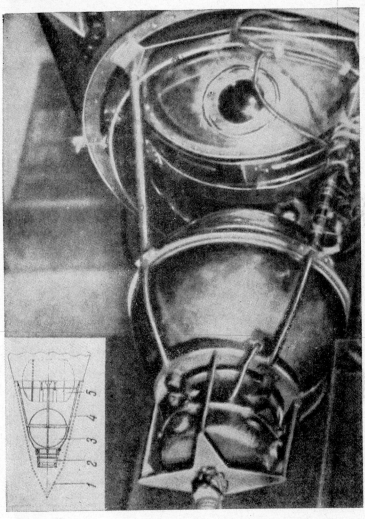

■ FIG. IX.—Installation of Containers with Scientific Instrumentation on Second Soviet Artificial Satellite. Layout of instrumentation as follows: 1—protective cone ejected after satellite is put in orbit; 2—instrument for investigating ultraviolet and X-ray radiation of the sun; 3—spherical container with instrumentation and radio transmitters; 4—stressed frame for attachment of instruments; 5—pressurized cabin with experimental animal.

■ FIG. X.—Mockup of Planned Vanguard Artificial Satellite *(United States).* A—photocells with memory unit; B—ionization chamber for recording of ultraviolet radiation; C—thermistors for determining temperature of satellite; D—instrument for measuring erosion caused by the impact of micrometeorites; 1—radio transmitter; 2—acoustic amplifier of clicks from impacts of micrometeorites; 3—memory unit for impacts of micrometeorites; 4—telemetering system; 5—memory unit for ultraviolet measurements; 6—amplifier for ultraviolet measurements; 7—mercury battery.

necessary to find a take-off angle such that the horizontal velocity of the rocket at the ceiling, where it must go into circular orbit, will be as high as possible.

On the whole, this problem coincides with the ballistic problem of defining the angle at which a missile must be fired to attain maximum range.

On receiving a sufficient acceleration at the earth's surface, the rocket will begin to move in the arc of an ellipse one of whose foci coincides with the center of the earth. At the ceiling, in apogee, when the velocity of the rocket is directed parallel to the earth's surface, the engine will again be cut in so as to raise the velocity to the local circular velocity (Table 23).

■ **TABLE 23**

Launching of an Artificial Satellite on a Ballistic Elliptical Arc

Take-off Angle, in Degrees	Central Angle of Ballistic Curve*, in Degrees	Height to Which Artificial Satellite Is Launched, in Kilometers	Velocity Departure from Earth's Surface, in Meters Per Second	Velocity of Arrival in Circular Orbit, in Meters Per Second	Circular Velocity, in Meters Per Second	Additional Velocity on Circular Orbit, in Meters Per Second	Total Velocity of Launching Satellite, in Meters Per Second	Duration of Flight into Circular Orbit Min.	Sec.
40	10	505	4,304	3,055	7,617	4,562	8,866	6	14
35	20	898	5,649	4,056	7,408	3,352	9,001	9	34
30	30	1,167	6,460	4,729	7,274	2,545	9,005	12	27
25	40	1,304	6,999	5,267	7,209	1,942	8,941	14	59
22.5	45	1,321	7,201	5,512	7,202	1,690	8,891	16	7
20	50	1,304	7,369	5,747	7,209	1,460	8,829	17	8
15	60	1,167	7,623	6,224	7,274	1,050	8,673	18	51
10	70	898	7,788	6,723	7,408	685	8,473	20	6
5	80	505	7,882	7,275	7,617	342	8,224	20	51

* The angle between the two straight lines joining the center of the earth with the beginning and end of the ballistic arc.

As shown by calculation, when an orbital rocket is launched at the optimum angle, this method permits an artificial satellite to be put into an elliptical orbit with a perigee not higher than 1321 kilometers. Such an altitude is entirely adequate, since even at lower altitudes the resistance of the air will be practically unnoticeable.

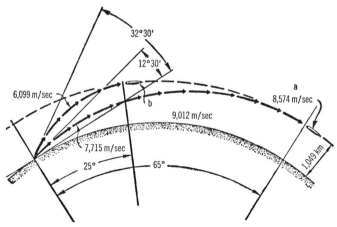

■ FIG. 31.—Launching of an Artificial Satellite on a Ballistic Elliptical Arc: the Orbital Rocket on Take-off Is Given a Velocity in a Direction Making an Angle with the Horizon and, at the Ceiling, a Velocity in a Horizontal Direction. As indicated in the sketch, take-off for one and the same altitude may be made at one of two possible angles. (a)—Total velocity, 8574 meters per second; (b)—total velocity, 9012 meters per second.

In launching an artificial satellite on a ballistic elliptical arc to an altitude less than the maximum altitude, the take-off may be made at one of two possible angles (Fig. 31).

In the case of take-off at the smaller angle, the total velocity will not be over 3.8 per cent more than the total velocity on launching on a semi-ellipse; at the same time, the method of launching on a ballistic arc is safer since, on launching on a semi-ellipse, when the take-off is horizontal, the slightest loss of velocity would result in the fall of the rocket. At a smaller angle, a smaller total velocity is needed if the resistance of the air is neglected. This case may occur on launching artificial satellites from heavenly bodies having no atmosphere, for instance, from Moon or Mercury.

It may prove more advantageous to take off at the greater angle from a heavenly body with an atmosphere, in particular from the earth, since in this case the rocket must overcome the resistance of the air over a shorter portion of its path. It is true that, by comparison with launching in a vacuum on a semi-ellipse, the losses on launching at the greater angle on a ballistic arc may increase to 8.2 per cent, but the losses due to the resistance of the air on take-off at the smaller angle are so great that, if the influence of the atmosphere is taken into account, it will be more advantageous to launch the satellite on the ballistic arc at the greater take-off angle.

Summarizing the above, we arrive at the following conclusion: Neglecting the resistance of the air, the total velocity at take-off on a ballistic elliptical arc is found to be somewhat higher than at take-off on a semi-ellipse, but is considerably lower than in the case of take-off on a rectangular trajectory. Since, on launching an artificial earth satellite, the rocket must pass through the earth's atmosphere, i.e., fly in a resisting medium, the launching on a ballistic elliptical arc will in practice be more advantageous than on other trajectories.

■ Launching an Artificial Satellite on an Indirect Trajectory[3]

If anyone were asked whether it would be preferable, from the point of view of saving fuel, to fly an aircraft from London to Moscow by way of New York, he would undoubtedly take the question as a joke. Not only are these cities in opposite directions from London, but New York is 2.5 times farther from Moscow than London. It is clear that such a detour would involve an immense unnecessary fuel consumption. The situation is entirely different in astronautics, especially on flight from the earth to an artificial satellite (or in launching a satellite). In many cases on flight into a circular orbit on a special trajectory, which we will call indirect (Fig. 32), the total velocity will be smaller than if a semi-elliptical transitional trajectory is followed.

Assume that astronauts start out from the earth for an artificial satellite at a distance of 50 earth radii from the center of the earth, i.e., in the region of the lunar orbit. Following a semi-elliptical trajectory, the rocket will gradually approach the orbit of the artificial satellite. However, it is sometimes more advantageous, in order to reduce the fuel consumption, to fly an indirect trajectory with a preliminary detour. For this purpose, the rocket must at first rise on a semi-elliptical curve to an altitude about twice the distance between the earth and the artificial satellite. When the rocket reaches the highest point, the astronauts will again cut in the engine, to direct the rocket toward the artificial satellite on a new semi-elliptical trajectory. After reaching the orbit of the satellite, the rocket must be retarded: its velocity must be decreased by 173 meters per second.

This path, in which the rocket will describe something like an incomplete deadman's loop, will be somewhat longer than the usual

[3] Proposed by the author in 1954.

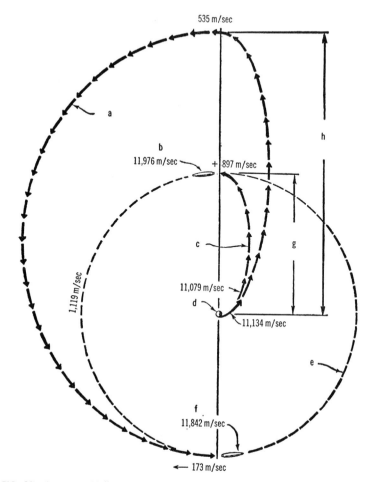

■ FIG. 32.—Astronauts Will Sometimes Be Forced To Fly to an Artificial Satellite Not by the Shortest Way (in a Semi-ellipse) but by a Longer Way (on an Indirect Trajectory) Which Will at First Take Them Farther Out, Economizing Fuel but Losing Time. (a)—Indirect trajectory with preliminary detour; (b)—total velocity 11,976 meters per second; (c)—semi-elliptical trajectory; (d)—earth; (e)—orbit of artificial satellite; (f)—total velocity, 11,842 meters per second; (g)—50 earth radii; (h)—100 earth radii.

semi-elliptical trajectory. But the advantage in the total velocity of the rocket by comparison with a flight over the shortest path will amount to 134 meters per second and the saving in fuel, related to the weight of the empty rocket at an exhaust velocity of 4 kilometers per second, will be 66 per cent. This is explained by the fact that during a flight on a longer and flatter trajectory, the engine need be cut in only for shorter time intervals.

One may imagine a case when such an indirect route, an "astronautic loop," might mean salvation of a crew that had ascended on a semi-ellipse, used up too much fuel, and was therefore unable to bring the ship into the circular orbit of the satellite. In this case, the pilot might give the rocket an additional acceleration, and the rocket would cross the orbit of the satellite, continuing on its upward course. Then reducing the speed of the ship at apogee by the aid of the engine, the crew would return to the satellite on a new semi-elliptical trajectory. Such a flight would of course take more time, but less fuel would be used, and the crew would still be able to reach the assigned goal. If the radius of the circular orbit of the artificial satellite is larger than 11.9 earth radii, then its launching on this indirect trajectory would demand a smaller total velocity than launching on a semi-ellipse. For the same size of circular orbit, the total velocity imparted to the rocket would be smaller, the greater the maximum distance of the indirect trajectory.

The saving in total velocity when using the indirect trajectory of launching by comparison with launching on a semi-ellipse might theoretically reach 8 per cent. The saving in fuel would be somewhat greater.

An "astronautical loop" might be utilized in certain interplanetary flights, for instance in a flight to the moon, for studying interplanetary space, etc. Finally, a theoretical calculation shows that the launching of an artificial planet to a great distance from the sun on an "astronautical loop" would demand a smaller consumption of fuel than on a semi-elliptical curve.

The indirect trajectory may be of advantage not only for flight from the earth to an artificial satellite but also for passage from one satellite to another, more distant, satellite.

■ Theoretical Case of Launching of an Artificial Satellite at Minimum Fuel Consumption

To transform a body into an artificial satellite of a planet, revolving close to its surface, it is theoretically necessary to expend as much energy as would be required to lift the same body a distance equal to the radius of the planet. This is half as much as would be required to entirely remove the body from the gravitational attraction of the planet and allow it to escape into space.

With increasing desired altitude of flight, the potential energy of the satellite increases, while its kinetic energy (energy of motion) decreases since the circular velocity decreases (cf. above). At an altitude equal to half the radius of the earth, the kinetic energy of an artificial satellite equals its potential energy. For an artifical satellite launched to the orbit of the moon, the potential energy would be almost a hundred times as great as the kinetic energy.

■ **TABLE 24**

Kinetic, Potential, and Total Mechanical Energy of an Artificial Satellite

Radius of Satellite Orbit, in Radii of Central Body	Kinetic Energy of Satellite*	Potential Energy of Satellite*	Total Mechanical Energy of Satellite	Ratio of Kinetic Energy to Potential Energy
1	1.000	0	1.000	1:0
1.1	0.909	0.182	1.091	1:0.2
1.3	0.769	0.462	1.231	1:0.6
1.5	0.667	0.667	1.333	1:1
1.7	0.558	0.824	1.412	1:1.4
2	0.500	1.000	1.500	1:2
2.5	0.400	1.200	1.600	1:3
4	0.250	1.500	1.750	1:6
7	0.143	1.714	1.857	1:12
10	0.100	1.800	1.900	1:18
30	0.033	1.933	1.966	1:58
50	0.020	1.960	1.980	1:98

* The energy of the zero artificial satellite is here taken as the unit.

Table 24 shows that the kinetic energy of an artificial satellite decreases with altitude and that its potential energy increases at the same time. The unit of measurement taken is the mechanical energy of the zero artificial satellite. As indicated in the table, the potential energy of the satellite increases considerably more rapidly than its kinetic energy decreases; therefore, as we just stated, the total mechanical energy of the satellite increases with its altitude.

Thoretically, in the absence of losses, it would be sufficient, for launching an artificial satellite to a certain altitude, to give the rocket at the earth's surface a velocity such as to make its kinetic energy at take-off equal to the total mechanical energy of the satellite at the planned altitude.[4] The value of this velocity indicates the limit below which the value of the total velocity, necessary for launching a satellite to the given altitude, must not drop no matter what the launching trajectory may be. This minimum velocity increases with increasing altitude of the orbit, in view of the fact that, in this case (as we know), the total mechanical energy of the satellite also increases.

In all methods of launching an artificial satellite discussed above, the total velocity imparted to the rocket to place it in circular orbit has exceeded the theoretical minimum velocity. Might there not be a method of launching a rocket, though only of a purely theoretical type, that would minimize its total velocity?

Assume that a weightless rope, stretched over the earth's surface, with one end attached to the earth, has its other end attached to an instantaneously accelerated rocket. The length of the rope is equal to the altitude at which the orbital rocket will fly (Fig. 33). The rocket

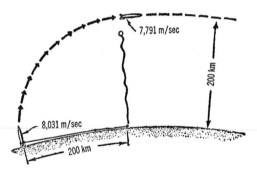

FIG. 33.—In a Cable-Launching of an Artificial Satellite (Theoretical Case), the Fuel Consumption Would Be Minimum. The necessary velocity would be imparted to the rocket all at once, at the very surface of the earth; the rocket would then fly in a curve with engine off.

is launched vertically at the minimum velocity theoretically sufficient to transform the rocket into an artificial satellite of the earth (disregarding the resistance of the air). But since the rocket is attached to a rope or cable, it cannot take off along the vertical: the stretched

---

[4] The energy expended in launching an artificial satellite is relatively small. This will be clear from a comparison of this energy with the work performed by an aircraft engine. The aircraft may have a flying weight of the order of 3 kilograms per horsepower of power developed by the engine. In fifty hours, its engines will produce an amount of energy which, if completely utilized for increasing the speed of the aircraft, would be sufficient to give the aircraft zero circular velocity (not taking account of the weight of the fuel consumed).

cable would curve its trajectory. With the engine shut off, the rocket will fly in an arc. As it rises higher, its motion will slow down. At the instant of reaching the ceiling, when the velocity of the rocket will be directed horizontally, its magnitude will be equal to the calculated circular velocity at that altitude. At this time, the cable is detached from the rocket, which then begins to revolve around the earth in a circular orbit.[5]

Assume that such a rocket satellite is to move in a circular orbit, at an altitude of 200 kilometers, at the circular velocity of 7791 meters per second corresponding to this altitude; then it will be sufficient to accelerate it at the earth's surface to a velocity of 8031 meters per second. If the exhaust velocity of the gas from the engine is 2.5 kilometers per second, then, by Tsiolkovskiy's formula, the amount of fuel must be 19.4 times as great as the empty weight of the single-stage rocket.

In this cable (moored)-launching of an artificial satellite from the surface of the earth, the fuel consumption would be the theoretical minimum. This is due to the fact, in contrast to free take-off, no fuel is expended in this case on curving the trajectory: the trajectory is curved by the cable. Moreover, with cable-launching, the necessary velocity can be given to the rocket all at once, on the ground itself.

This method of launching an artificial satellite is, of course, merely of theoretical interest. Nevertheless, the conclusions derived here permit determining the conditions of launching of an artificial satellite at minimum energy consumption and, consequently, will help in finding a way to solve the problem of the most economical launching of an artificial satellite.

Since the velocity indicated here is the lowest for launching an artificial satellite to a given altitude, or for reaching such a satellite already in orbit at that altitude, it may serve as the unit in the comparison of the total velocities that are necessary for this purpose (Table 25).

It is interesting to note that the minimum velocity, theoretically

---

[5] The converse reasoning is also possible. In imagination, let us throw, on a moving artificial satellite, a weightless cable attached by its other end to the earth at the exact subsatellite point. Then the satellite will begin to fall toward the earth along the arc of a circle and will strike the ground at a velocity greater that the velocity of its circular motion in orbit. The velocity of this crash will equal the minimum velocity of launching of the artificial satellite.

■ **TABLE 25**

Minimum Velocity, Theoretically Necessary for Launching an Artificial Satellite

Altitude of Flight, in Kilometers	Minimum Launching Velocity of Artificial Satellite, in Meters Per Second	Percentage by Which the Minimum Velocity of Launching a Satellite Exceeds Local Circular Velocity	Altitude of Flight, in Kilometers	Minimum Launching Velocity of Artificial Satellite, in Meters Per Second	Percentage by Which the Minimum Velocity of Launching a Satellite Exceeds Local Circular Velocity
0	7,912	0	3,000	9,090	14.89
200	8,031	1.50	4,000	9,312	17.69
300	8,088	2.22	5,000	9,493	19.98
400	8,142	2.91	6,000	9,640	21.84
500	8,194	3.56	6,378	9,690	22.47
1,000	8,431	6.56	7,000	9,765	26.39
2,000	8,806	11.30			

necessary for launching an artificial satellite into a predetermined circular orbit, is equal to the velocity at perigee of an artificial satellite moving in an elliptical orbit, having a major axis equal to the diameter of this circular orbit and having its perigee at the very surface of the earth.

The launching of an artificial satellite into circular orbit with minimum fuel consumption may also be represented as follows:

From the point A of the earth's surface a body of known mass is launched in a horizontal direction on an elliptical orbit (Fig. 34). According to the laws of celestial mechanics, at the moment when the body reaches the point B, which is the end of the minor axis of the ellipse, it will have a velocity equal to the local circular velocity, although it will not be directed horizontally but will make a certain angle with the horizon. How can such a body be forced to begin moving in a circular orbit passing through the point B? For this purpose, let us eject upward, from the point D on the surface of the earth, another body of the same mass as the first body with the same initial velocity directed horizontally and, consequently, moving on an identical trajectory. Let us select the point D such that the bodies will meet at the point C of the circular orbit. At this instant, both bodies must have the same velocities equal to the local circular

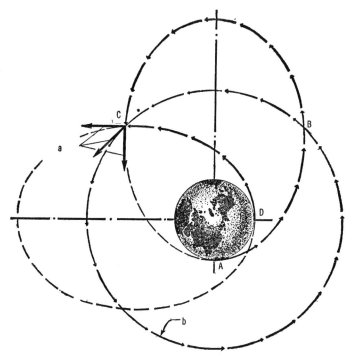

FIG. 34.—If Two Bodies Leaving the Earth's Surface at the Points A and D Are Linked Without Energy Losses, at the Point C, These Bodies Will Begin To Move in a Circular Orbit If the Take-off Velocity Was the Theoretical Minimum. (a)—Circular velocity; (b)—orbit of satellite.

velocity. If the bodies are forced to link at the point C, without loss of energy, then they will acquire a common velocity, likewise equal to the local circular velocity and forming the same angles with the velocities at which the bodies arrived at the point C. They will there-fore continue to move on together, in the circular orbit passing through the points B and C.

It is the initial velocity at which each of these bodies commenced its motion on the elliptical trajectory that will be the minimum velocity theoretically necessary for launching an artificial satellite into the circular orbit passing through the points B and C.

We note that, as indicated in Table 25, the minimum theoretical velocity of launching an artificial satellite increases with the altitude of the desired orbit.[6] The total velocity for certain actual launching

[6] This is explained by the fact that the energy expended on the additional vertical lift of the rocket exceeds the saving in energy due to the decrease in orbital velocity with altitude.

trajectories, however, as discussed above, does not always increase with altitude.

■ Crossing the Atmosphere

If a rocket takes off more or less vertically, the density of the air along its path will decrease rapidly, so that the resistance of the air decreases. On the other hand, the resistance of the air also increases, owing to the increased velocity of the rocket during take-off. Which of these factors will have the predominating influence? Will the resistance of the air register, on balance, a net increase or decrease with the altitude of the rocket? Calculations show that, on the first segment of its path, the influence of acceleration will predominate and the resistance of the air will increase. Later, however, the resistance of the medium, having reached its maximum value, begins to decrease (the factor of rarefaction of the air will predominate) and gradually drops to zero. Under certain simplified conditions, it is possible to calculate the mass of fuel consumed by a rocket moving at constant acceleration in crossing the atmosphere at any desired angle to the horizon. Table 26 gives the corresponding data for various exhaust velocities.[7]

■ TABLE 26

Consumption of Fuel in Kilograms per Square Decimeter of Cross Section of Flying Device when a Rocket, Moving at an Acceleration of Thrust Four Times as Great as the Acceleration of Gravity at the Earth's Surface, Crosses the Atmosphere

	Exhaust Velocity of Gases from Rocket, in Kilometers Per Second			
Take-off Angle	2.5	3	3.5	4
90°	1.873	1.451	1.182	0.995
80°	1.925	1.491	1.213	1.022
70°	2.093	1.618	1.316	1.108
60°	2.430	1.870	1.518	1.276
50°	3.022	2.321	1.879	1.575
40°	4.142	3.159	2.535	2.127
30°	6.535	4.930	3.940	3.274

It is often asserted that the resistance of the air encountered by the rocket is proportional to its pressure. This is untrue. The resistance

[7] A. Shternfeld, "Consumption of Fuel by a Rocket Crossing the Atmosphere at Constant Acceleration," *Dok. Akad. Nauk SSSR*, Vol. 49, No. 9, 1945.

of the air is proportional to its density, but the density of the atmosphere is not at all proportional to the pressure of the air. For instance, the ratio of the pressure of the air at an altitude of 5 kilometers to its pressure at sea level is 0.53, while the ratio of air densities is 0.60. For an altitude of 10 kilometers, the respective ratios will be 0.26 and 0.34.

On crossing the atmosphere, the rocket skin will be strongly heated. In spite of this, the phenomenon of heating will involve no particular danger, since it will be short-lived. Some authors have proposed the utilization of the heat liberated to evaporate liquified gases under high pressure, subsequently expelling such gases through the nozzle to accelerate the motion of the rocket; however, the resultant advantage would apparently be negligible. In any case, to prevent the heating of the skin during take-off from exceeding the safe limits, the rocket might be provided with a cooling system with a relatively small amount of liquid coolant.

We can get an idea on the influence of the air on a cosmic rocket during take-off from the behavior of a high-altitude rocket, since the velocities of both such rockets will be very similar in the dense layers of the atmosphere; at an altitude of hundreds of kilometers, however, the velocity of the rocket will have no substantial effect either on the resistance of the medium or on the heating of the rocket hull.

Theoretical and experimental data seem to indicate that, at a velocity of the order of 2.5 kilometers per second, a space rocket is already at an altitude where the resistance of the air has no longer any effect on its velocity, its temperature, or the stability of its motion. The expenditures of energy to overcome the resistance of the air by space rockets will be considerably smaller than the gravitational losses and will amount only to several percent of the total energy expended on the acceleration of the rocket.

In a paper read before the Second International Astronautical Congress, Kuemmer (Germany) came to the conclusion that, in a special case studied by him, 8 per cent of the total fuel supply of the lowest rocket stage weighing 500 tons would have to be consumed in overcoming the resistance of the air on take-off of an orbital rocket.

During the launching of an orbital rocket on various trajectories, its speed within the atmosphere would not exceed 2.5 kilometers per second. The resistance of the air and the aerodynamic heating at such velocities have been well studied. In the opinion of Perkins (United

States), the loss in velocity due to the resistance of the air on launching an artificial satellite amount to what he claims are only a little more than 100 meters per second.

Thus we see that, as assumed earlier and as confirmed by the launching of the first Soviet artificial satellites, the crossing of the atmosphere by an orbital rocket will involve no serious difficulties.

■ General Conditions of Launching an Artificial Satellite

No matter what the method of launching a satellite, only the nose section of the compound orbital rocket, carrying the artificial satellite, will reach the planned altitude. At that level, the velocity of the rocket will have been brought up to the circular (or elliptical) velocity, and this instant will be the beginning of existence of the simplest artificial satellite. This at once makes it unnecessary to drop the last empty tanks and other spent parts of the engine. They will no longer burden the artificial heavenly body revolving around the the earth. Even if these parts are separated from the rest of the rocket, they will not fall back on the ground but will continue to move together with the rocket, revolving around the earth in its previous orbit, as was actually the case when the first artificial satellite and its carrier rocket were launched.

The question of the choice of a trajectory for launching an orbital rocket, or for subsequent flight to the artifical satellite (in each case, the trajectory is one and the same) is of great importance. The trajectories requiring a relatively low fuel consumption are very complicated. In flying on these, a rocket must constantly vary the direction of acceleration of its motion (Oberth, German Federal Republic; Loden, Great Britain). But if a rocket flies on a simplified trajectory (for instance, rising vertically at first and then changing to horizontal flight at the ceiling), then the fuel consumption may prove to be greater than for reaching the nearest planets on a correctly calculated trajectory.

In free space, at a given exhaust velocity, the final velocity acquired by a rocket depends, as we already know (see above), exclusively on the relative amount of fuel consumed. This is also largely true for take-off from an interplanetary station. The situation is different for take-off from the earth. In this case, a more rapid combustion should yield a better effect, and the active portion[8] of the trajectory should be as close as possible to the surface of the earth.

In fact, in the gravitational field the fundamental law of rocket motion (Tsiolkovskiy's formula) is expressed differently than in free space. This will be clear from even the brief explanation below: If the exhaust of the gas takes place under conditions where the engine thrust is less than the "instantaneous" weight of the rocket (the weight, of course, is continuously decreasing), then all of the fuel will obviously burn without the slightest effect: the rocket will not move from the spot (just as a helicopter will not break away from the ground if its blades are not rotating rapidly enough). If the weight of the fuel in the rocket is reduced to such an extent that the rocket as a whole begins to weigh a little less than the thrust, it will take off but will not rise high. If the fuel supply is still further decreased, the rocket will take off faster and rise higher. But such a decrease in fuel supply on the rocket cannot continue without limit. Although the gain of velocity in unit time, i.e., the acceleration, will in fact increase under these conditions, at the same time the total time of engine operation to combustion cutoff will also be shortened. Thus, with too low a fuel supply, the ceiling of the rocket will decrease (it will, of course, become zero if the rocket is not supplied with any fuel). On the other hand, if the rocket is supplied with increasing amounts of fuel, then, in the first trials, as the fuel supply is increased, the rocket will rise ever higher; however, in later trials, if the fuel supply is still further increased, the rocket will be overloaded, and the ceiling will begin to drop. Finally, the rocket will be unable to become airborne.

In other words, on take-off from the earth's surface, an increase in the relative supply of fuel is useful only up to a certain limit.

The faster a space rocket reaches the necessary velocity, the less fuel will it require. In fact, the earth's gravity will decrease the rocket thrust, but this loss will be smaller, the less time the engine will have to counteract this force.

Suppose that we have two rockets. One of these is moving in free space at an acceleration of 15 meters per second, while the other

---

[8] The active part of a trajectory is that part of the trajectory along which the engine is operating. The passive part of the trajectory is that part of the trajectory along which flight is effected with the engine off.

rocket is moving at an acceleration twice as great. Two seconds after its motion begins, the first rocket will have a velocity of 30 meters per second, while the second rocket will reach the same velocity at the end of the first second.

Now let these rockets take off vertically from the earth's surface. The gravitational attraction of the earth will decrease their velocity every second by about 10 meters per second. After two seconds, the first rocket will have a velocity of $(15 - 10) \cdot 2 = 10$ meters per second, while the second rocket, after one second, will be moving at velocity $(30 - 10) \cdot 1 = 20$ meters per second. A comparison of this result with what it would be in free space shows clearly that the gravitational forces (see above) will have a smaller effect on a rocket with higher acceleration. This type will need less fuel to reach any definite velocity (neglecting the resistance of the air).

Thus an immense fuel saving could be realized if we were able to accelerate a rocket instantaneously to the necessary velocity, and then to have it continue flight with engine off. But since this is impossible in practice, the rocket should be launched at the maximum possible acceleration. The magnitude of this acceleration is limited by the power of the engine, by the mechanical strength of the instrumentation and, in the case of human flight, by the endurance of the organism.

It follows from this that, with increasing thrust, the fuel consumption will decrease and, consequently, the design of the orbital rocket will be simplified. However, the G-force will also be increased as a result; the human organism is unable to withstand too great a G-force. For this reason, to deliver cargo to an artificial satellite, rockets with maximum acceleration must be used, while to deliver human beings, the rockets must have a relatively low acceleration.

■ Optimum Take-off Trajectories

During the rise of a rocket it must simultaneously overcome the earth's attraction and the resistance of the air. From the point of view of fuel saving, these two factors pose directly opposite demands. On the one hand, as already mentioned, the higher the acceleration of a rocket, the more rapidly will it reach the necessary velocity and altitude and the smaller will be the necessary fuel supply. On the other hand, the higher the acceleration of a rocket, the greater the resistance of the air, and the more fuel will be needed to overcome it. Further, although in vertical upward flight the earth's gravity considerably brakes the rocket, this effect is compensated, in such a flight, by the decrease—fastest of all in this case—in the density of the air and, consequently, also in its resistance. For horizontal flight, however, the earth's attraction has only a slightly retarding effect on the rocket, while the resistance of the air will be greater. If, for instance, the magnitude of the reactive force, i.e., the thrust, produced by the operation of a rocket engine is four times as great as the force of gravity, then the gravitational velocity losses will amount to 25 per cent in vertical flight, and 3.5 per cent in horizontal flight.

These contradictory conditions complicate the solution of the problem of selecting the optimum trajectory of flight of an artificial satellite to orbit. As shown by calculations, the following take-off trajectory will be relatively economical: the rocket takes off at a certain angle, and after having reached a considerable velocity, turns in such a way as to direct the engine thrust almost parallel to the earth's surface. Thus the rocket, while gaining horizontal velocity, continues to coast upward by inertia, until it reaches the circular velocity (Fig. 35).

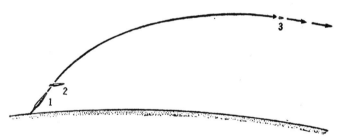

■ FIG. 35.—One of the Possible Launching Trajectories of a Satellite at Relatively Low Fuel Fuel Consumption: The rocket takes off at a certain angle (1) and after reaching a considerable velocity turns in such a manner as to direct the engine thrust almost parallel to the earth's surface (2). While gaining horizontal velocity, the rocket continues to rise until the instant of attaining circular velocity (3).

With the object of reducing the resistance of the air, certain authors suggest carrying the orbital rocket, which is to launch a minimum artificial satellite, to a definite altitude by dirigibles or spherical balloons, as is sometimes done in launching high-altitude rockets (Oberth; Van Allen, United States). In this case, in the attempt to raise the ceiling, the fact that the rocket takes off from a higher level also plays a certain role. There is, for example, a plan in existence to launch a three-stage orbital rocket from a stratosphere balloon at an altitude of 24 kilometers. If the artificial satellite weighs 14 kilograms, then the starting weight of the rocket would amount to 6100 kilograms. The diameter of such a stratosphere balloon with a skin of plastic foil would be 5.5 meters (Stehling, United States).

High-altitude rockets are sometimes launched from an aircraft at the instant of an incipient steep climb. In that case, the rocket will gain a certain velocity from the accelerating aircraft. Similar plans have been proposed for orbital rockets. According to one such plan, turbojet and ram-jet engines could be used to give the initial acceleration to the orbital rocket while it is crossing the densest layers of the atmosphere. Two possible solutions are considered in this case. A winged flying machine with a turbojet engine would lift the orbital rocket to an altitude of 20-25 kilometers, where it would reach a velocity of the order of 2000 kilometers per hour. Then the engines would be jettisoned and the ram-jet engines would take over, bringing the velocity up to 5000 kilometers per hour at an altitude of 35-40 kilometers. From this altitude, the winged flying machine with the ram-jet engines would descend to the ground, and the single-stage or multistage liquid-fuel orbital rocket would be cut in. According to another version, the orbital rocket would be carried by an aircraft with a ram-jet engine, which in turn would be mounted on a carrier aircraft with a turbojet engine (N. A. Varvarov, U.S.S.R.).

Trajectories for transition to a circular orbit with continuously operating engine (without a transitional passive stage) have been proposed. Such trajectories, however, are of no practical interest since, if they are limited to low fuel consumption, the trajectories will be flown at relatively low levels in the very dense layers of the atmosphere. If, on the other hand, the satellite orbit is raised beyond any dense atmosphere, the acceleration due to the operation of the engine will be slight, while the fuel consumption will be enormous. For this reason, in launching an artificial satellite, the active part of the trajectory should not represent a single unbroken arc but several arcs, separated by passive portions. For instance, the high-altitude rocket Nike Cajun, after combustion cutoff of the first stage and before ignition of the second rocket, coasts upward by inertia for a short time (10-20 seconds). Thus the rocket enters the rarefied layers of the atmosphere before developing its maximum velocity. (This interval of time, however, must be short enough for the rocket not to rise too high, otherwise the aerial stabilizers or air rudders will be of no further use). For a three-stage rocket, it is preferable to schedule the separation after the combustion cutoff of the second stage. When the rocket reaches the ceiling, the third stage goes into operation and raises the velocity of the satellite to the local circular velocity.

The circular velocity can probably also be attained with a winged rocket (F. A. Tsander, U.S.S.R.). Although such a solution of the problem of flight with an artificial satellite is rarely encountered in the modern literature, it is not without scientific foundation. At the Fourth International Astronautical Congress, some scientists (Fiecke, Deunert, Neuber, and Gebauer) demonstrated that a certain fuel economy in flight to an artificial satellite could be obtained by using a winged rocket.

■ Launching of Large Satellites in Sections

Artificial satellites of large dimensions will be launched gradually, in sections. Of course, it will be possible to join the individual rockets into a single structure only if all the rockets have the same velocity. We recall the fact that when two railroad trains are moving in the same direction on parallel tracks at almost the same speed, the passengers on the two trains will be in constant sight of each other. If the railroad tracks were sufficiently close to each other, then the passengers on the two trains could freely pass from one rushing train to the other.

It is obvious that rockets flying from the earth to an artificial satellite, at the instant of making fast to the satellite, will have to match their velocity to the velocity of the platform.

Since the velocity of the rocket, at the instant of reaching the circular orbit of the satellite, will be smaller than the velocity of the satellite itself, the two velocities can be matched only after a certain period of flying in orbit.

It is of interest to determine the position with respect to the satellite (ahead of it or behind it) in which the rocket must be when mooring to the platform. Assume that the rocket is behind the satellite on its orbit. It must then, by means of its engine, develop a velocity higher than that of the satellite in order to overtake the latter; then, the engine must again be turned off to retard the rocket and thus to match the velocities of both satellite and rocket. All this will require large fuel consumption. It will therefore be more advantageous for the rocket to reach the orbit ahead of the satellite. In this case, however, the motion of the rocket need not be retarded, as one might think at first. It is more advantageous to proceed in the opposite manner: to accelerate the motion of the rocket so that, at the moment of reaching circular velocity, it meets the satellite.

An orbital rocket flying to an artificial satellite must move exactly in the plane of the satellite orbit. Otherwise additional fuel will be necessary to match the velocities of the rocket and satellite at the instant of "mooring." Ferrying flights from a given rocket base to an artificial satellite should therefore not be more frequent than twice a day, since any point of the earth's surface will pass the plane of the satellite orbit only twice a day. The time between one take-off and another will be less than 12 hours. But these two trajectories of flight to the satellite will generally not be identical, and one trajectory should be given preference over the other. For this reason, only one flight a day will, in practice, be made from a given point to one and the same satellite.

Exceptions, however, are possible. Assume, for instance, that, in overflying a rocket base, an artificial satellite at the same time passes the northernmost or southernmost point of its orbit. Naturally, in that case, the rocket base will be in the plane of the satellite orbit only once a day. On the other hand, the number of possible flights can be increased to as high as sixteen a day when a polar or equatorial artificial satellite is involved. In this case, a flight on an identical trajectory can be accomplished during the course of each synodical period of revolution of the satellite.

Flight from the earth to an artificial satellite, just as a successive launching of rockets from which a large artificial satellite is to be assembled, is a complex problem and resembles the problem of firing from an oscillating gun at a target moving at immense speed. A gunner, firing a gun on a ship rolling on the waves of the sea, faces such conditions. The gun is loaded. The gunner sights through the sighting telescope in which the target has flashed for an instant. The gunner quickly pulls the firing lanyard: If he delays a single instant, the projectile will plunge into the sea close to the side of his own ship or else will fly high into the sky. In our case, however, there are certain features which facilitate the problem: We know exactly the path of the satellite, its velocity, and its position at each instant of time. It is thus possible to calculate, in advance, the time of take-off, to determine the trajectory of the rocket over the portion of the path along which the engines operate, to plan the program of accelerations and velocities, and therefore to indicate exactly the point in space at which the encounter of rocket and satellite must take place.

It is most convenient to have a flight to the satellite always follow one and the same trajectory. This is possible, provided the satellite periodically overflies the launching pad.

▪ Correction of the Take-off Trajectory and Orbit of the Satellite

A space rocket, and in particular an orbital rocket, must differ from ordinary rockets (for instance, rockets used for atmospheric research) not only in the indices of altitude, range, and velocity. There is another highly important criterion for determining the suitability of a rocket as a space-flight device, namely, the accuracy of its arrival at destination. Here the accuracy of the control of orbital rockets must be far greater than the accuracy of control, e.g., in marine navigation or in aviation. The slightest deviation in the velocity of flight or in the direction of motion is impermissible, and sometimes even fraught with great danger. An orbital rocket must therefore be provided with a fuel supply to compensate possible errors.

This is particularly important for liquid-fuel rockets in which, as a rule, not all of the propellant is consumed and a certain amount of combustible or oxidant[9] remains at the bottom of the tanks.

The experience obtained in the launching of *Viking* type rockets

[9] The cause of this is the inaccurate operation of the metering devices regulating the feed of the fuel components. For instance, when the supply of fuel to the combustion chamber is stopped and the flame extinguishes, a certain amount of unused oxidant remains in the tanks, thus reducing the velocity, range, and altitude of flight of the rocket. The indices obtained with liquid rockets may be considerably improved by the creation of ideally operating fuel metering devices, which would supply the fuel components to the combustion chamber in strict proportion to the combustible and oxidant remaining in the tanks at a given instant. But even under considerably simpler, static conditions, such devices usually operate with an accuracy not greater than 2 per cent.

makes it possible to estimate the fuel supply necessary for trajectory correction. These rockets, in most cases, reached heights somewhat above the mean predicted altitude, but still considerably lower than the theoretical maximum altitude (for example, an altitude of 219 kilometers was obtained in a case where the maximum calculated altitude should have been 354 kilometers). On the basis of these data, Rosen and Snodgrass (United States) attempted to find what the altitudes and velocities attained by three orbital step rockets would be if, for some reason, 2.5 per cent of their fuel remained unused. The payload of these rockets, at a take-off weight from 4.5-5524 tons, was assumed to be from 45 kilograms to 36.5 tons, and the altitude of the orbits from 322 to 1730 kilometers. It was found that in this case the ceiling of two of these rockets would be considerably lower than its planned level, while the third rocket could not go into circular orbit at all. The altitude and velocity of the satellite envisaged by the calculation could still be obtained, but only if the exhaust velocity were increased 3-5 per cent (by improving the propellant), or if the take-off weight were increased 10-20 per cent (by increasing the fuel supply).

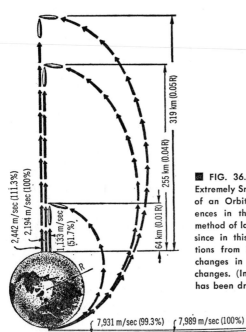

■ FIG. 36.—In Launching on a Semi-Ellipse, Extremely Small Deviations in the Initial Velocity of an Orbital Rocket Involve Immense Differences in the Ceilings Attained. The vertical method of launching is free of these drawbacks, since in this case only relatively large deviations from the calculated velocity will cause changes in the altitude equal to the above changes. (In the sketch, the size of the earth has been drawn to less than scale.)

However, even if an adequate amount of fuel is available, the correction of the trajectory may still prove highly complex since an insignificant difference in the take-off velocity involves tremendous changes in the rocket ceiling. Assume for instance that it has been decided to launch a rocket in a semi-ellipse to an altitude of 255 kilometers. For this, we need a take-off velocity of 7989 meters per second (Fig. 36). If the autopilot lags slightly and the velocity developed is 0.23 per cent greater, then the rocket will rise, as shown by calculations, to 319 kilometers, i.e., its ceiling will be 25 per cent higher. In other words, here the altitude is increased a hundred odd times as much as the velocity. If, however, the take-off velocity is 0.72 per cent lower, then the rocket will rise only to 64 kilometers, i.e., to a quarter of its planned altitude.

In launching a satellite on a different transitional trajectory, a deviation from the necessary velocity might result in considerably less deviation from the program. Compare these results, for instance, with the case of the rectangular launching discussed above. For a vertical take-off to an altitude of 255 kilometers, an initial velocity of 2194 meters per second is required. To raise this ceiling by 25 per cent, the velocity would have to be increased to 2442 meters per second, i.e., by 11.27 per cent. For a decrease of the ceiling to a quarter, however, the velocity would have to be decreased to 1133 meters per second, i.e., by 49.26 per cent.

Obviously, from the viewpoint of the possibility of correction of the launching, a rectangular trajectory is preferable, but this method of launching, as already noted, is quite uneconomical.

The velocity of the rocket must be carefully regulated not only on departure from the earth but also, to the same extent, at the instant of its passage into the planned orbit.

If the velocity of a satellite which is to revolve in a circular orbit is not adjusted with sufficient accuracy to the design value, then the satellite will be unable to remain at the prescribed altitude and will begin to descend, no longer moving in a circle but in an elliptical orbit located inside the planned circular orbit; this may lead to a subsequent fall of the satellite onto the earth's surface. An artificial satellite launched to an altitude of 200 kilometers is threatened by this danger already if its actual velocity is only 60 meters per second less than its design value. For a flight altitude of 500 kilometers, the maximum permissible deviation in velocity increases to 145 meters per second. With a further increase in the altitude to which the satellite is launched, the permissible deviation of the velocity increases, but only to a certain limit; more specifically, to 1500 meters per second for artificial satellites flying at an altitude of about 35,000 kilometers. For satellites flying at an altitude of 6000-7000 kilometers above or below this height, this value decreases by only one per cent. At still greater distances from the earth, this deviation in velocity, which would involve the fall of the satellite onto the earth's surface, gradually decreases, and approaches zero (Table 27).

■ TABLE 27

Maximum Permissible Losses of Altitude of a "Circular" Artificial Satellite, Assuming Absence of Atmosphere

Radius of Circular Orbit of Artificial Satellite, in Earth Radii	Loss of Velocity at Which a "Circular" Artificial Satellite Will Fall Back to the Earth, in Meters Per Second	Radius of Circular Orbit of Artificial Satellite, in Earth Radii	Loss of Velocity at Which a "Circular" Artificial Satellite Will Fall Back to the Earth, in Meters Per Second
1.1	182	6	1,503
1.2	336	10	1,435
1.3	468	20	1,223
1.5	682	30	1,078
2	1,027	40	975
3	1,338	50	897
4	1,454	70	787

The above statements refer to the case of the absence of atmosphere. In reality, however, the resistance of the atmosphere may lead to the destruction of an artificial satellite even at a smaller error in velocity than above noted. If, due to such an error, a satellite passes into an elliptical orbit lying in the more or less dense layers of the atmosphere, it will be heated by friction and may burn up, like a meteor, without even reaching the ground. But even if the satellite does not burn up and crosses the entire atmosphere intact, it will bury into the ground like a meteor when it strikes the earth.

As we see, it is one of the most difficult problems to ensure stability of motion of an artificial satellite. The motion of satellites whose orbits are located close to the earth's surface will be particularly unstable.

These arguments also speak eloquently of the difficulties involved in the building of an artificial satellite. Actually, in launching a satellite to an altitude of 200-500 kilometers, a deviation in the velocity by 1-2 per cent of the design value is sufficient to cause failure of the mission. But even if the design value of the circular velocity is exactly maintained, success is not always certain; at some definite altitude, the necessary velocity must be directed strictly horizontally, otherwise the orbit obtained will not be circular but elliptical. If, in this case, the velocity of the artificial satellite is deflected upward, it will pass through apogee first; if, however, the velocity is directed downward, the artificial satellite will first pass through perigee, which may be located even beneath the earth's surface, which means that the satellite will crash. Quite obviously, to ensure the necessary direction of velocity presents an additional difficulty. All this, incidentally, also indicates the high level of Soviet rocket engineering in launching artificial satellites.

It is interesting that, if the direction of the velocity at the end of the active segment of the path is not maintained while the value of the design velocity is accurately maintained, then the period of revolution of the satellite would not be modified. Such an error would involve a change in the positions of the apogee and perigee, whose heights may vary over a wide range.

The above-mentioned deviations of the velocity of a launched artificial satellite from the rated value must definitely be corrected, since they threaten the satellite's very existence. In particular, during the time of motion of the rocket on the active segment of the trajectory, the autopilot must continuously correct the angle of yaw, pitch, and roll of the rocket. It should be mentioned at this point that the periodic angular deflections of the rocket, alternately to the left and right of the principal direction of motion, are called "yaw." The keel rolling and the lateral inclination of the rocket about its longitudinal axis are termed "pitch" and "roll," respectively, as in marine navigation. The corresponding angles of deflection characterizing these motions are continuously measured by the aid of a gyroscope system, which also feeds electric impulses, proportional to the values of the deviations, into a correcting mechanism.

The course of the artificial satellite must be checked by the aid of the most delicate instrumentation and its trajectory corrected not only on launching but also during the time of the entire flight, especially if the artificial satellite is to move at relatively low altitudes, in the ionosphere, where the influence of the resistance of the air is already sensible.

Theoretically, an artificial satellite is under the influence of various gravitational fields: those of the earth, the moon, and the sun. For example, at a point equidistant from the earth and the moon, the forces of attraction, which must at that place be proportional to the masses of the interacting heavenly bodies, will be at a ratio of 1 : 81.5.

The perturbing influence of the gravitational fields of the sun and moon on the motion of an artificial satellite manifests itself in a slow oscillatory motion of the satellite about its theoretical orbit (according to Kepler's laws). The same influence on the motion of the satellite will be exerted by mountain ranges. No doubt, flights over ocean shores will also manifest their effects (since the density of the earth is considerably greater than the density of water), like flights over denser regions of the earth's crust, since these factors, to some extent, modify the character of the gravitational field of the earth.

The oblateness of the earth will have a considerably greater perturbing effect on the orbit of a low-flying artificial satellite than the attraction of the sun and the moon. Without changing the inclination of the orbit with respect to the plane of the equator, it will rotate the plane of the orbit in such a way that the line of its intersection with the plane of the equator will be in retrograde rotation (cf. above).

In the case of a greatly elongated elliptical orbit, the perturbing influence of the moon will become very marked, especially after the artificial satellite has made a certain number of revolutions. Figure 37 shows how an elliptical orbit, with its perigee at an altitude of 200 kilometers and its apogee at a distance of about 260,000 kilometers from the earth's center, changes after five revolutions. These studies were made by V. A. Yegorov at the Mathematical Institute, Academy of Sciences U.S.S.R., using a high-speed digital electronic computer.

Thuering (Federal Republic of Germany) studied the distortion of the orbit of an artificial satellite under the influence of the perturbing action of the gravitational forces of the moon and sun and determined the amount of fuel necessary to correct the deviations that would arise. He came to the following conclusions: If an artificial satellite moves at an altitude of 1730 kilometers and the rocket engine

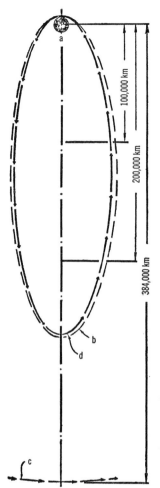

100,000 km

200,000 km

384,000 km

■ FIG. 37.—Variation in Shape of an Elongated Elliptical Orbit under the Influence of Lunar Perturbations (V. A. Yegorov, U.S.S.R.). The sketch shows the change in the orbit of a satellite after 5 revolutions. (a)—Earth; (b)—fifth revolution of satellite; (c)—first revolution of satellite; (d)—orbit of moon.

correcting its motion continuously ejects gases at an exhaust velocity of 3 kilometers per second, then during a year the consumption of fuel will be 1.1 per cent of the total mass of the artificial satellite. However, to compensate the influence of the oblateness of the earth on the orbit of an artificial satellite under similar conditions, the fuel consumption necessary would have to be 6.5 per cent of the mass of the satellite.

The method of continuous compensation of the perturbations is particularly unsuitable for an artificial satellite of the earth flying around the moon (cf. later in text). At an exhaust velocity of 95 kilometers per second (the atomic rocket of the future), it would take a mass of fuel equal to 1/10 the total mass of the satellite to correct the trajectory in a single circling flight around the moon, according to Thuering's calculation. But in that case, at an exhaust velocity of 3 kilometers per second (a thermochemical rocket), the mass of fuel would have to be 19.44 times as great as the final mass of the satellite, which is completely unthinkable.

We note, however, that the perturbing action of the moon and the sun need not necessarily be completely compensated. Insignificant changes in the shape of the satellite orbit might be of no danger. Moreover, a colossal economy of fuel could be obtained if the trajectory were to be corrected, not continuously, but only from time to time.

In launching artificial satellites (as in flight to a space platform), a correction may also prove to be necessary in the case where the rated velocity has been reached (in magnitude and direction) at the planned altitude, but, at the end of the last active segment, the orbital rocket emerges ahead or behind the platform or satellite that is its destination. On the ground, an automobile driver would slow down his motion to meet a car moving in the opposite direction. An astronaut, however, would have to accelerate his motion in this case, to make the orbit of the rocket longer than the orbit of the satellite (Fig. 38) and to meet the satellite after one revolution. If the rocket

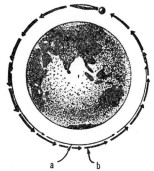

■ FIG. 38.—If an Orbital Rocket Flying Toward an Artificial Satellite Is in Front of It, then, To Reach the Satellite, It Would Have To Accelerate Its Motion and Make a "Correcting Circle." (a)—Orbit of satellite; (b)—orbit of rocket.

is behind the satellite, then the "correcting circle" would have to be made shorter than the satellite orbit.

The perturbations in the trajectory of an artificial satellite caused by the ebb and flow of tides, distorting the shape of the earth, would apparently be attenuated by the retarding action of the air and the influence of the earth's magnetic field.

In very high layers of the atmosphere, the radiation pressure of the sunlight on the artificial satellite might, under certain conditions, be more powerful than the resistance of the air encountered by the satellite. In the opinion of some authors, this phenomenon could be utilized to correct the trajectories of artificial satellites, and in this way to prolong their life indefinitely. But this view is entirely erroneous. In fact, the strongest pressure of light rays is exerted on a surface that completely reflects them. Such a surface, placed at the same distance from the sun as the earth, would be repelled by the solar rays with the force of approximately 1 milligram per square meter. An absolutely black body would experience a radiation pressure of the solar rays only half as great. In both cases, obviously, we have to do with a completely negligible force; to correct the trajectories of a satellite, it would be far simpler and more effective to make use of a miniature rocket engine.

5

Construction of Artificial Satellites

■
■
■

The prototype of the orbital rocket is the rocket with a very great radius of action, the intercontinental ballistic rocket. The launching of such a rocket is conducted so as to obtain the maximum horizontal velocity component.

The fact that a relatively small increase in the velocity to which an intercontinental rocket is accelerated greatly increases its radius of action is characteristic for such a rocket. For example, to reach a point 9,000 kilometers away, an initial velocity of 7 kilometers per second is necessary. But this velocity need be increased only 12.5 per cent in order to double that radius of action.

The longer the range of flight, the greater the velocity that must be developed by the rocket on acceleration. At the same time, the angle of take-off of the rocket with respect to the horizon decreases. Finally, if a rocket is to reach the antipodal point of the globe, this angle must be decreased to zero, i.e., the takeoff must be in a horizontal direction and the velocity must rise to the circular velocity (neglecting the resistance of the air). In this case, however, the intercontinental rocket would not fall on the antipodal point of the globe, since now it would fly parallel to the earth's surface. It would continue its motion indefinitely as an artificial satellite of the earth.

Thus an intercontinental ballistic rocket, gradually increasing its radius of action, is transformed into an artificial earth satellite. In fact, the Soviet artificial satellite was launched on the base of an intercontinental ballistic rocket.

The opinion has been repeatedly expressed that the current work on intercontinental ballistic rockets will exert a great influence on the solution of certain problems of space flight: These two problems are related, since the specifications for such rockets differ only slightly from the specifications for orbital rockets.

In contrast to aircraft, which usually fly parallel to the earth's surface at a more or less constant speed, the superlong-range rocket will fly at varying speed, at constantly varying altitudes. The trajectory that an intercontinental ballistic rocket would follow represents an arc of an ellipse, one of whose foci coincides with the center of the earth. Such a trajectory is the most economical (the rocket engine will give it, essentially, only the initial impetus). Regardless of the direction in which the rocket is dispatched and the distance it is to cover, it will usually start vertically. This is done mainly to ensure faster crossing of the dense layers of the atmosphere. But already at a relatively low altitude, the rocket will be turned by a definite angle and placed on course. The more distant the objective of the flight, the smaller must be the angle between the horizon and the velocity imparted to the rocket by its engine. In the case of a flight, for example, from Anadyr (Bering Sea) to Odessa, which is 7500 kilometers from Anadyr, this angle will be 28°. In this case, the earth's gravitation will somewhat interfere with the acceleration. In each second, the rocket engine will accelerate the flight of the rocket by 40 meters per second more, while the earth's gravity will decrease this value by 5.5 meters per second.

The compound rocket is today considered to be the most suitable type of rocket for intercontinental flights.

Assume that a nonstop flight from Anadyr to Odessa is made with a six-stage rocket. The lowest stage gives the rocket a velocity of

2 kilometers per second and lifts it to an altitude of 30 kilometers, where this stage is separated and the second stage goes into operation. After covering an arc 192 kilometers long by the aid of the second-stage engine, the rocket reaches an altitude of 120 kilometers. Here the third stage engine is cut in and gives the rocket, at an altitude of 270 kilometers (after covering a path of 575 kilometers along an arc), the velocity of 6.7 kilometers per second that is necessary to reach its planned destination. The engine is then cut and the rocket continues its flight by inertia, like a shell ejected from the muzzle of a gun (the remaining three stages of the rocket are necessary for the landing). By this time, the rocket has left most of the thickness of the atmosphere behind it, and, despite the immense velocity of the rocket, the air no longer offers any resistance to its motion.

As the rocket ascends, its motion gradually slows down. At an altitude of 500 kilometers its velocity amounts to 6 kilometers per second, and at an altitude of 1000 kilometers, to 5.3 kilometers per second. Finally, at the "ceiling," located at the level of 1235 kilometers, the flight of the rocket undergoes its greatest deceleration, but its velocity even now still amounts to only slightly less than 5 kilometers per second.

As the rocket rises, ever new expanses of the earth's surface unfold before the eyes of the travelers. Points hundreds of kilometers behind the place of departure, Anadyr, become visible. At the moment the rocket has covered about a third of the distance to Odessa, Anadyr will be 1600 kilometers from the horizon line. Fifteen minutes after the start, when the rocket reaches its ceiling, the horizon will be still wider: The field of view will now include Greenland, Iceland, the Scandinavian Peninsula, and the Urals, while Novaya Zemlya will lie almost "underfoot."

After the rocket has passed the uppermost point of its trajectory, its velocity will again begin to increase, and at an altitude of 270 kilometers, it will again reach 6.7 kilometers per second as on take-off. At this moment, retardation produced by the rocket engine (or by the resistance of the air), will begin. The entire process of retardation will take three minutes, as long as the period of gaining velocity had taken, and the rocket will land smoothly. The entire flight will take 30 minutes 3 seconds. Since the difference in local time (not zone time) between Anadyr and Odessa is almost 10 hours, it follows that, on landing in Odessa, the passengers of the intercontinental rocket will find that they have seemingly retraced several hours in time. If they had taken off at sunset, the day for them would have been "prolonged" by 9½ hours. If the voyage took place at night on January 1, they could celebrate New Year twice.

According to biblical legend, Joshua, son of Nun, succeeded, for a short time, to stop the motion of the sun in the sky. To the passengers of the intercontinental rocket, flying westward, the sun pays even greater homage: It not only stops its motion in the sky, but even turns backward, rushing at high speed in the direction from west to east.

On the return from Odessa to Anadyr, on a similar rocket, the sun will hurtle westward by day much faster than usual, since this time the rocket will be moving "to meet" the sun.

As stated above, the building of an intercontinental passenger rocket, capable of making the gigantic jump from Anadyr to Odessa in half an hour, is a very difficult task. Might it not be easier to build a rocket that could cover the distance Anadyr-Odessa not in ½ hour, but in 1 hour or in 1½ hours, in view of the fact that it is simpler, after all, to build an aircraft with a cruising speed of 300 kilometers per hour than one with a speed of 900 kilometers per hour. The answer to this question may seem paradoxical.

It is theoretically possible to launch a rocket so as to fall at a predetermined place after any desired period of time, since an infinite number of elliptical arcs between this place and the starting point can be drawn. In practice, however, it is easier to construct a rocket, connecting these cities in the above shorter interval of time than in the longer time. In fact, if the rocket is to fall at the appointed point later, it would have to be thrown higher, in order to cover a longer distance, but this would require a greater acceleration. If, however, the rocket is launched at a lower initial velocity, then it will not reach its destination at all.

For a rocket to reach any point on earth from some definite starting point, its radius of action would obviously have to be half the length of the earth's circumference. However, a glance at a map of the northern hemisphere will be sufficient to convince the reader that, for a start from Europe, it will in most cases be sufficient if the radius of action of the rocket is only a quarter the length of the earth's cir-

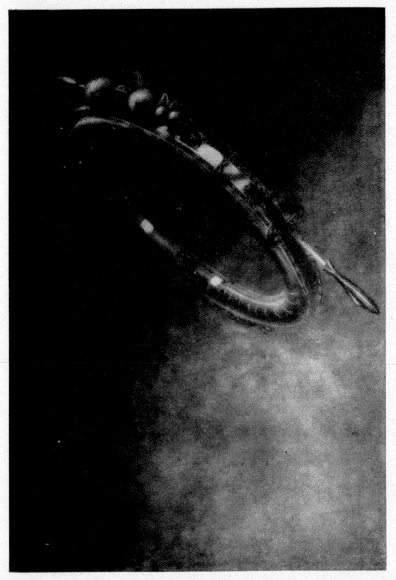

■ FIG. XI.—Approximate Design of Artificial Satellite of the Earth. From such a platform, space ships will depart on interplanetary journeys. The rotation of the satellite about its axis will produce artificial gravity on it *(according to A. Shternfeld, Artist N. Kolchitskiy).*

FIG. XII.—One of the Possible Versions of the Design of a Manned Artificial Satellite: The Satellite Is Made Up Mainly of Spent Rockets. In the part of the artificial satellite visible in the foreground, weightlessness prevails; in the rotating part, artificial gravity is present (according to A. Shternfeld, Artist V. Vorontsov).

■ FIG. XIII.—Interplanetary Station (according to von Braun). 1—Radio center; 2—meteorological station; 3—sleeping quarters; 4—observation post; 5—television station for transmission of photographs; 6—emergency respiration equipment; 7—computer; 8—telescope control desk; 9—aerophotographic laboratory; 10—aerophotosurveying control desk; 11—air-conditioning plant; 12-13—astronomical station; 14—water-circulation system; 15—scales; 16—unloading platform; 17—elevator; 18—emergency respiration equipment; 19—propellant; 20—portholes; 21—temperature controls; 22—inner wall with struts for antimeteorite skin; 23—antimeteorite skin; 24—ring for anchorage; 25—deck reinforcement; 26—pumping station; 27—doors; 28—micro-atmospheric tester; 29—air-conditioning plant; 30—electric power plant; 31—air analysis laboratory; 32—ventilation system; 33—electric system and water line; 34—pipeline for carrying off mercury vapor; 35—piping for condensation of mercury vapor; 36—mirror of helio plant; 37—ladder; 38—space boat; 39—mooring tower; 40—air lock; 41—air lines; 42—loading hatch; 43—pressure suits; 44—tower engine; 45—mooring; 46—antenna.

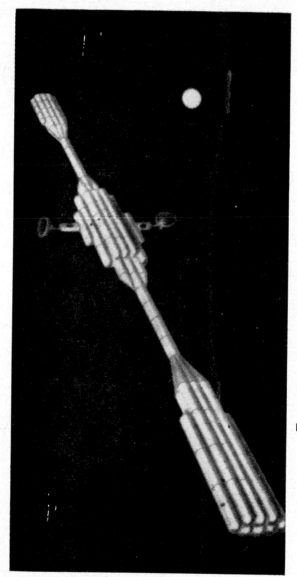

■ FIG. XIV.—Artificial Satellite (According to *Krafft Ehricke*).

cumference. Actually, for a start from any point in Europe, it is possible, by flying this distance, to reach almost any populated point of the dry land of the globe. These points include Europe, Asia, Africa, North America, the Northwestern coast of South America, and other places on the globe.

On August 27, 1957, the Soviet newspapers published a *Tass* dispatch that a superlong-distance intercontinental multistage ballistic rocket had been launched in the U.S.S.R. This dispatch stated: "Tests of the rocket have been successful and completely confirm the correctness of the calculations and design adopted. The flight of the rocket took place at a very high altitude, never reached previously. After covering an immense distance in a short time, the rocket fell in the assigned area. The results show that a rocket can be launched to any region of the globe."

Below, we will discuss the significance of this fact for the construction of orbital rockets.

■ Construction of Orbital Rockets

Design of the Rocket

What will be the appearance of orbital rockets in general, i.e., rockets that will serve either for launching artificial satellites of the earth or for maintaining communications with them? Rockets of various designs may be used for launching satellites. For example, if three- or four-stage rockets burning ordinary fuel are used for this purpose, then their take-off weight will be several hundred times as great as the payload. The stages of the rocket, tightly fitted to each other, will be enclosed in a streamlined shell, in order better to overcome the resistance of the air in passage through the atmosphere (Fig. 39). The nose section of the rocket will carry the payload or cabin for the fliers. The equipment of such a cabin will be quite simple, since a flight on a circular orbit will take only from several minutes to one hour.

In a thermochemical orbital rocket, the tail and center sections will have to be jettisoned, which will be an immense material loss since the weight of the rocket head constitutes only a small part of the total structural weight of the rocket. However, the spent stages of the rocket can be returned to the ground either by parachute, or by the aid of wings (apparently retractable wings) to convert the no longer

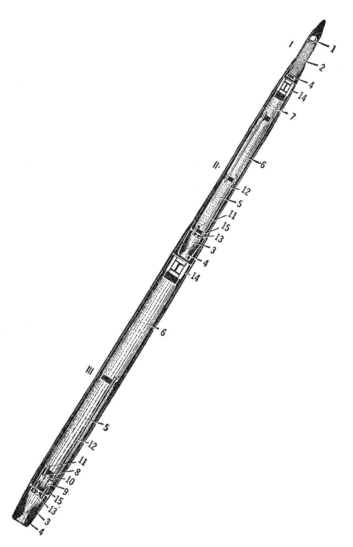

■ FIG. 39.—One of the Possible Versions of an Orbital Rocket: I—head section of rocket; II—middle section of rocket; III—tail section of rocket; 1—artificial satellite; 2—powder sticks; 3—combustion chamber; 4—nozzle; 5—combustible tank; 6—oxidant tank; 7—tank with compressed gas for feeding fuel to combustion chamber; 8—pump for combustible; 9—oxidant pump; 10—turbine; 11—line for combustible; 12—oxidant line; 13—hinged engine mount; 14—autopilot; 15—autopilot levers for turning the engine.

required stage into a glider. The spent stages, after descending intact to the ground, will be reusable. We note that, as far back as the end of the Twenties, rockets were built in which the stabilizers were automatically expanded at the ceiling and were transformed into lifting wings, after which the rocket descended in a glide (Tiling, Germany).

To prevent a rocket from rotating during the time of engine operation, the thrust must always pass through its center of gravity. The fuel tanks must therefore be so constructed that, as the fuel is expended, the common center of gravity is displaced along the axis of symmetry of the rocket, despite the fact that, as a rule, the weight of the combustible consumed is not equal to the weight of the oxidant consumed.

When a rocket moves through the atmosphere, the center of pressure of the air must be located on the axis of symmetry, preferably aft of the center of gravity, as is the case in arrows shot from a bow.

In practice it is very difficult to obtain a strictly axial direction of the jet thrust, especially in cases where there are several combustion chambers for which it is impossible to produce entirely identical operation.

The "parasitic" rotation of a space rocket can be eliminated by the aid of air or gas rudders. These allow the rocket to rotate, if necessary, during the time of engine operation. The same object is attained by varying, for a certain time, the orientation of the engine relative to the axis of symmetry of the rocket. For this purpose, the rocket is not installed rigidly in the rocket frame but is suspended on hinges.

If there are several engines, the same result can be obtained by varying the feed of the fuel into the proper chamber or into several chambers. In that case, the resultant thrust will not pass through the center of gravity of the rocket, and therefore a turning moment will arise which is necessary to turn the rocket or to counteract the parasitic rotation.

The rocket may also be provided with properly arranged special nozzles of small size, to be connected at the moment when the rocket is to be rotated. The automatic displacement of some mass within the rocket, so that the rocket will turn as required, is also possible.

To obtain stable motion, the stabilizing elements may be controlled by automatic gyroscope devices, which are set in rotation by compressed air or gas stored in cylinders, by a steam-gas generator, or by some other method. The displacements of the control elements may be transmitted to the rudder by the aid of an electric current, a pneumatic transmission, or a mechanical drive. Such mechanisms, known as servomotors, are widely used in technology.

Air stabilizers were formerly considered to be most convenient devices for ensuring stability of the rocket in the dense layers of the atmosphere. Recently, however, designers have come to the conclusion that such stabilizers, which are generally rather heavy, are unsuitable, since during the first stage of flight they exert no stabilizing action because of the low velocity of motion; when the rocket, after having picked up speed, is at a high altitude, such stabilizers still fail to yield an effect since, because of the low density of the air at great altitudes, the action of the air on the stabilizers is negligible. Air rudders suffer from the same shortcomings. Besides lightening the rocket structure, the abandonment of stabilizers decreases the resistance of the air on the active part of the trajectory. But even gas rudders are far from perfect: the combustion products, having a high temperature and moving at immense velocity, exert a destructive action on such rudders. However, it is practically impossible to produce intense cooling of the combustion products. Gas rudders are therefore highly fragile, and some orbital rockets are designed entirely without air stabilizers and also without either air or gas rudders. The stability of a rocket and the variation of its course are secured in this case by a hinge suspension of the engine, which, obeying the control devices of the autopilot, deflects the gas jet away from the longitudinal axis of the rocket in any desired direction.

At each given instant, the engine is placed in its proper position in the gimbals by the aid of a lever system. The servomotor for turning the axle of the engine uses (in particular) a hydraulic transmission, and the power necessary for this purpose is tapped from the turbine shaft. To supply the fuel components, a flexible pipeline is used, running from the rocket body to the unit of the gimbal hinge of the engines. To reduce the resistance of the air and to protect the rocket from aerodynamic heating, a special protective cap of pointed shape may be placed on it; this cap can be jettisoned as soon as the rocket has passed through the dense layers of the atmosphere.

During the time of motion of a step rocket along the passive part of the launching trajectory, the autopilot can take care of the correction of the trajectory and the launching of the nose section at a predetermined altitude by the aid of auxiliary nozzles through which the inert gas that has previously served to maintain the pressure in the tanks is exhausted.

At the Seventh International Astronautical Congress held at Rome in 1956, the Italian scientist Robotti proposed the following method of launching an artificial satellite: An orbital compound rocket with a winged tail section is first lifted by a jet aircraft, special or standard, to a great altitude (for instance to 14,000 meters) where it is separated from the aircraft and begins independent flight. The tail section, after combustion cutoff, is returned to the ground in a gliding flight. On take-off from the earth's surface, the entire system, i.e., the orbital rocket together with the carrier aircraft, is given an initial acceleration by means of a rocket car.

To realize this project it is proposed to utilize the Bumper two-stage rocket (V-2 plus Wac Corporal), provided with delta wings, 9 meters in span and the same in width. At the moment of start, the wing loading is 300 kilograms per square meter and decreases as the fuel, consisting of 4200 liters of combustible and 4700 liters of oxidant, is consumed. In this case, the center of gravity of the flying device is considerably displaced, which demands special measures. It is also necessary to solve a number of other problems. For example, on crossing the troposphere, in contrast to the rapid crossing of the atmosphere by wingless rockets, the tanks of a winged rocket, containing liquid oxygen, would become coated with a thick layer of ice due to the condensation of water vapor. For this reason, some other substance with a high boiling point would have to be used as oxidant, or the tanks would have to be coated with a heat-insulating material. Possible freezing of the fuel on the inner wall of the tanks, due to the low outside temperature in some layers of the atmosphere, as well as a rise in pressure of the fuel vapor to above the permissible level would have to be anticipated.

Orbital rockets for manned flights would have to be given considerably greater over-all dimensions and higher power than rockets for launching satellite robots. This requirement is due not only to the fact that the weight of a human being plus his vital necessities is greater than that of automatic instrumentation but also to the fact that facilities for a safe return to earth will have to be provided.

The increase in over-all dimensions of rocket engines involves thicker combustion-chamber walls, which makes them very difficult to cool. Moreover, gantry tests of large-caliber rockets are very expensive. This indicates the advisability of replacing large engines by groups of rocket engines of lower power (Von Braun). A rocket flying device with a large number of engines of smaller size will be more reliable in operation than a device with a smaller number of engines of greater power. If engines of one and the same type can be installed in varying numbers on the different stages of step rockets, series production of such engines could be scheduled. This would make their production less expensive, speed up the rate of production, and increase their safety, since it will be possible to subject them to more careful machining and testing. In particular, the series production should be restricted to two or three types of powerful standard rocket engines, which, in different combinations, could be used for both cargo and passenger rockets capable of reaching circular velocity.

According to a project initiated in 1952 by a group of specialists, headed by the above-mentioned scientist, Von Braun, for the construction of an interplanetary platform at an altitude of 1730 kilometers (radius of orbit 8100 kilometers) and also for subsequent delivery of crew and cargo to this station, three-stage rockets, with a take-off weight of 6400 tons and a payload of 25 tons, would be used. All three stages of the rocket would be enclosed in a conical shell 60 meters in height (without counting the stabilizer), with a base of 20 meters in diameter.

Gatland, Kunesch, and Dixon (Great Britain) consider the Von Braun project unrealistic and propose building three-stage rockets, automatically taking off into a circular orbit, with an initial weight of 520 tons, of which 5.2 tons are payload (Figs. V, VI) (the exhaust velocity of the rocket will be 2.8-3 kilometers per second). With certain modifications in the design of the rocket and an increase of its initial weight to 700 tons, a glider could be transported to the artificial satellite for subsequent descent to the earth's surface.

Under the influence of the above work and others, Von Braun improved his original project for an orbital rocket in 1956. The main improvement consists in the fact that the ratio of the payload to the take-off weight of the rocket is now increased to one quarter, despite the fact that the dimensions of the rocket are considerably reduced. In the second version, the rocket is more elongated: Its height will be 50-58 meters (depending on the shape of the head) and its

■ **TABLE 28**

Characteristics of the Orbital Rocket According to the 1956 Von Braun Project

	1st Stage	2nd Stage	3rd Stage*
Thrust, in tons	2,500	320	40
Initial weight of rocket to combustion cutoff of stage, in tons	1,280	180	26
Empty weight of stage alone, in tons	140	14	2.1
Final weight of rocket after combustion cutoff of stage, in tons	320	40	15.7
Fuel, in tons	960	140	10.3
Fuel consumption per second, in tons	11.15	1.12	141
Operating time of engine, in seconds	84	124	73
Altitude of final point of active part, in kilometers	40	64	102
Velocity at end of active part, in meters per second	2,350	6,420	8,260

* *This does not include the 2.5 tons of fuel consumed in the transition to circular orbit at an altitude of 1,730 kilometers, when the rocket is given an additional velocity of 460 meters per second after the engine, with a 40-ton thrust, is turned on for 17 seconds.*

diameter 11.7 meters. Table 28 gives the characteristics of orbital rockets for delivery of 10-ton loads into a circular orbit with the same radius (8100 kilometers) as before.

Automatic Controls

On board an aircraft, the crew uses semiautomatic or even entirely nonautomatic instrumentation. It is another matter in space flights. Actually, manual control is unsuitable in this case, since a sharp movement of the hand or foot takes about half a second, while during this time the velocity of the rocket could increase by 20 meters per second, which would raise the ceiling of the rocket by additional tens of kilometers. The slightest deflection in the take-off angle of the rocket would also have serious consequences. Other typical examples could be given. For this reason, the operating conditions of the engine and the control of the air and gas rudders must be automatically regulated. Finally, for recording the wide variety of instrument readings, automatic devices will be required.

Thus, the entire control of the flight of an orbital rocket must be effected automatically, according to a predetermined program. The pilot, however, must make certain that the automatic devices are in good working order, check the results of their operation, and take the necessary decisions. It must be borne in mind that, at the beginning of rocket motion, the movements of the pilot will be impaired, due to the effects of the G-force, while in the first moments after cancellation of gravity, he may lose his orientation.

The automatic accelerographs will be able to program the thrust of the rocket engine along the active part of the trajectory. The direction of flight of the rocket can be programmed and corrected by gyroscopic instrumentation.

For instance, during the time of flight of the rocket along the active part of the trajectory, the autopilot will be able to correct the angles of yaw and pitch by appropriate rotations of the axis of symmetry of the main engine. To eliminate rotations of the rocket about the longitudinal axis, special rocket jets may be placed on the rocket skin, and arranged in planes perpendicular to this axis.

The successful operation of the gyroscopes is primarily a result of their high-precision machining. The flywheel of the gyroscope can be manufactured with a tolerance of only 2.5/100,000 of a millimeter. The allowable deviation of the diameters of the gyroscope bearings from the rated values is only 2.5/1,000,000 of a millimeter (which corresponds to 1/20 the diameter of a hair).

Specialists consider that even the microscopic specks of dust getting into the gyroscope may cause no less of a disaster than a handful of grit in an automobile transmission (Berger). Gyroscopic instrumentation is therefore made carefully airtight, and in its manufacture special precautionary measures are taken: The assembly shops are entered through air locks, after careful cleaning of the shoes on a foot mat; in the shops themselves smoking is forbidden, draftsmen are not allowed to tear paper or use erasers, and invalids are used by preference for the work, since their enforced immobility minimizes the friction of clothing and shoe soles; the special work clothes for the assembly operations are made of nylon, etc.

In view of the fact that the assembly of gyroscopes must take place in a completely dust-free atmosphere, a factory for using such equipment has been built in the Arizona desert (United States), without windows. Air is admitted to the factory rooms through special filters, and is completely renewed every 9 minutes (Bosquier, France).

The details of the production of autopilots for orbital rockets we have given here may seem of secondary importance. They must, however, be taken with the utmost seriousness, since the successful launching of an artificial satellite depends largely on such "trifles."

■ Gantry Tests of Orbital Rockets

The preliminary tests of orbital rockets are run under special laboratory-type conditions. These are what are termed gantry tests. In such tests, conditions similar to those under which the orbital rocket must fly can be produced. For the laboratory study of the process of the discharge of the exhaust gases from a rocket in the upper layers of the atmosphere, the pressure of the air at the outlet of the exhaust nozzle is reduced and, in some cases, is brought almost to the vacuum level. If necessary, the metering of the fuel components, the intensity of the cooling of the combustion chamber and nozzle, etc., are varied.

In gantry tests, the following quantities, varying with time, are automatically recorded: thrust, consumption of combustible and oxidant, pressure and temperature in the tanks and at various points of combustion chamber, nozzle, piping, pumps, etc. During the operation of rocket engines, they are viewed from behind a thick armored wall with peepholes of unbreakable glass; mirrors, periscopes, still and motion-picture cameras, television, and other installations are also used. Motion-picture photography and television permit following the combustion process, even inside the rocket engine.

Color motion-picture photography is used for spectrographic examination of the fiery jet emerging from the nozzle of a rocket engine (Herman and Silverman, United States). The speed of motion-picture photography of the combustion processes is 1000 or even as much as 10,000 frames per second. At the same time the instrument boards with the mounted instruments are also photographed on the motion-picture film, permitting an exact definition of the time variation of the different parameters characterizing the operation of the rocket engine.

The use of motion-picture photography in fire tests also permits safe observation (explosion of the combustion chambers of rockets during tests of new types of fuel is a fairly frequent occurrence). In many cases, the magazines with motion-picture film are undamaged after explosions, while the motion-picture camera itself is put out of commission.

A gantry for static tests of rockets with a thrust as high as 160 tons has been set up at Lake Denmark, N.J. (United States). The largest gantry of this type in the United States is at the White Sands experimental base. Fire tests of a rocket engine with a thrust of about 230 tons, which is almost ten times as great as the thrust of a *V-2* rocket, can be run on such a gantry. Near Baltimore (United States), the Glenn Martin Company has built a five-story test gantry of 30 meters height for testing the engines of the Vanguard orbital rockets (Fig. VII). This gantry is equipped for simultaneous testing of two rockets.

In the wind tunnels used for measuring the resistance of the air acting on the rocket in flight, the stationary rocket or a model of it is exposed to a jet of air having a velocity corresponding to the velocity of motion of the rocket in various parts of its trajectory in the atmosphere. At present, the velocity of the airflow past a small rocket model has been brought up to more than 6 kilometers per second. The degree of heating of the rocket shell during its motion along both the active and passive parts of its trajectory is also studied in wind tunnels. For testing the retarding action of parachutes at supersonic speeds, rocket carriages sliding on rails are also used. For example, the North American Aviation Company has built, for running aerodynamic tests, rail rocket sleds which, under a thrust of 22.7 tons, have developed a velocity of 792 meters per second (2850 kilometers per hour) in 4.5 seconds from start.

■ Flight Tests of Orbital Rockets

Flight tests of orbital rockets, naturally, resemble the analogous tests of high-altitude rockets.

For photographing attack aircraft and flying missiles, motion-picture theodolites have been used since 1929. Such a camera not only photographs the missile itself but simultaneously records its azimuth,[1] its angle of ascent and the time; from 2 to 4 exposures per second are made. Mutually synchronized theodolites permit an accurate reconstruction of the trajectory of the missile, as well as its position and velocity as a function of time.

Gantry tests of rocket engines, as well as flight tests, are recorded by the method of accelerated motion-picture photography ("slow-motion photography"). At the end of World War II, the Germans equipped certain guided missiles with motion-picture cameras. After the war, the British military authorities made flight tests of V-2 rockets on German soil, and the tests were photographed and made up into a documentary film. Since 1946, motion pictures have been made of the flight tests of guided missiles of various types in the United States. In recent years the French military authorities have also taken motion pictures of the flight of rockets and guided missiles in the Sahara. For the exact photography of a rocket in flight along various parts of its trajectory, cameras with the most varied characteristics, taking from 25 to 180 frames a second, must be used. The data of such motion-picture photography are processed on automatic computers. For instance, 24,000 calculations must be made for an exact reconstruction of the flight of a high-altitude rocket, which can be done by an automatic computer in 10 hours.

■ Acceleration Tests of a Manned Orbital Rocket

How is a manned orbital rocket to be tested before sending it out into space? How can one make sure that it will be able to become a satellite of the earth?

Assume that an artificial rocket is designed to revolve around the earth at an altitude of 1000 kilometers. The circular velocity corresponding to this altitude is 7356 meters per second. In addition to the work necessary to impart this velocity to the rocket, a certain amount of work must be performed to lift the rocket to the assigned altitude and overcome the resistance of the atmospheric envelope of the earth. Finally, one must also take account of the losses in the correction of the trajectory, in view of possible inaccuracies in the

---

[1] The azimuth is the angle between the plane of the meridian and the vertical plane passing through the flying device.

operation of the mechanisms and instruments, of the losses due to the quite insignificant but still constantly present resistance of the extremely rarefied air in the orbit of the artificial satellite, and also of certain other losses. Bearing all this in mind and making the necessary calculations, it will be found that to perform the assigned function the rocket must be able, on completely consuming its fuel, to develop an ideal velocity of 9460 meters per second.

For testing the orbital rocket under flight conditions, it can first be given half the ideal velocity (in this case 9640 : 2 = 4820 meters per second) and then, by means of its engines, it can completely counteract this velocity. This proves convincingly that the rocket is capable of developing the velocity necessary for becoming an artificial satellite of the earth. We may also put the rocket into flight on a suitably corrected trajectory resembling that of an intercontinental rocket. As shown by calculations, in our case the rocket could cover 2405 kilometers, i.e., for instance, the distance between Moscow and Karaganda or between Kiev and Nar'yan-Mara, in 14 minutes 43 seconds.

In such a preliminary flight, the rocket engine would be started for a short time, but the rocket velocity would increase at the maximum rates permitted by the physical endurance of the human organism. The rocket would take off, for example, at Moscow with an acceleration of the reactive force of 50 meters per second. Because of the earth's attraction, however, the acceleration of motion decreases to 43.2 meters per second.[3] After 96.4 seconds at an altitude of 127.8 kilometers, when the rocket has flown 200.5 kilometers, the engine will shut off. At this moment the rocket will have a velocity of 4161 meters per second (in free space its velocity would be 4819 meters per second). From this moment on, with engine off, the rocket will fly in the arc of an ellipse. After the rocket has passed through its ceiling at an altitude of 539 kilometers, its velocity will again begin to rise, and, at the altitude level of 127.8 kilometers, it will reach the same value that it had at combustion cutoff, i.e., 4161 meters per second.

[2] The acceleration of the reactive force (sensible acceleration) is the value of the thrust divided by the flying mass of the flying device at a given instant, i.e., the acceleration the rocket would have in free space.

[3] The take-off is at an angle to the vertical, and the acceleration of the reactive force is geometrically added (by the parallelogram rule) to the acceleration of gravity, i.e., the acceleration of free fall.

At this moment, braking by means of the rocket engines must begin. This will last 96.4 seconds, the same time as the take-off period, and the rocket will then start landing. The entire flight will last, as already stated, a little less than a quarter of an hour. This is about the manner in which a number of experimental launchings of the orbital rocket will be made to test the structural strength, the reliability of operation of the instrumentation, and the proper training of the crew.

When the pilot sits at the controls of a ship of similar design to the rocket we have described, no longer intended for testing but for an actual space flight, he will not decelerate the motion of the device but will rather increase its velocity according to a predetermined program until it reaches the magnitude necessary to transform the rocket into an artificial satellite (for this purpose, the engine will have to operate, with interruptions, somewhat over 3 minutes).

■ Acceleration and Deceleration Tests of the Manned Orbital Rocket

To realize a manned artificial satellite, it is not sufficient merely to give a rocket an orbital velocity. It is also necessary to be sure that the human cargo will be able to return unharmed to earth. However, to investigate the possibility of a safe descent, it will be necessary to run tests at considerably higher rates of acceleration than in the case we have just considered, and then to retard this velocity by any available methods, for instance, by the combined action of the resistance of the air and of the rocket engines. It is possible that we will succeed in utilizing atmospheric oxygen for combustion of the propellant in the braking engines. (Questions connected with deceleration by making use of the resistance of the atmosphere during descent from an artificial satellite are discussed later in the text.)

No doubt, attempts to launch artificial satellites with human passengers will not be undertaken before relevant experiments have been successfully completed with manned superlong-range and intercontinental rockets with greater radii of action and higher rates of acceleration.

On such rockets, the pilots will be trained not only to reach the orbital velocities (i.e., velocities at which the rocket can move in a closed orbit) but also to reduce such velocities by means of the resistance of the air and of a rocket engine.

This is why flights on such rockets are a preparation for the flight of man to an artificial satellite, and for living on such a satellite.

The persons participating in flights on an intercontinental rocket will receive the necessary hardening for flight on an orbital rocket, since the physiological sensations of a passenger on an intercontinental ballistic rocket will not differ from those in a space rocket: namely those involving the G-force during acceleration and deceleration, and the complete absence of gravity during the entire flight with engine off.

■ Layout of Artificial Satellites

Artificial satellites will differ substantially from all terrestrial structures, but nevertheless will not resemble heavenly bodies. It would be difficult and uneconomical to create, in space, a sphere consisting of a dense mass like the planets and their satellites. It would be entirely impossible to supply such a sphere or other artificial heavenly body with an atmosphere: the negligible force of gravity of such a structure could not, of course, retain an atmospheric envelope.

The first Soviet artificial moon is a very small structure: a sphere 58 centimeters in diameter, weighing 83.6 kilograms (Fig. VIII). The body of the satellite is made of aluminum alloys. Its shell is carefully machined and polished, to ensure good visibility of the satellite. The shell protects the instrumentation not only from micrometeorites but also from sharp fluctuations of temperature.

The satellite is equipped with radio apparatus. The four rod antennas are 2.4–2.9 meters in length. During take-off of the orbital rocket, these antennas are held against the shell. After separation of the satellite as an independent body, the antennas, attached to the shell of the satellite by means of hinges, are detached and separated, assuming the position shown in Fig. VIII. The antennas are the only parts mounted on the outer surface of the satellite, while all the remaining apparatus and power supply are placed inside the shell. The airtight satellite is filled with nitrogen which, because of the constant forced circulation, regulates the heat exchange between the instruments and the parts.

At the beginning of flight of the first satellite, it was preceded by the protective cap of the nose section of the orbital rocket, which had been ejected after the stage had reached the necessary velocity, and was followed by the stage that had ejected the satellite itself.

The second Soviet artificial earth satellite, in contrast to the first satellite, consisted of the last stage of the step rocket itself; all the scientific and measuring apparatus was located in this stage (Fig. IX). This arrangement of the instrumentation substantially simplified the problem of determining the coordinates of the satellite by optical observation means since, as shown by the experience with the first satellite, observation of the carrier rocket proved far simpler than of the satellite itself (the carrier rocket was several stellar magnitudes brighter than the first satellite). The total weight of the apparatus, experimental animal, and power supply on the second artificial satellite was 508 kilograms 300 grams.

The front part of the last stage of the rocket, on a special frame, carried an instrument for investigating the solar radiation in the ultraviolet and X-ray regions of the spectrum, a spherical container with radio transmitters and other instruments, and a pressurized cabin with an experimental animal, a dog. The apparatus for studying the cosmic rays was mounted on the body of the rocket. A special protective cone protected the instruments and containers installed on the frame from the aerodynamic and thermal influences that act during flight on the rocket in the dense layers of the atmosphere. After the final stage of the rocket was put in orbit, the protective cone was ejected.

The radio transmitters in the spherical container operated on frequencies of 40.002 and 20.005 megacycles. Their power supply, the system of heat regulation, as well as the sensitive elements recording the variation of temperature and other parameters were also placed in this container. In its design, the spherical container resembles the first Soviet artificial satellite.

The pressurized cabin containing the experimental animal (dog) was of cylindrical shape. The cabin for the animal, like the spherical container, was made of aluminum alloys. Its surface was polished and specially treated to give it the necessary values of the coefficients of radiation and absorption of solar radiation.

At the Fifth International Astronautical Congress held at Innsbruck, Austria, in 1954, the American scientist Levitt proposed a project for a satellite in the form of a sphere that would be a good reflector of solar rays. The rubber shell of the sphere, covered with aluminum foil, was to be lifted on a three-stage rocket and, after the head rocket reached the circular velocity, it was to be inflated with gas. The thin aluminum sphere would not lose its shape even after the gas was lost and the rubber shell contracted. Such a beacon satellite, 3 meters in diameter, which would reflect both light rays and radio waves, could be serviceable for geodetic and gravimetric measurements.

According to a French project, an inflatable artificial satellite of spheroconical shape would have a diameter of 10 meters with a length of 15 meters and would weigh 50 kilograms. It could be made of a special fabric or of polyethylene, covered with a fluorescent lacquer to render observation possible during its passage through the earth's shadow, at night. The shells of the projected American inflatable artificial satellites are made of fabric, covered with an aluminum composition.

At the end of 1955, a model of an artificial satellite, reproducing the design of the satellite to be launched during the International Geophysical Year (Fig. X) was exhibited at New York. The spherical shell of the model was made of transparent plastic. The shell of the actual artificial satellite, half a meter in diameter, will be made of magnesium alloy 0.7 millimeter thick and will weigh 1.8 kilograms, which will be 18.5 per cent of the total weight of 9.7 kilograms. The magnesium shell of the satellite was covered with successive layers of copper, zinc, nickel-silver alloy, and, finally, pure gold. This shell was to protect the instrumentation not only from micrometeorites but also from sharp temperature fluctuations.

Owing to the electrical conductivity of metals, the shell of a satellite designed for investigating the electric currents in the ionosphere cannot be made of metals. In particular, aluminum, which is so suitable in all other respects, cannot be used for this purpose. The shell must be made of an insulating substance such as a plastic, preferably white to ensure optimum visibility.

In order to have one and the same side of the satellite always turned toward the sun, over a long period of time (with the object of constant study of the solar radiation and utilization of the solar energy for charging a storage battery), the gyroscopic effect is used. On the ground the artificial satellite, suspended in gimbals, is placed in rapid rotary motion about an axis parallel to the solar rays. For the satellite, special board instruments have been developed, of over-all dimensions considerably smaller than American industry has ever before produced. The radio transmitter, for instance, will be the size of a cigarette box. It is assumed that the energy of the electric batteries will be exhausted long before destruction of the artificial satellite.

For the smallest artificial satellites, a conical form has also been proposed, since it is difficult to place a sphere or a cyinder in the nose section of a rocket. The spherical form of the satellite, in contrast to all others (for instance to the cylindrical form), permits motion in relatively dense layers of the atmosphere in a smooth trajectory with no nodes whatever that might distort the data transmitted to the earth.

Automatic rockets alone are insufficient for studying the process of launching and operating artificial satellites; rockets with scientific and technical personnel would also be required, the more so since we are concerned with the discovery of new phenomena and with finding out how man will adapt himself to the conditions of weightlessness.

There are still many difficulties in the way of the creation of a manned artificial satellite. The most complex problem is the necessity of ensuring return of the crew to earth, which involves greater difficulties than the launching of a satellite. For this reason alone, it is still impossible today to build a manned artificial satellite. But the experience that will be obtained in the launching and operation of the first automatic artificial satellites will serve as a foundation for the subsequent construction of manned satellites.

The contours of large artificial satellites have not yet been sufficiently worked out, but it is entirely clear that their designers will not be restricted by the need for giving the satellites a streamlined shape. In view of the absence of resistance of the external medium, that would retard the motion of a satellite, it may have any desired outline. For instance, a satellite may be given a toroidal shape[4] in the form of an immense hollow ring within which all the necessary conditions for life and work of the crew will be provided. On the outer walls of the structure there may be hand rails, and grapples, as well as decks and all devices necessary for the mooring and assembly of space rockets.

The cabins will not be very spacious: the designers of artificial satellites will be forced to economize weight and thus in part also volume.

If a torus consists of individual "cars" connected by flexible air-

[4] A body of revolution, shaped like an automobile inner tube, is called a torus.

locks, then its size can easily be increased by hooking on new "cars" (Fig. XI).

The cabins of a satellite must of course be hermetically sealed off from the surrounding space. In addition, the inner air-locks, doors, and partitions must provide a tight seal for the individual rooms. The hatches must be clamped by locking devices with plastic gaskets. The entrance doors, framed (for instance) in rubber, must open inward and not outward. Thanks to this, the pressure of the microatmosphere[5] will also help to provide tight closure of the doors, on whose other sides there is airless space. The skin of the satellite must be integral and seamless. Contact between the metal frame and the window panes must be particularly tight. These panes must be unbreakable, and have about the same coefficient of thermal expansion as the metals into which they are built or sealed.

The leakage of gas from the cabin of the space ship is not of great importance for brief flights, during which the vitiated micro-atmosphere is still periodically expelled into airless space and replaced by a new microatmosphere. But the leakage of gas to outside is very undesirable when continuous regeneration (purification) of the micro-atmosphere is used, which will be the case during long flights, or in cabins of permanent space platforms.

In many respects, the design of a manned artificial satellite will recall that of a submarine. The shell of the satellite, however, will not be subjected to compression, as in the case of deep submergence of a submarine, but to tension, which considerably simplifies design prob-lems.

Like the earth's atmosphere, the windows and skin of the artificial satellite will stop the ultraviolet rays of the sun which travel through interplanetary space and, in large doses, are harmful to the human organism. If necessary, special curtains may also be drawn over the portholes. It may be found that, because of the danger from meteors and harmful radiations, no window in direct communication with the outside can be provided in the compartments of the artificial satellite. In that case, a narrow channel with a system of lenses and mirrors will be used to bring in the light rays. Observations will be made in this case by means of a periscope, as in submarines.

In some astronomical instruments, quartz lenses, which transmit

[5] The air enclosed in the cabin of a flying device will be called microatmosphere.

ultraviolet rays, must be used. We note that quartz becomes brownish from their action.

Von Braun proposes building an artificial satellite in the form of a torus of rubberized material, made of glass fiber or of an impermeable nylon-plastic fabric, that can be inflated with air. But it will hardly be possible to find a material capable of serving as a protection from cosmic rays. It is more probable that, for this purpose, the skin will have to be made of several layers of different materials (Wiese, Federal Republic of Germany).

As we will see later, the object and persons on the satellite will be weightless. Therefore, it will evidently be necessary to build satellites with artificial gravity; by forcing the satellite to rotate about its own axis, we can produce a centrifugal force on it which will replace the force of gravity (the questions of weightlessness and artificial gravity are discussed in detail below). Combination satellites can also be built: In one part of the structure weightlessness will prevail, while in the other part there will be artificial gravity. In this case, it would be desirable to have the intensity of this artificial gravitational force remain more or less constant; for instance, in the case of a toroidal satellite, this should be the case throughout the entire ring of the satellite. Otherwise, when an astronaut moved about inside the satellite, he would experience undesirably sharp variations in the force of gravity. For this purpose, the satellite would have to be so constructed that its center of gravity coincided with its geometric center. When loads are shifted on the artificial satellite (for instance, from one storeroom to another in diametrically opposite direction) precautionary measures would have to be taken to maintain the centering of the structure. It would be more difficult to satisfy the condition of coincidence of these two centers during unloading operations. Figure XII shows such a structure on which there is a rotating cabin with artificial gravity. The satellite is assembled mainly of tanks and other parts of the head stages of orbital rockets. Such a system for the artificial satellite would make it possible to keep on increasing the dimensions of the structure all the time.

Projects for artificial satellites in the form of a wheel have been widely publicized. Figure XIII shows a project for one such wheel-shaped satellite worked out by Von Braun. On the basis of Von Braun's project for an interplanetary station, Derbin (United States) has proposed an improved version of such a station which, in the author's opinion, is more advantageous with respect to construction time and fuel consumption.

The center of the artificial satellite has a hollow cylinder serving as a mooring point for orbital cargo rockets. From the cylinder hub radiate telescoping tubular spokes, connecting the center of four "rims," each having a perimeter of 218 meters. The artificial satellite is constructed on the same principle as the tube of a telescope, in which the individual sections of the tube are joined by overlapping parts. The living rooms will consist of 20 compartments, each 9 meters in diameter and 11 meters in length. These are made of inflatable nylon-plastic bags with a diameter of three meters and a "thickness" of one meter in the collapsed state. All 20 compartments would form a torus or still retain the common cylindrical shape. To prevent leakage of air, if a compartment were struck by a meteoric body, the skin has an inside lining of self-sealing rubber. The living rooms can be connected with the body of the artificial satellite by means of special passages. By rotating the entire structure, a centrifugal force, equal to the force of gravity on the earth's surface, may be produced on the satellite. To prevent parasitic moments, the rocket engine for correcting the orbit of such a satellite must be mounted in the hub of the structure.

In the opinion of Ehricke (United States), an artificial satellite with a crew of four would have to have a volume of 566 cubic meters and weigh about 225 tons. It would take 50 flights of cargo rockets from the earth's surface for its erection. To supply such a satellite with everything necessary, about one ton of cargo would have to be brought up from the ground every month. To supply an expedition to Mars, consisting of three ships with a total crew of eight men, 3000 tons of cargo would have to be transported to the space platform. This would require six hundred trips of cargo rockets. Figure XIV shows a plan for a large artificial satellite according to Ehricke, built on the principle previously (in 1950) proposed by the author along these lines, according to which the space platform would be built up of bodies (in particular tanks) delivered to the orbit of the last stages of orbital rockets.

According to Noordung (Austria), a space platform would consist of several individual parts (living rooms, observatory, helio plant) connected with each other by flexible pipes, electric cables, etc.

The delivery of food products and of oxygen for respiration from the earth to the platform is a complicated and expensive operation. At the same time, of course, no shortage of solar energy would be felt on the satellite. K. E. Tsiolkovskiy has proposed capturing its immense flux and using it to grow plants in extraterrestrial greenhouses, which the inhabitants of this heavenly island could use for food. This would also solve the question of the natural cycle of the air. Such a greenhouse, however, would have to be of immense size. If the greenhouse were to have only a single function of the greenhouse, that of regeneration of the air and were to grow only inedible plants, then the area of the greenhouse could, of course, be somewhat reduced. But even in this case it would still be an enormously large structure. For instance, for the continuous regeneration of a "ration" of air for one person it would take 28 square meters of surface of leaves of the heliophilic catalpa (a deciduous shrub), well illuminated by the sun's rays (F. Green, Canada). In this case, the sunlight entering the greenhouse would first have to pass through special filters to absorb that part of the spectrum that would kill the plants.

The use of chlorella, a microscopic alga, might also prove advantageous for regeneration of the microatmosphere. This alga liberates 50 times its volume of oxygen in sunlight, in a single hour. Finally, a discovery made recently in this direction, that adenosine triphosphate can be used to grow green foliage in the open air, may bring the solution of this problem nearer (Kanin, Ordway). However, since the plants may wither, one cannot completely count on the natural cycle of air and water, thus making an automatic air-conditioning plant necessary on a manned satellite.

At the beginning of 1956, Romick (American Rocket Society) proposed building an artificial satellite in the form of an entire city with a population of 20,000 (Fig. XV). As far as can be judged from the published paper, the Romick project is based on data repeatedly published in the literature on astronautics and contains nothing that would make it practically realizable. As for the dimensions of the satellite on which 20,000 people are to live, it is not necessary to emphasize that these dimensions have no influence on the possibility of realizing the project: if a satellite for 100 persons can be built, it can be built for 1000 or for 20,000, just as well. The question, however, as to whether such a large satellite would be practically necessary does evoke doubt. It is possible that, in giving the number of the population of the space island as 20,000, the author of the project imagined that it would be easier to find the path to the mind and hearts of his countrymen. We can only be glad that the idea of the "father of astronautics," K. E. Tsiolkovskiy, on the establishment in cosmic space of whole "cities" endowed with artificial gravity, continues to give food for technological thinking.

■ Assembly of the Satellite

The construction of large artificial satellites, and later of stations on the moon and planets, will demand the use of entirely new methods of erection.

Imagine that a rocket, launched at circular velocity is sufficiently large to accommodate living quarters, laboratories, workshops, store rooms, moorings for space ships, and many other things. This, then, would be an artificial satellite, a flying observatory, or a landing station for cosmonauts traveling from the earth to the moon and to the planets. It is obvious, however, that such a large rocket could not be built. The construction of a large space platform would therefore evidently be accomplished as follows: A certain time after launching of the first rocket, a second rocket would follow it and, by means of radio control, would approach close to the first one. Then, in exactly the same way, a third, a fourth, and more rockets would be launched, until a heavenly body, of dimensions adequate to accommodate persons living on it and all the necessary supplies, mechanisms, and instruments, had finally been formed.

In this connection, we recall that the refueling of aircraft in flight has long been accomplished. In building artificial satellites, obviously, this experience would be utilized, despite the fact that the velocities and altitudes here are considerably greater. The position and velocity of the artificial satellite at any instant could be determined in advance with greater accuracy than for an aircraft. Indeed, the route and velocity of an aircraft depends on the weather and the behavior of the engine, while an artificial satellite is completely free from the influence of meteorological conditions and moves with engine off.

Yu.V.Kondratyuk considered that "it would be desirable to establish the delivery of fuel and all objects . . . , capable of enduring without damage acceleration of several thousand meters per second per second (with proper packing, everything excepting delicate instruments), into interplanetary space by the rocket-artillery method, separately from human beings. . . ." He wrote further:

"The rocket-artillery delivery of cargo to the base [i.e., to the artificial satellite] will be accomplished in the following way: At a time previously arranged, a missile-rocket will be fired from the earth, with supplies for the base . . . from a gun. . . . From the moment of firing the missile-rocket, light signals, which may be produced by explosion of a mixture of magnesium and saltpeter, are automatically and periodically transmitted. The period from signal to signal must be such that during this time the missile-rocket cannot go outside the field of view of the large telescope of the base. . . . . From the instant of firing, the large telescope of the base, pointed in advance at the place where the firing is to take place, does not let the missile-rocket out of its field of view. . . . A short time before the nearest approach of the missile-rocket to the base, when the missile-rocket is already freely distinguishable in the larger of the two instruments of the rocket at the base, this rocket is now directed toward the missile rocket, approaches it, and, after reducing the relative velocity to zero, it makes the missile-rocket fast and tows it to the base, using, if necessary, the fuel supplies on the missile-rocket."

Thus it will be possible to build the artificial satellite in advance on the earth and test, down to the smallest details, the reliability of its structure and the possibility of establishing on it the necessary living conditions for the crew. Then, disassembled into its component parts, the satellite can be put into an orbit planned in advance, on which these parts will be again assembled into a single whole.

All the parts of the artificial satellites must of course be so designed that they do not exceed the over-all dimensions of the "holds" of the orbital rockets. The mirrors of the telescopes intended for extraterrestrial observatories, however, will, as a rule, be too large for shipment in one piece on orbital rockets. They will therefore have to have a mosaic structure, which will allow their transport in parts. Cross (Great Britain), for example, has proposed the construction in space of a telescope with a plastic mirror 25 meters in diameter, weighing 68 kilograms in all. "Satellite" telescopes with mirrors of sodium foil, of considerably larger dimensions, have also been proposed. Naturally, all of these will also have to be of the built-up design.

For the dispatch rockets leaving the earth to be able to dock on the artificial satellite, marine experience can be utilized. Mooring lines (for instance, a chain hawser) will be thrown from the satellite to the rocket, which will allow the two flying devices to be pulled together.

The following variant is also in question: Instead of sending the rockets consecutively to the satellite being constructed, all the rockets may be sent off simultaneously, in the form of a squadron. In this case, the difficulty of finding the previously launched rockets by the individual new rockets will be eliminated, and the assembly of the artificial satellite can take place in less time, since there is no need to wait for the arrival of the separate parts from the earth. This will reduce the meteor danger for the workers (cf. below).

6

Man in Cosmic Space

■
■
■

■ Harmlessness of High Velocities for the Organism

Let us now consider the question whether man is physiologically able to endure the phenomena connected with flight to an artificial satellite, with living on it, and with the subsequent descent to the earth's surface.

During such a space voyage, subjective feeling of malaise may be caused primarily by the disturbance of the normal sensation of gravity. Let us first mention that there is no velocity that the human organism could not endure, provided that it is not accompanied by excessive acceleration. In fact, does the rotation of the earth about its axis disturb us to even the slightest extent? Yet, on the equator, the peripheral velocity of objects on the earth's surface reaches 1675 kilometers per hour. Does the earth's motion around the sun at a velocity of over 100,000 kilometers per hour disquiet us? Do we, finally, notice at all the motion of our entire solar system in cosmic space, at the velocity of 70,000 kilometers per hour? Bearing these facts in mind, we can state that the human organism is capable of safely enduring any velocity.

The flight from the earth to an artificial satellite and back may be compared to a gigantic jump into space, during which the astronauts will be, at times, subjected to the action of increased gravity, and, at times, will be in a state of weightlessness. We observe similar phenomena during an ordinary long jump or high jump. When we leave the ground with a single surge, we feel the increased weight of our body. This stage of the jump is analogous to the take-off of the rocket from the ground. From the moment when our soles leave the ground and our body is carried along for a certain distance, we fly without feeling our weight. This stage of the jump is similar to the motion of a rocket ship with engine off. When, finally, our feet once again touch the ground, our velocity begins to be decelerated, and again we feel our weight. This third stage of the jump is analogous to the period of retardation on descent from an artificial satellite.

■ In the World of Increased Gravity

When a train starts suddenly, the passenger experiences a backward jerk, and if there is a wall behind him, the passenger is pushed against it. A so-called G-force is created whose source is the accelerated motion. The action of the G-force on the organism is exactly the same as the action of gravity. It is precisely the action of the G-force, caused by the thrust of the rocket engine, that will be felt by the astronaut in the rocket cabin. At the start, this force is naturally greater than the force of the earth's attraction, otherwise the rocket would not move from place, and it has therefore been given the name of "overload" or G-force (one speaks of a force of 3 G, 5 G, etc., having in mind its comparison with the ordinary force of gravity on the earth).

If, by the aid of a rocket engine, we were to impart a uniformly accelerated motion to a ship in free space, we would feel exactly the same sensations on board such a ship as on a planet attracting us with a constant force.

During the catapulted take-off of an aircraft, the pilot receives a force of 4 G, i.e., he feels himself four times as heavy as ordinarily; pilots in stunt flying often take as much as 8 G, and for swimmers who dive, it is an ordinary thing to take 16 G during submergence. It must, however, be borne in mind that on a catapult the G-force lasts for a few seconds, while in diving into the water (more accurately, during retardation in the water after a fall), it lasts for only negligible fractions of a second. We also know that the velocity on ordinary transportation means may go through a prolonged period of increase if the acceleration is low. These examples by no means prove, however, that man is able to endure the G-force necessary to reach circular velocity for a sufficiently long time.

Is it possible to establish, before making a space flight, what G-force a man can endure without danger to life, and for what time he can take it?

The centrifugal force created during rotary motion also produces a G-force. G-forces of long duration and of any desired magnitude can be obtained by this method. The subject is placed in the cabin of a rotary machine, a sort of a carousel, which is then placed in very rapid rotary motion (Fig. XVI). By proper selection of the radius and the velocity of rotation, the same sensations may be induced in the test subject as he would experience in a rocket during take-off. The results obtained in such an experiment indicate that a rocket crew can endure, without untoward effects, the accelerations required to develop the circular velocity: a force of 4-5 G for several minutes is endured without pain by most of the test subjects.

The tolerance of a human being for a G-force depends substantially on the position of the body during the time of operation of the engine. A subject, for example, will react differently to a G-force if he is lying supine or prone than if he is sitting. If he is standing, the subject feels the weight predominantly in his legs. In other positions, the sensation of gravity as well as the general fatigue of the body will differ. Thus, we tire less sitting than standing, and least of all lying down. The most effective method of reducing fatigue under G-forces is to place the subject in a special, individually fitted suit.[1] Experiments have shown that even the less improved "anti-G" suits, used since World War II, in which increased pressure is provided in the region of the feet and the lower part of the torso to retard the flow of blood away from the head and facilitate the blood supply

[1] This proposition was advanced by the author of this book in 1933 in a paper submitted to the Committee on Astronautics at Paris.

to the brain, make it possible for a subject to tolerate 3 G without ill effect and for a length of time exceeding the period of operation of the engine of an orbital rocket.

We note that the tolerance for high G-forces depends on the individual characteristics of the organism and, in part, on training. G-forces that are tolerated with relative ease by one person may be fatal to another.

The sensation of the direction of the force of gravity or reactive thrust arises in human subjects as a result of the interaction of visual reactions with the changes in the tonus of the muscles and organs of the sense of equilibrium. The otoliths (ear stones) located in the vestibular apparatus in two membraneous sacs (the sacculus and utriculus), irritate, by their weight, the receptors (sensitive cells) of the lower walls, thus inducing the sensation of the direction of the force of gravity. During accelerated motion in any direction, the otoliths, suspended in the tissue fluid, because of their inertia irritate the receptors located on the various walls of the vestibular apparatus, and in this way the force of reactive thrust (and of linearly accelerated motion) in any direction is sensed. As for angular accelerations, these are perceived by the semicircular canals of the labyrinth.

■ Life Under Conditions of Weightlessness

We have seen that, after attaining circular velocity beyond the boundaries of the atmosphere, the rocket will no longer fall back toward the earth but will revolve around the earth as a satellite. The same thing will happen with persons on a rocket satellite. They will, likewise, not fall back toward the earth, i.e., they will not feel the force of the earth's attraction. In exactly the same way, on the earth, the rapid spinning of the planet around the sun makes it impossible for us to feel the force of the sun's gravitation and lets us feel only the gravitation of our own planet. On the satellite, however, its own gravity will be insensible because of the extremely small mass of this artificial heavenly body. Consequently, the astronauts will feel no weight whatever.

In the literature on astronautics, the concept "weight" is usually taken to mean the force that acts on objects and persons in the cabin of a space ship, forcing them against the floor, and not the force of attraction toward the earth which, of course, never actually disappears. It is precisely the action of this pressure rather than the force of the earth's gravitation that will be sensed by astronauts; this force stretches the spring of a balance (a spring balance) or the filament of a plumb line. (In airless space this force is due exclusively to the thrust of the rocket engine, while in air it is due to the combined action of the thrust of the rocket engine and the resistance of the air.) In its absence, objects will not exert mutual pressure, and human subjects will feel no force holding them against the floor, i.e., they will "lose their weight."

The Human Organism under Conditions of Weightlessness

The influence of weightlessness on human beings and animals may to some extent be studied during the vertical fall of an aircraft or during a delayed parachute jump (before the parachute opens). It has also proved possible to study the action of weightlessness of the human body during high-altitude flight of a jet aircraft. To stage such experiments, the aircraft is made to climb to high altitudes in very rarefied layers of the atmosphere, and at the instant when it has reached maximum speed after the climb the engines are cut. The aircraft then begins to move in a so-called parabola of weightlessness, like a hurled stone, experiencing only the insignificant resistance of the air. Under these conditions the force of gravity disappears almost completely ("almost," since there is still a certain resistance of the medium).

One might also, moving in this parabola, cut in the engine at low power in order to compensate the resistance of the external medium. In that case, the aircraft will move along the same trajectory and at the same velocity as in airless space, thus producing the state of ideal weightlessness.

In another version, to produce a parabola of weightlessness, the pilot first puts the rocket airplane into a dive. For this purpose, on the initial segment of the dive, the aircraft descends at increasing speed on an inclined line. The aircraft then goes for an instant into horizontal flight and then almost immediately into a flight curving upward in an arc. The radius of curvature of the path and the speed of flight are so matched that the G-force felt by the pilots does not exceed, for instance, three times the force of gravity at sea level. When the aircraft has reached a speed of the order of 800 kilometers per hour, the engine is cut off, and the aircraft, encountering no perceptible resistance of the air in the stratosphere, moves in an arc close to a parabola, with its high point about 2.5 kilometers above the level at which the engine was cut. In this case, the aircraft moves along the ascending branch of the parabola for 23 seconds and then, for the same period of time, along the descending branch. At the moment the aircraft reaches the former altitude, the engine is turned on, and the maneuver "parabola of weightlessness" can be repeated.

To increase the dimensions of the "parabola of weightlessness" and thus the length of the experiment, a jet aircraft may be put into a dive together with the parent aircraft that has carried it to high altitude. In producing a parabola of weightlessness by this method, a preliminary dive considerably raises the attainable ceiling.[2]

In this way, the state of weightlessness can be produced for about one minute on a jet fighter. On a modified aircraft, this time can be prolonged to 2-3 minutes.

Experiments have shown that the sensation of weightlessness for a period of one minute does no damage to a subject although, in the first moments, he will lose all control over his movements (they become very abrupt and jerky).

Diringshofen (Federal Republic of Germany) first succeeded in repeatedly producing the condition of weightlessness for 8-10 seconds in himself, and he described the sensations experienced by him as pleasant. Recently, a number of experiments were made on weightlessness in jet aircraft which reached an altitude of over 27 kilometers. Eger, who made this type of flight, found that his power of orientation was already affected after 8-10 seconds in the state of weightlessness; at the thirteenth second he felt himself to be rotating in an indeterminate direction, and at the fifteenth second he had the feeling of being lost in space, so that the test had to be stopped although it was technically possible to prolong the state of weightlessness to half a minute. In 1951, Ballinger (United States) directed experiments on the vertical ascent of a jet aircraft with one passenger. In 30 flights, the condition of weightlessness was maintained for 15-20 seconds. The

[2] This method of raising the ceiling was proposed and calculated by me in 1935. Cf. A. Shternfeld, *Introduction to Cosmonautics*, op.cit., pp. 223-225.

pilot and passenger were both strapped to their seats by means of belts and used an orienter. Neither vertigo nor uncoordinated movements were observed. At the Fourth International Astronautical Congress, Bek (Argentina) reported that, during his experiments on the influence of weightlessness in a vertical dive, the subjects withstood the tests considerably better when they were strapped to their seats. In similar experiments with turtles, the animals painstakingly attempted to pick up a bit of food, but only one turtle, with lesions in its organs of equilibrium, succeeded in doing this properly. Experiments staged on Aerobee rockets also showed that mice with damaged organs of equilibrium, in contrast to a normal mouse, exhibited good tolerance of the state of weightlessness. A normal mouse behaved more quietly when its shelf was removed than another mouse that had no support from the start.

At the Seventh International Astronautical Congress, Gerathewohl (United States) reported the results of 300 experiments on the influence of a brief period of weightlessness to which 16 subjects were exposed during special experimental flights in 1955-1956.

In view of the great significance of this question for astronautics, we will discuss these experiments in greater detail. The tests were run with a *Lockheed T-33* aircraft. During each flight, the aircraft made four dives from an altitude of 6100 meters to 5300 meters at an angle of 40° to the horizontal. The dive lasted 15 seconds. In the first dive, the subject while in the state of weightlessness kept his eyes open, whereas during the second dive he closed them. During the third dive, he was asked to follow an object "floating in the air," and also his own hands. During the first three dives, the subject held a small screen in front of his eyes. During the fourth dive, he no longer used it but looked toward the outside. After returning to the original altitude, the subject sometimes asked the pilot to make an additional dive to confirm his previous sensations. If he felt ill, however, the experiment was stopped, a stream of pure oxygen was supplied to the cabin, the temperature of the microatmosphere was brought to the necessary level, and the aircraft returned to the airfield. If the subject felt well, he was immediately after the dive subjected three times to the action of weightlessness at 30-second intervals, in an engine-off flight along a parabolic arc. During flight on the ascending branch of the parabola, the engines were completely inoperative; on the descending branch, the propellers were turning at 25 per cent below normal speed (to compensate the resistance of the air). The transition from one parabolic path to the other took place along matched circular arcs with engine off. On these transitional segments, the centrifugal acceleration reached values almost three times as high as the acceleration of free fall. In concluding the experiments, at the special request of the subject, the pilot executed two turns of the aircraft about its longitudinal axis, to the right and to the left. When this was done the subject checked again on his sensations, especially the visual ones.

The subjects themselves usually analyzed and reported their sensations. A series of data was collected by the physician who accompanied the "patients" aboard the aircraft.

The sensitivity to the physiological action of weightlessness was found to be subject to extreme variations, not only in different persons but even in one and the same person, depending on the circumstances. While many persons reacted satisfactorily to loss of weight, others became more or less seriously indisposed. Some of them experienced nausea, with the after-effects being felt for many hours after landing. As in the above-mentioned Ballinger experiments, no pathological processes were noted in the circulation during a brief period of weightlessness, while voluntary motions of the head under conditions of weightlessness induced no unpleasant sensations.

The 35-year old pilot Stallings (United States) who has a thousand flying hours on jet aircraft to his credit and has been subjected over 200 times to the influence of weightlessness (mainly on an aircraft piloted by himself), reports that motions of the limbs were effortless and that muscular coordination was completely undisturbed. There was no difficulty in orienting the aircraft with respect to the ground. The directions "up" and "down" underwent no changes. According to Stallings, the state of weightlessness induced a pleasant sensation in him. He noted no disturbing symptoms with respect to vision, hearing, or respiration under the condition of weightlessness.

Gerathewohl, who tested the action of weightlessness on himself for a period of 47 seconds, characterized his sensation as follows at the Seventh International Astronautical Congress: "I never felt as well in my life, and if I could pick my own way of resting, my choice would undoubtedly fall on the state of weightlessness."

Another subject, 46 years of age, with abundant experience of

■ FIG. XV.—Various Phases of the Construction of an Artificial Satellite of the Earth. *(According to the Romick Project.)*

■ FIG. XVI.—Centrifuge for Investigating the Influence of G-Forces on the Human Organism *(United States)*.

■ FIG. XVII.—The Dog "Malyshka" after Returning from an Altitude of 110 Kilometers, to Which She Had Been Taken in a Rocket.

■ FIG. XVIII.—The Dog "Layka" in the Pressurized Cabin after Being Placed on the Second Soviet Artificial Satellite.

■ FIG. XIX.—Artificial Satellite with Solar Power Collector
(According to Smith and Ross).

flight on gliders, states, on the contrary, that during the time of weightlessness he lost the sense of "up" and "down."

The subjects disturbed by weightlessness included 20-year old novices as well as pilots over 30 years of age with 1000-1500 flying hours behind them.

The effect of weightlessness, in many respects, depends on the training and on the duration of the state of weightlessness. It would be very risky to draw generalizing conclusions from the results of the brief action of weightlessness as to the effect of protracted weightlessness. Simons (United States), for example, considers that the latent period of development of "space sickness" is considerably longer than the short periods during which it is possible today to produce the physical conditions of weightlessness. In the case of seasickness, which to a certain extent resembles "space sickness," the latent period, even for novices, lasts not less than 15-20 minutes. Gerathewohl, on the other hand, believes that persons easily able to tolerate weightlessness for a short period of time will also be able to endure it for a longer time. If it should be possible to select persons immune to "space sickness," the design of manned artificial satellites and space ships would be greatly simplified and their realization facilitated.

Mice, dogs, and monkeys have successfully withstood states of weightlessness, although this state was incomplete, for considerably longer time than human subjects (up to 3-4 minutes). In experiments staged in the U.S.S.R. under the direction of A. V. Pokrovskiy, dogs were carried to an altitude of 110 kilometers (and then up to 200 kilometers). During the fall of the rocket back to the ground, dogs in pressure suits with the appropriate devices were ejected by means of a catapult. One catapulting took place at an altitude of 90-85 kilometers and another at an altitude of 50-35 kilometers; from an altitude of 4 kilometers downward, their descent to the ground continued by parachute. All nine experimental animals landed safely (three dogs went through this twice—see Figure XVII). The motion pictures, electrocardiograms, measurements of the dogs' temperature and pulse, etc., made during the flight showed that on the whole the animals adapted well to the condition of weightlessness, reacting to it differently according to their individual peculiarities.

Thus we see that a brief state of weightlessness does no harm to living organisms or, at least, is harmless for many persons. A stay on an artificial satellite may, however, last for many days or even whole weeks and months, and therefore we are able today to formulate only more or less well-founded hypotheses as to the subjective feelings of cosmonauts.

Some investigators believe that even under prolonged weightlessness the heart will still operate normally, since its activity resembles the mechanical work of a pump with a closed cycle. The heart needs only to overcome the friction of the blood against the walls of the blood vessels. Such arguments are unreliable, however, since cardiac activity is closely connected with the more delicate central nervous system.

The situation with respect to respiration will be somewhat more complicated. It is well known, for example, that during a brief fall, in the first moments of a parachute drop, stoppage of respiration usually takes place. If, however, flight on an artificial satellite, which as a result of the absence of weight will be perceived by man precisely like a fall, lasts for a long period of time, then the use of apparatus for artificial respiration may be necessary. The ingestion of food can occur even in the absence of gravity, since the passage of food is due to contraction of the muscles of the esophagus (liquids can be swallowed even when the head is lower than the torso). The peristaltic processes (the rhythmic contractions of the walls of the intestines, stomach, and other hollow organs, aiding the travel of food in the body) can likewise proceed under conditions of weightlessness.

Under ordinary conditions, the physiological processes take place with the body in any position, whether standing, sitting, or lying. Consequently, a change in the positions of the bodily organs relative to the direction of the force of gravity will have no substantial influence on their functions. It is true that it is very difficult to keep the head for a long time below the torso. This indicates that, in certain unusual body positions, the force of gravity has a harmful effect on the organism. But this does not mean at all that, for other normal positions of the body, the existence of the force of gravity is necessary.

On the other hand, in view of the fact that most physiological functions are accomplished under the action of muscular forces, osmotic processes (passage of liquids through semipermeable membranes), etc., we have every reason to expect that the absence of gravity will cause no substantial disorders in the activity of the organism.

Such are the results of studies of the influence of weightlessness on the living organism at sea-level conditions. The launching of the second Soviet artificial satellite with an experimental animal has opened entirely new opportunities for studying the adaptability of the organisms to the conditions of the world without gravity. On the second Soviet artificial satellite, an experimental test of the action of prolonged weightlessness on the living organism was staged for the first time. This experiment proved encouraging: The physiological behavior of the dog on board the satellite, in a specially equipped pressurized cabin, was satisfactory not only during the first hours but even for several days.

This gives us reason for supposing that the astronaut will not lose control over himself even at the beginning of flight during the sensation of loss of weight and that he will be able, during this time, to establish acceptable living conditions on board the cosmic vehicle.

Work and Life under Conditions of Weightlessness

Let us discuss briefly the physical phenomena which will take place, under conditions of weightlessness, during everyday life on an artificial satellite and which, naturally, will differ substantially from the customary physical phenomena on the earth.

In the absence of gravity, the concept of "up" and "down" in its usual sense will disappear, since "down" is considered only by convention to be the direction toward the center of the earth. An object dropped from the hand will not fall "down." People will be able to rest in any position. Walking will become impossible, since there will be no pressure of the sole of the foot against the supporting surface and, consequently, there will be no friction, which is necessary for moving about. It will be possible to move around inside the artificial satellite by holding on to the walls or to fixed objects, and then pushing oneself away from them.

It should be noted that, although bodies will indeed be weightless on an artificial satellite, it will still be necessary to exert a definite force for a certain length of time in order to bring them into motion, or to stop them, or even to slow down their motion, since they naturally will not lose the property of inertia, inherent in any mass.

On emerging from an artificial satellite into outer space beyond the atmosphere, the astronaut will obviously have to maintain contact with the satellite by means of a cable. He will be able to take along a heavy object attached to only a thin cable, and by pushing away from it in one direction he will be able to displace himself in the opposite direction (on the basis of the law of the conservation of the position of the center of mass under the action of external forces alone). He will be able to produce the same effect with a small rocket or pistol, but such methods involve the irrecoverable loss of mass.

It will be impossible to use ordinary furniture or tools. To hold any object at a definite place it will have to be fastened. For instance, a bottle with liquid would have to be attached to the wall. In preparing food, the pans will have to be covered with lids and placed in rotary motion by the aid of a special centrifuge to make their contents adhere to the wall. Electromagnetic instruments, which would operate well under the condition of weightlessness, will be very convenient. Liquid poured from a vessel would collect into a sphere, because of the action of surface tension. On its contact with a solid body, the forces of cohesion might exceed the forces of surface tension, and then the liquid would flow along the surface of the body. Handling liquid would in general be rather inconvenient. Washing would be possible only by means of a moistened sponge or towel. To empty a bottle it would be necessary literally to pull it away from the liquid it contained or to make use of the centrifugal effect, moving the bottle in a great arc or, finally, to use a pump or rubber ball.

If, under the condition of weightlessness, a match is struck on a box, the head will flare up but the match will not light. Neither candle nor gas flame will burn. The reason is that, under terrestrial conditions, the combustion products (the burning gases), because they are lighter, will rise (the phenomenon of convection), thus giving access to new portions of the oxygen necessary to maintain the flame. Under conditions of weightlessness, however, the gases would not be lighter than the air surrounding them. They would accumulate around the flame and extinguish it. To maintain a flame it will be necessary to supply a continuous jet of oxygen to the burner. It will, of course, be more convenient to use electric heating devices.

Under conditions of weightlessness, the dust contained in the air will not settle on the floor or on other surfaces, which will constitute a health hazard. To control the dust, electric filters may be used.

The clothing of astronauts will have to be so designed as to remain on the body regardless of the force of gravity.

Thus the control of many phenomena and functions on an artificial satellite will be somewhat impeded. On the other hand, certain functions (for instance the moving of loads) will be substantially easier in a state of weightlessness.

■ Artificial Gravity

This means that experimental proof that a person's sensations would be completely normal under the condition of weightlessness is as yet unavailable. It is possible that special drugs would have to be used to maintain the normal activities of the human organism (Oberth). As a result of a prolonged stay in the state of weightlessness, cosmonauts are also threatened, to a greater or lesser degree, with loss of the viability of most muscles.

A radical solution of the problem would be to create an artificial G-force to replace the force of gravity if the absence of gravity proved to be disastrous to the human organism.

At first glance it would be simplest to create an artificial gravitational field by maintaining uninterrupted operation of the engine, but at reduced power, as proposed by Esnault-Pelterie (1912). This method, however, would involve excessive consumption of fuel.

There is an exceedingly simple method of creating artificial gravity, namely, the rotation of the artificial satellite. According to K. E. Tsiolkovskiy's idea, advanced as far back as the end of the last century (1895), a space vehicle such as an artificial satellite would consist of two interconnected parts. At the necessary moment of time, these parts would be separated from each other while still remaining connected by cables, and then would be put into circular motion, by the aid of small rocket engines, about their common center of gravity. Obviously, in an airless ambient medium, after the system had reached the necessary angular velocity, further rotation would continue by inertia without participation of the engines.

As already stated (see above), the artificial gravity produced might be confined to some limited part of the artificial satellite by means of its rotation.

Thus we see that, from the point of view of physiology, there will be no insuperable obstacles to the stay of human beings on artificial satellites. During the operation of the engine while flying to the artificial satellite, the cosmonauts would undoubtedly be able to tolerate 4 G for several minutes. This would make it possible to give the rocket the circular velocity under rather economical conditions of engine operation.

As for flight on the rocket after combustion cut off and on the artificial satellite, we are not entirely certain that the absence of gravity for a long period of time would not damage the human organism. But even if there were damage, this would not be an obstacle to the creation of manned artificial satellites, since it is technically entirely possible to produce the sensation of gravity by means of rotation.

■ Harmful Radiations

As everyone knows, the atmosphere of our planet is a reliable protection, for all living things on the earth, from the harmful radiation of the sun. The oxygen contained in the upper layers of the atmosphere absorbs these radiations and is converted into ozone. This takes place as follows:

Under the influence of the ultraviolet rays of the sun, molecules of oxygen are dissociated (split). This process is accompanied by a considerable absorption of the energy of the solar rays in the ultraviolet region of the spectrum. The free atoms of oxygen that are formed on dissociation subsequently unite with molecules of oxygen, as a result of which molecules of ozone which consists of three oxygen atoms are formed.

The ozone is located in the stratosphere at a variable altitude from 16 to 50 kilometers. This indicates that the ultraviolet rays of the sun are absorbed by exactly these layers of the air. Consequently, even an artificial satellite flying very low would not be protected from the action of ultraviolet radiation. It is true that the use of altitude rockets Viking No. 11, and others) has recently made it possible to establish (Tanner, Great Britain) that the ultraviolet radiation of the sun is considerably less intense than had been assumed on the basis of observations made on the ground. It is therefore possible that the skin of the satellite itself will be a sufficient protection from these radiations. If this is not so, then the space between the walls of the skin could be filled with a layer of oxygen, which, acting like the atmospheric oxygen, i.e., being transformed into ozone, would form a barrier against the ultraviolet rays of the sun. As for the port holes of artificial satellites, it is well known that even ordinary glass strongly absorbs ultraviolet light.

We note that a small amount of this radiation is necessary for normal functioning of the organism (hygienists consider that the windows of dwellings should be provided with glass passing ultraviolet rays).

The solar spectrum also contains the harmful X-rays, but the control of these radiations will involve no trouble on artificial satellites, since they are readily absorbed by almost all structural materials.

The space outside the atmosphere is aso penetrated by cosmic rays (most of which are stopped by the earth's atmosphere) which consist mainly of protons and alpha particles (nuclei of hydrogen and helium). If it is borne in mind that these particles have a velocity close to the velocity of light and that a square meter of the surface of an artificial satellite would be bombarded every 10 minutes by a million (and perhaps by several millions) of these particles, then it becomes clear how serious is the danger of exposure of an artificial satellite to cosmic rays. But it is not only this so-called primary radiation that constitutes a hazard for the human organism. On collision of cosmic rays with the skin of an artificial satellite (or with a pressure suit), secondary cosmic radiation would also be formed, exactly as it is formed when cosmic rays enter the earth's atmosphere. According to data of the Naval Research Laboratory (United States), only 9 per cent of the cosmic rays recorded are primary radiation.

It should be noted that, on the other hand, man on an artificial satellite will no longer be subjected to the action of radiation produced by the radioactive disintegration of minerals in the earth's crust, which at the earth's surface is more than twice the dose of the cosmic rays that penetrate to that level through the thickness of the atmosphere and amounts to 1/5000 roentgen.[3]

We still know very little about the influence of cosmic rays on

[3] The roentgen is the unit dose of X-ray and other radiations.

the human organism. Laboratory experiments in this direction are still in the embryonic state. The paper read by Simons, of the Department of Space Biology in New Mexico (United States), before the Seventh International Astronautical Congress, is of great interest in this respect. This paper was devoted to the action of cosmic rays on small animals. A total of 25 stratosphere balloons was used in the experiments. Each of them lifted a load of 135 kilograms to an altitude of up to 30 kilometers. Each flight lasted up to 30 hours. The results of the measurements were transmitted by radio. The experimental animals were placed in spherical aluminum capsules 76 centimeters in diameter. Capsules of organic glass maintain their airtightness even better. In daytime tests, the capsules were cooled with water, while in the case of night experiments they were coated with heat-insulating materials. The experiments were staged at geomagnetic latitude 50°. As a result of injury by primary cosmic rays, large spots, of a size considerably larger than had been expected, appeared on the skins of black mice. In other experiments, no disturbances were noted, even after 24-hour exposure. After the experiments, the experimental animals were kept for a long time under careful observation.

The Swiss scientist Eugster staged the following experiment to determine the action of cosmic rays on the human organism: A small piece of preserved human skin was lifted by a rocket to an altitude of several tens of kilometers and was subjected to the action of the cosmic rays. After descent of the rocket, this skin was successfully grafted onto a human subject and was found not to have lost its viability. On a larger scale, similar experiments were later staged in the United States.

When the cells of the retina are damaged by cosmic rays, a man does not lose his sight, since the surrounding cells remain unaffected. The same is true of the sensitive cells of the organs of hearing (according to the data of the United States Navy School of Aviation Medicine at Pensacola, Florida).

How will cosmic rays act, however, on persons who stay for a long time on artificial satellites? This question still remains open.

Graul (Federal Republic of Germany), in discussing the radiobiological problems of space flight, came to the conclusion that the phenomena connected with flight in cosmic space may have a pernicious effect on the human organism only if the voyage lasts longer than several months, and that the damage done by cosmic and ultra-violet radiation differs for different persons.

It may also be possible to investigate the influence of the primary cosmic rays on biological processes under laboratory conditions.

To protect man from primary and secondary cosmic rays, according to some authors, it would be possible to cover an artificial satellite with a lead armor of 10 centimeters thickness. At altitudes above 100 kilometers, 35 per cent of the cosmic rays are stopped by a layer of lead 2-4 centimeters thick. But the ferrying of even a considerably thinner armor to an artificial satellite would involve incredible difficulties. Hydrogen, and compounds that contain it (such as water or hydrocarbons), are an excellent means of protection from the action of cosmic rays. Hydrogen in the solid state is most suitable for this purpose, since in this case the particles bombarded by the cosmic rays would not mix with the remaining hydrogen. A steel shield would weigh 18 times as much as one of water or kerosene. Solid hydrogen might simultaneously serve as an armor to protect the artificial satellite from puncture by meteoric bodies (Dufer, United States).

■ The Meteor Hazard

The fear is often expressed that an artificial satellite might encounter large meteoric bodies and that even a micrometeorite, as a result of its immense velocity, will possess a greater destructive energy than, say, a stone hurled at maximum force at an artificial satellite. How great is this danger and what are the methods of protection from it?

Our planet undergoes continuous "bombardment" by meteoric bodies. Several thousand meteorites fall on the earth's surface each year. These stone bodies or, far more seldom, iron bodies, are of various size before entering the earth's atmosphere; the diameter of some of these may be as high as several meters or more. As for meteoric dust particles, 10,000-100,000 of them fall on the earth every second. The total weight of meteoric bodies falling on the earth during a day is estimated at 10-15 tons (B. S. Orlov, B. Yu. Levin, U.S.S.R.).

On crossing the atmosphere, meteoric bodies are heated to incandescence by the resistance of the air, and the resultant flash is sometimes brighter than the sun. The apparent length of the path of a meteor in the atmosphere (its "train") is usually more than 300 kilometers.

When a large meteorite falls on the earth there is a violet explosion, and most of the mass of the meteorite is transformed into gas, the remainder flying in all directions in the form of fragments. A crater with a diameter sometimes running up to several kilometers is formed on the earth's surface at the point of impact of a meteorite. The impact of so large a meteorite, however, is an exceptionally rare phenomenon, and an artificial satellite is, as a practical matter, not in danger of colliding with such a body.

It has been established in recent years that the total mass of micrometeorites is considerably greater than the mass of all visually observed meteors. The flux of micrometeorites 0.0005 millimeter in diameter over a cross-sectional area of 93 square meters close to the earth is 4900 units an hour. For micrometeorites 0.01 millimeter in diameter, this value drops to 0.49 unit an hour, and for meteorites 1 millimeter in diameter, to 0.0000005 unit per hour, i.e., one impact in 230 years (Tanner, Great Britain). Similar data have been obtained by Grimminger, who calculated the probability of stone meteorites striking an artificial satellite with a surface of 93 square meters, moving around the earth at a height of 483 kilometers. For a meteorite with a diameter of 5.21 millimeters (the size of a drop of water), the mean period of time between two successive falls of meteorites on the satellite was found to be 38,800 years; with a diameter of 1.12 millimeters, 388 years, and with a diameter of 0.24 millimeter, 3.88 years.

In spite of such apparently encouraging conclusions from the theory of probability, an artificial satellite cannot be considered absolutely safe from being struck by a meteorite, even of large size, at the very beginning of its flight.

A brief bombardment by meteoric dust particles constitutes no menace for the artificial satellite, in spite of the immense velocity of meteorites, which may be as high as several tens of kilometers a second. The impact of micrometeorites on altitude rockets, for example, leaves such insignificant traces that they can usually be detected on highly polished plates only under the microscope, and it is very rare that the diameter of such "craters" reaches 2-3 millimeters, with a depth of only several microns, the crater being fringed by temper colors. We note, however, that the frequency of impact of micrometeorites on altitude rockets is still relatively high: At an altitude of 35 kilometers there are an average of 2.2 hits a second. In another experiment staged in the United States in 1953, 66 hits in 144 seconds were recorded at altitudes from 40 to 140 kilometers (equivalent to 4.9 hits per second per square meter). Finally, in 1955, in an experiment using considerably more sensitive instrumentation, 114 hits were recorded, of which 101 occurred at altitudes from 85 to 103 kilometers, and the others at lower levels. In this experiment, there were an average of 175 hits per square meter per second.

Since modern rockets rise above the meteor appearance level, the possibility of their collision even with a larger meteoric body, which could cause considerable damage, is theoretically not impossible. As for an artificial satellite, especially if it revolves around the earth for a long time, even microscopic meteoric bodies might gradually destroy its skin. "The drop wears away the stone not by its strength, but by its steady drip," says an ancient proverb. As a result of the frequent impact of meteoric dust particles, the shiny part of the satellite's skin will evidently become dark and dull in time, which will involve an undesirable temperature rise within the satellite. For this same reason, the transparency of the cabin windows may become inadequate.

Meteorites of sizes from a sand grain or pebble up represent the greatest danger of all. The impact of such meteoric bodies on an artificial satellite may destroy it, since the slightest puncture will impair the hermetic seal of the pressurized cabins, and the air will begin to escape rapidly. This may constitute a considerable hazard for the personnel, since, at a pressure of 47 millimeters mercury (Hg), the water contained in the human organism begins to boil. Of course, experiments have shown that at a sharp drop in external pressure a human subject still retains control of his faculties for about 15 seconds, and this time may be sufficient to turn on the oxygen apparatus of the pressure suit.

It must be noted that no effective methods of protecting an artificial satellite from meteor hazards have as yet been found. Some technicians have suggested a double (or multilayer) skin as a protection from the consequences of a collision with meteorites, in the hope that the explosion caused by the impact of a meteoric body on the outer skin will not impair the integrity of the inner skin. Whipple has proposed attachment of an armored skin to the satellite by means of compression struts, at a distance of 2-3 centimeters from its shell. Langton (Great Britain) considers chrome steel to be the most suitable metal for use as shock-absorbing armor. At a thickness of 1 millimeter, such an armor would be sufficient protection even from the relatively large meteorites that are encountered, on the average, once in two years.

A small puncture due to the impact of a meteorite might be temporarily closed by a rubber plate which itself would be forced against the wall by the internal pressure of the air. It would be still better to use an elastic patch covered with a layer of adhesive. Micrometeorites, however, would be able to produce punctures that could not be detected by the naked eye, and these, too, would have to be plugged.

The opinion has also been expressed that meteoric bodies that puncture the thin walls of the ship may possibly do less damage than those which explode and penetrate into the heavy armor.

The meteor hazard can perhaps be eliminated by the aid of radar installations which automatically would change the path of the artificial satellite. The maximum velocity of a meteorite relative to the sun in the "neighborhood" of the earth is 42 kilometers per second. The maximum velocity of an artificial satellite relative to the sun, however, is not over 11 kilometers per second plus the velocity of the earth (about 30 kilometers per second), i.e., not over 41 kilometers per second in all. Consequently, even in the opposed motion, meeting a satellite, the impact velocity of a meteorite on a satellite cannot exceed 83 kilometers per second. For this reason, if radar detects the approach of a meteoric body at a distance of 1000 kilometers, the automatic devices would have 12 seconds available, which would be entirely sufficient to change the satellite's course.

It must, however, be noted that artificial satellites, because of their tremendous velocity, lack the "flexibility" possessed by ground transportation facilities. Whereas a pedestrian finds it easy to walk around obstacles on his path, an automobile driver traveling at high speed will find it difficult, and a rocket aircraft still more difficult, to turn aside quickly. Naturally the possibility of rapid swerving of an artificial satellite from its orbit is very doubtful. In this field, scientific thought is still faced by a gigantic task.

It is not impossible that the problem of protection from meteor hazards will be solved by shooting down meteoric bodies. It goes without saying that the radar detection of meteors menacing a satellite as well as the aiming and firing of antimeteorite machine guns would have to be automatic: as soon as a meteor threatening the satellite was detected, the automatic radar-controlled devices would no longer let it out of the "field of view." They would establish the velocity, the direction of motion, and the position of the "enemy" at each instant. After a fraction of a second, atomic machine guns would go into action. The meteoric body "aimed" at the satellite, on collision with a bullet, would explode at a certain distance from the satellite, and only a negligible fraction of the "spray" could hit the artificial satellite. The particles would apparently be no more dangerous than meteoric dust, against which the skin of the ship would be sufficient protection.

The upper layers of the atmosphere might also serve as partial protection from meteors if the satellite moves sufficiently close to the surface of the earth at an altitude where, on the one hand, the air is already so rarefied that it hardly opposes the motion of the satellite and yet, on the other hand, is sufficiently dense to protect the satellite from the fastest minute meteors. An altitude of about 200 kilometers may be considered to be such a height. Although at this altitude the density of the air is tens of millions of times less than at sea level, the larger part of the small meteors does not penetrate down to this level.

It is possible that, during the passage of "meteor showers," when meteoric bodies fall on the earth in whole swarms, artificial satellites would have to descend to denser layers of the atmosphere (but not lower than 100 kilometers), which would offer them partial protection. To overcome the resistance of the air it would be necessary, at this time, to connect a small rocket engine and also to take measures for protecting the satellite shell from aerodynamic heating. During the "meteor shower season," the crew of the satellite could also live in a suitably equipped "meteorite shelter" (in this case, only the most necessary instruments would have to be protected from meteorite hits).

Whipple considers that, for an artificial earth satellite moving close to our planet, the meteor danger would be greater than for an interplanetary ship, since the earth attracts meteoric matter. Conversely, other authors believe that the earth would partially shield the space ship from the impact of meteoric bodies.

Interesting theoretical studies on the absorption of the energy of meteorites by shock-absorbing shields have been staged by the British scientist Langton. In his calculation he assumes that the total kinetic energy formed on impact of a meteoric body on the armor is transformed into thermal energy, which is completely absorbed by the armor and the meteor. The armor is considered punctured if the molten metal, even at a single point, has touched the inner surface of the skin. Langton comes to the conclusion that, to absorb the thermal energy of meteoric bodies of average size with a velocity up to 30 kilometers per second, a metal armor of 1 millimeter thickness would be practically sufficient. The mechanical action of a meteoric body on the armor, however, would make these results considerably less favorable, although it is difficult to say to what extent.

In conclusion we note that the most convincing proof for the harmlessness of micrometeorite impacts on the skin of an artificial satellite is the experience gained with the first and second artificial satellites. Despite being struck by micrometeorites, the satellites revolved normally around the earth, and their instrumentation, particularly the radio transmitters, operated without trouble.

■ Problems of Food and Respiration

Although the problems of supplying astronauts with oxygen, water, and food in a hermetically sealed cabin of the artificial satellite can be solved even in our own days, specialists still face considerable work in refining their results. These questions are not of a secondary nature if we consider that large artificial satellites may revolve for many years around the earth. Little work has been done up to now on the questions of air conditioning and water circulation aboard an artificial satellite.

There are great differences in the views of various authors as to food rations and air supply that astronauts will require. Some of them put the food ration below 4 kilograms, others as high as 10 kilograms per person per day. The ration of dry food products ranges from 0.5 to 1.2 kilograms. For completely dehydrated food products, the lower limit would seem closer to the truth. A little over 1 kilogram of oxygen should be sufficient for oxidation of these products (it must not be forgotten that the respiratory process is closely related to the digestive process: the more we eat, the more oxygen we absorb). In view of the fact that carbohydrates, on combination with oxygen, yield fewer calories than do proteins and fats, the latter two groups should predominate in the diet for astronauts.

In high-grade food products, however, the carbohydrates, in conjunction with oxygen, can successfully compete with fats as far as heat value is concerned. Thanks to this fact, the astronauts' menu can be diversified with a minimum weight of provisions. In particular, the favored food of the North American Indians, pemmican (a paste of dried meat and berry juices), in view of its high heat value and its long keeping qualities, will probably be highly prized on an artificial satellite.

The water ration has been set at 2 kilograms per man per day. The proposal that water and oxygen should be stored in the form of hydrogen peroxide seems reasonable. This would allow a reduction in the volume of the oxygen tanks, since the oxygen would be, as it were, packed in the water. Further than that, a certain amount of heat is liberated on decomposition of hydrogen peroxide into water and oxygen, and this heat could be utilized for heating the living quarters.

A plant for recycling the water could be advantageous only for permanent satellites. In this case the amount of water on the space platform would increase constantly because of the synthetic water continuously produced in the organism by oxidation of the hydrogen contained in dry food products.

At the San Diego Symposium on Astronautics (1957), much attention was paid to the question of the delivery of food, etc., to astronauts on an artificial satellite. The methods of sustaining life for an astronaut on an artificial satellite in case of depletion of food, water, and oxygen were also studied.

■ Pressurized Space Suits

Naturally, cosmonauts could leave an artificial satellite and move in outside space only in pressure suits, and through an air-lock. After donning their pressure suits, the cosmonauts would pass from the cabin into the air-lock and then hermetically close the door through which they had entered. Next, the air would be pumped out of the lock, and only then would the outer door be opened.

Pressure suits have already been designed and produced for a stay in a highly rarefied and even airless medium. Projects of a pressure suit for extraterrestrial flight are also being worked out (Oberth and others). Such a pressure suit differs fundamentally from a pressure suit designed for flights at extreme altitudes. It must not only provide the cosmonaut with a normal medium for respiration but also produce the necessary temperature in airless space; the suit must stop the harmful radiation of the sun and stars and protect its occupant from cosmic dust and micrometeorites moving at an immense speed. For this purpose, pressure suits with a multilayer skin are proposed.

Constant temperature will be maintained in the presure suit by a thermostat, both in the solar rays and in the shadow of the earth. This automatically will also compensate the fluctuations in the equilibrium temperature of the pressure suit in its various position with respect to the direction of the sun's rays.

The microatmosphere of the pressure suit will be renewed by the constant motion of a fresh air jet in one direction, produced by a special apparatus. The water obtained in this process may be used by the astronaut in the pressure suit for drinking purposes.

A pressure suit of soft fabric is unsuitable for airless space; because of the internal pressure, such a suit would assume the shape of the greatest volume permitted by the area of the fabric, and the motions of the astronauts would be greatly impeded. The pressure suit would have to be rigid and maintain a constant volume under all motions. In order to ensure the cosmonauts freedom of motion, the pressure suit must be provided with joints having the necessary degrees of freedom. Providing mobility for the fingers would constitute an extremely difficult problem of design. For this purpose it is more convenient to use external rods, controlled from inside the pressure suit. For protection from the consequences of impacts, it is proposed to cover the lining of the pressure suit with a cloth jacket.

The small pressure difference inside and outside the space suit, in contrast to a diving suit, will keep its weight relatively light, despite its complex design.

■ **Training Astronauts for Orbital Flight**

Despite the fact that the entire process of take-off and placing the artificial satellite in orbit would be accomplished by automatic devices, extensive training of astronauts for orbital flight will still be necessary.

The minutes of flight with the engine on will be the most tense for the crew of a space rocket: the attainment of the necessary velocity at a predetermined altitude and the exact direction of motion at this moment will largely decide the success of the launching of the artificial satellite as a whole. A driver, a navigator, or a pilot can always correct any deviation of an automobile or aircraft from the prescribed path. In contrast to the driving of terrestrial transportation means, the control of a space rocket during take-off will be very difficult not only on account of the increased gravity that the pilot will experience but also because he will have to act instantaneously.

It is therefore entirely natural that astronauts will need proper physical preparation. They will require increased physical tolerance for G-forces and absence of gravity, for the low barometric pressure of the microatmosphere in the space ship, and for the great fluctuations of temperature. Piloting a space ship and other operations will demand not merely detailed knowledge but also great skill and intensive preliminary training. In the realization of space flight, also the biological factors—the man, his health, his endurance—will by no means be of minor importance.

In preparing for flight along the active part of the trajectory, the crew may be trained on the centrifuge, which can be rotated in such a way that the centrifugal force increases in exactly the same way as the sensation of weight will increase under the actual conditions on an orbital rocket. Under terrestrial conditions, it will be possible to train personnel to tolerate weightlessness only for very short periods of time.

Prolonged training of astronauts as well as comprehensive testing of various devices of the artificial satellite under laboratory conditions similar to flight conditions is an obligatory stage on the path toward realization of manned orbital rockets and artificial satellites. Such training may also be given in the so-called simulator or model of the artificial satellite. For example, in the opinion of Amico (United States), the simulator for a space vehicle must be equipped with instruments and units for scientific measurements, control, and other purposes and must also have emergency equipment. All the instruments must be put into operation, and an exact reproduction of the physical conditions of "flight" must be created. The cabin of the simulator must, with extreme accuracy, reproduce the cabin of the projected orbital rocket (or of the artificial satellite). The equivalent pressure of air, the corresponding temperature, the acceleration, the illumination, the various radiations, etc., must all be established in it. Automatic devices must regulate the nominal velocities of motion, the inclination of the vehicle relative to the celestial vault, the pressure in the tanks and pipelines, the fuel consumption, etc.

During a simulated flight at maximum velocity, the navigational problems connected with following any assigned trajectory will also be solved. The experimental plant will also include a system of remote radio control.

In reproducing the active part of the trajectory, during which the engine operates, it will be necessary to take account of the decrease in gravity and in air density with altitude, the variation of the aerodynamic resistance, the changes in the mass of the rocket, in particular during successive ejection of the auxiliary stages. Any desired air pressure can be obtained in the altitude chamber, the action of the reactive force may be replaced by centrifugal force, etc. However, a simulator will have a number of disadvantages. It will be impossible, for instance, to produce a state of prolonged weightlessness under laboratory conditions, it will be difficult to create the equivalent of the various hazards to which cosmonauts are exposed in flight, such as cosmic rays, impacts of meteoric bodies, etc. These faults may nullify the value of the entire experiment.

In the performance of their duties during the time of "take-off," cosmonauts will have to be dressed in protecting "anti-G" suits (cf. above), in order to verify the possibility of working under these conditions. The crew must not only master the normal system of servicing the equipment of an orbital rocket but must also be capable of rapidly making use of the rescue devices.[4] The effectiveness of the rescue facilities is important in the case of puncture of the ship skin by a meteoric body; strong heating of the skin or excessive cooling; failure of the oxygen plant; breakdown of the control or communication systems, the electric power system; etc.

Proper functioning of the automatic devices in flight will be under constant supervision by the crew. Therefore, the astronaut must learn to keep track of the instrument readings and to react properly to them.

---

[4] Training in proper use of rescue facilities is highly important. In aviation, for example, pilot training includes a program for meeting all possible cases of disaster, which in reality might hardly occur more than once in twenty years of service.

In turn, the actions of the cosmonauts in the simulator must be checked and recorded from outside. This will make it possible to analyze their errors.

Under the direction of instructors and checkers, the crew must first master the individual operations (navigational, rescue, etc.), and only after thorough preparation will a general test of the entire "space vehicle" (for instance, of an orbital rocket or an artificial satellite) be staged. In the general test, the actions of the crew in the cabin of the simulator will be watched by a staff of specialists in various fields of knowledge, rather than by individual instructors.

Such a program of operations is necessary not only for reaching the ultimate objective, namely the rational planning of space vehicles and the training of qualified personnel to service them, but also for day-to-day progress in this field. We note that the training, for instance, of test pilots for jet aircraft usually takes several years.

7

On Board
an Artificial Satellite

■
■
■

■ Days, Nights, and Seasons on the Artificial Satellite

When, after the dispatch of automatic scouts of the universe, human beings are sent into space and when they become inhabitants of the new heavenly body, an artificial satellite of the earth, they will see much to which they had been unaccustomed: The motion of the heavenly vault will be new, the changes of seasons unusual, and other phenomena, will seem strange.

On an artificial satellite, as on earth, day and night will alternate. But here they will not be similar to the days and nights on earth. Since the number of revolutions of the space platform around the earth during the day may be as high as sixteen (this number varies with the altitude of flight), day and night on the satellite during the course of a single earth day must alternate the same number of times. Night on a satellite is a peculiar kind of eclipse of the sun. The earth occults the sun. The satellite enters the earth's shadow, which covers only a small part of its orbit; therefore night on the satellite is always shorter than day (Fig. 40). For example, on an artificial satellite making 16 revolutions in a sidereal day, the local day will last 1 hour 29 minutes 45 seconds, and the longest "winter" night, 37 minutes.

The orbit of an artificial satellite can be so designed that the satellite does not enter the umbra (or even the penumbra) of the earth for many days. For this purpose the angle $\propto$ of inclination of the plane of the satellite orbit relative to the direction of the solar rays (Fig. 57) must not exceed a certain value. As the orbit becomes larger, this angle increases.

Thus, for an artificial satellite moving at an altitude of 0.1 earth radius, the angle $\propto$ is 116°; for an altitude three times as great, it is 130°; and for an altitude equal to three earth radii it will be 166°. At the distance of the moon, the angle $\propto$ already exceeds 179°.

For given dimensions of the satellite orbit, the maximum length of the night (and the minimum length of the day) corresponds to the case when the plane of the orbit is parallel to the solar rays. But theoretically, even then, night need never set in on an artificial satellite, provided the satellite is revolving around the earth at a distance of more than the length of the umbra of the earth. This umbra extends for a distance 217 times as long as the radius of the earth, for 3.6 times the distance between the moon and the earth (cf. Fig. 57).

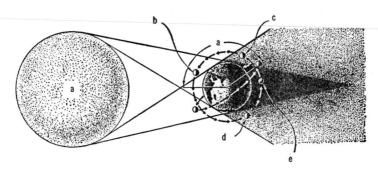

■ FIG. 40.—Dawn, Day, Dusk, and Night on an Artificial Satellite of the Earth. (a)—Sun; (b)—day on the artificial satellite; (c)—dawn on the artificial satellite; (d)—dusk on the artificial satellite; (e)—night on the artificial satellite.

In this theoretical case the satellite, without entering into the cone of the earth's umbra, will still pass through the earth's penumbra; during this time, the transit of the earth across the sun's disk will be observed from it.

It must be noted that this length of the earth's umbra corresponds to the mean distance from the sun. At aphelion of the earth's orbit, however, the umbra of the earth is elongated, and the satellite, if it is farther away from the earth than 217 earth radii, may enter the umbra of the earth. At perihelion, however, the earth's shadow is shorter, and a satellite which, at its mean distance from the earth was in that shadow, might now have no night.

■ TABLE 29

Length of Day and Night on an Artificial Satellite

Altitude of Path of Artificial Satellite, in Kilometers	Minimum Length of Day (Including Twilight)				Maximum Length of Night		
	Hrs.	Min.	Sec.	In Per Cent of Relative Length of Day, at Zero Altitude	Min.	Sec.	In Per Cent of Relative Length of Night, at Zero Altitude
0	0	42	13	100.00	42	12	100.00
200	0	51	09	121.2	37	15	88.24
1,000	1	10	07	166.1	34	55	82.71
2,000	1	32	08	218.2	35	01	82.94
3,000	1	54	40	271.6	35	51	84.92
4,000	2	18	11	327.7	36	56	87.49
5,000	2	45	06	386.3	38	06	90.24
6,000	3	08	58	447.6	39	20	93.17
6,378	3	18	59	471.3	39	27	94.28
7,000	3	35	56	511.5	40	35	96.13

Table 29 gives the lengths of day and night for altitudes of flight of artificial satellites as high as 7000 kilometers. We see that, as the earth recedes, the minimum length of the day continuously increases, while the maximum length of the night at first decreases and then begins to increase again.

Thus, when the orbital altitude of the satellite is increased from 200 kilometers to 1000 kilometers, the night is shortened by 2 minutes 20 seconds. At an altitude of 200 kilometers, however, the night is 6 seconds longer than at half that altitude.

On the artificial satellite, as on earth, the onset of night will be preceded by twilight (cf. Fig. 40). There will also be a twilight on the satellite before daybreak. But the dusk in the evening and the half-light before the dawn will result from causes entirely different from those on earth (where the light is scattered by the upper layers of the atmosphere). Here the cause will be the satellite's passage through the penumbra of our planet. The artificial satellite first enters the earth's penumbra and only then plunges into the umbra itself. While the diameter of the earth's umbra is gradually decreasing and finally tapers out into nothingness, the diameter of the earth's penumbra is continuously increasing. Whereas, during local night, the sun will not be visible at all on the satellite, it will be partially visible during twilight.

We have always hailed as wonders the sight of the rising and setting sun. The impressive colors of sunrise and sunset are explained by the passage of the sun's rays through a thick layer of air. In observing the rising and setting of the sun on an artificial satellite, the influence of the earth's atmosphere make itself felt more since the rays of the sun will sometimes travel over twice as long a path through the atmosphere before reaching the observer's eyes.

The rotation of the space platform about its center of mass will also affect the illumination of its individual parts, the more so since not only the direct rays of the sun will fall on the satellite but also the rays reflected by the earth and the moon.

The artificial satellite will also have its own seasons, due, as on earth, to the variation in the length of day and night; however, this variation will not be due to the same causes as on our planet. Whereas on earth the variations in the length of the day and night during the course of the year are due to the inclination of the earth's axis to the ecliptic, they are explained on an artificial satellite by the varying duration of the time spent by the satellite in the earth's shadow. The longer the satellite remains in the shadow, the lower will be its mean temperature. Nominal winter on the satellite will arrive at the period of the longest nights, and summer at the period of the longest days. In view of the fact that artificial satellites (even the largest ones) will be minute heavenly bodies, the temperature of the illuminated side, both on the north of the satellite and on the south, in contrast to the earth, will be practically one and the same. On satellites that rapidly rotate about their axes a practically constant temperature might be established on the entire satellite.

The entire course of the calendar on the satellite is determined by the fact that its circular orbit lies almost in one and the same plane, which is stationary relative to the fixed stars. Let us take, as an example, an artificial satellite overflying the poles at an altitude of 210 kilometers. The plane of the orbit of such a satellite, like the earth's axis, will be inclined to the ecliptic at an angle of 66°33'. Assume that at the time of the September equinox this plane is parallel to the solar rays.

At the instant when the satellite enters the earth's shadow, night begins on it. This will take place four minutes after the satellite has overflown the North Pole; during these four minutes, the satellite will still be bathed in the sun's rays, although the subsatellite points during this time will already be submerged in darkness. When the sun rises on the satellite, however, the surface of the earth will still be in the shadow, and it will again be four minutes until the satellite reaches the South Pole. In this way, the day on the satellite will last $4 \times 4 = 16$ minutes longer than the night, and its total length will be 52 minutes. At this time, the night will be longest on the satellite, and therefore winter will prevail on it.

On this satellite, June and December will be the height of summer, and the ends of March and September, midwinter. Thus, during a single earth year, there will be two winters and two summers on the satellite.

If, however, the circular orbit of a given artificial satellite lies in the plane of the ecliptic, then the length of day and night during the course of the entire year will not vary, and there will be no change of seasons. If the earth did not revolve around the sun, then the length of day and night of such a satellite would be the same as indicated in Table 29. But, as already stated in Chapter 1, the earth does make one revolution around the sun during the course of a year, and the satellite will make one revolution more in a year relative to the sun than relative to the fixed stars if the direction of the satellite's motion around the earth is opposite to the direction of the earth's motion around the sun, and one revolution less if these two directions are the same. Consequently, the length of the day and night will also differ, according to the direction of the satellite's motion.

This correction will increase with the orbital altitude of the satellite. While, for a satellite flying at a tenth of an earth radius, this difference is only ± 1 second, it will already be ± 1 minute for a satellite revolving at an altitude of three earth radii. For artificial satellites moving close to the moon's orbit in opposite directions, in circles of equal size, the difference in the period of revolution relative to the sun would already exceed four days.

The shape of the orbit will also affect the length of day and night on a satellite. Above, we have been considering only circular orbits. If, however, for the same period of revolution of a satellite its orbit is not circular but elliptical, then the length of day and night will vary. Assume, for example, that the diameter of a circular orbit is three earth radii. If we disregard the motion of the earth around the sun, then the maximum length of the night on the satellite will be 35 minutes 48 seconds. Consider now the elliptical orbit with a major axis likewise equal to three earth radii (and, consequently, with the very same period of revolution of the satellite), with its perigee lying at the very surface of the earth. If the apogee of the orbit is turned toward the sun, then night on the satellite will last 34 minutes 12 seconds. But if the perigee is turned toward the sun, then the length of the night will be 1 hour 6 minutes 10 seconds. For any other position of the satellites orbit, the length of the night will assume a certain intermediate value provided that the sun is in the plane of the orbit.

In general, the flattening of an orbit, regardless of its position, will result in a lengthening of the night by comparison with its length in the case of circular motion. We note that, in this case, the night will generally be longer at apogee than at perigee. This will be due to the fact that, although the earth's shadow is more narrow at apogee than at perigee (which we assume to be located at the surface of the earth), this will be compensated by the motion of the satellite itself being considerably slower.

The greatest variations in the length of the day (or night) during the course of the year should occur on a satellite with an orbit perpendicular to the plane of the ecliptic. We may agree conventionally to call "winter" that period of time when the satellite enters (as a rule, periodically), the earth's umbra (i.e., when there are not only days and twilights on it but also nights); "spring" and "autumn," the periods when the satellite enters the penumbra of our planet (i.e., when there is only day and twilight during the course of a day on the satellite); and, finally, "summer," the period when the satellite, during the course of many revolutions around the earth, entirely avoids both the umbra and the penumbra and is constantly washed by the sun's rays. The length of the seasons for a satellite with this orbital plane is given in Table 30. In compiling this table, it was assumed (for example) that, at the beginning of the "winter" or "spring" when the orbit touches the umbra or penumbra of the earth, the satellite itself is located precisely at the point of such contact. Actually, such coincidences will not, as a rule, take place. The change of seasons on the satellite will therefore take place somewhat differently than indicated in the table, but the values of the corresponding corrections cannot exceed the length of the period of revolution of the satellite around the earth.

■ TABLE 30

Length of Seasons on an Artificial Satellite Whose Orbital Plane Is Perpendicular to the Plane of the Ecliptic

Radius of Orbit, in Earth Radii	Length of Spring and Autumn, in Days	Length of Summer, in Days	Length of Winter, in Days	Radius of Orbit, in Earth Radii	Length of Spring and Autumn, in Days	Length of Summer, in Days	Length of Winter, in Days
1.1	0.56	51.86	129.65	4	0.56	152.67	28.84
1.2	0.56	67.51	114.00	5	0.56	158.63	22.88
1.3	0.56	80.01	101.50	7	0.56	165.38	16.13
1.4	0.56	89.53	91.98	10	0.56	170.40	11.11
1.5	0.56	97.20	84.31	15	0.56	174.29	7.22
1.7	0.56	108.93	72.58	20	0.56	176.23	5.28
2	0.56	121.17	60.34	30	0.56	178.17	3.34
2.5	0.56	134.20	47.31	40	0.56	179.16	2.35
3	0.56	142.53	38.98	70	0.56	180.38	1.13

The variations in the length of night on the artificial satellite will also depend on the orbital altitude of the satellite: The higher its orbit, the more rapid will be the lengthening of the night during the initial period of local winter, and the more rapidly will it afterward decrease.

This can be attributed to two causes. As we have seen, with increasing orbital altitude of the satellite, on the one hand, the length of the night on it is increased, while, on the other hand, the winter will be shortened. Thus, at an orbital radius of 1.1 earth radii the lengthening of the night on the satellite will not exceed 1.5 minutes, while for a satellite moving in a circle with a diameter ten times as great as the earth's diameter the corresponding value will reach 37 minutes. The smallest fluctuations in the lengthening of the night will occur in mid-winter on the satellite.

■ **TABLE 31**

Variation in the Length of Night during Winter on an Artificial Satellite Moving in a Plane Perpendicular to the Plane of the Ecliptic, at an Altitude Equal to the Radius of the Earth

Time Elapsed between Winter on Satellite (or Remaining to Midwinter), in Days	Length of Night		Ratio of Length of Night to Length of Longest Night in Midwinter	Time Elapsed between Winter on Satellite (or Remaining to Midwinter), in Days	Length of Night		Ratio of Length of Night to Length of Longest Night in Midwinter
	Min.	Sec.			Min.	Sec.	
0	39	27	100	20	29	32	74.9
5	38	54	98.6	25	22	5	56.0
10	37	13	94.5	30	4	7	10.4
15	34	14	86.8	30.17	0	0	0

As a typical example, Table 31 shows the variation in the length of the night throughout each of five local days during the course of winter on an artificial satellite moving at an altitude of one earth radius.

Knowledge of the length of day and night and of the length of the seasons on the artificial satellite is very important for determining the conditions and the time of its illumination by the rays of the sun, i.e., for its observation from the earth and for the study of solar radiation by means of instrumentation installed on the satellite.

■ **View of the Sky and Heavenly Bodies from an Artificial Satellite**

As soon as the orbital rocket is flying beyond the boundaries of the sensible atmosphere, i.e., one or two minutes after take-off, the celestial vault will lose its usual blue color and will become black. It is well known that absolute darkness never occurs on earth, even in places completely shielded from the sun, since sunlight scattered to some degree in the atmosphere does enter the zone of shadow. Conversely, the regions of space in the shadow of some nonluminous heavenly body appear to be in almost total darkness. The celestial vault is not lit up by the bright solar rays scattered in the atmosphere, and the stars and nebulae shine only faintly. The stars do not twinkle and are always distinctly visible if the eyes are shielded from the direct action of the solar rays; otherwise, the eye, after accommodation to bright sunlight, loses its power of distinguishing the stars.

The appearance of the sky seen from the artificial satellite will differ completely from its appearance seen from the earth's surface. To our eyes, the eyes of inhabitants of the northern hemisphere, most of the celestial vault of the southern hemisphere is invisible, in exactly the same way as most of the northern celestial vault is invisible to inhabitants of the southern hemisphere. From an artificial satellite, regardless of the direction of its motion, the entire celestial sphere will be visible during the course of a local "day" (i.e., during one revolution around the earth).

Apparent Motion of the Earth in the Celestial Vault

Let us first see how the motion of the earth in the celestial vault will appear to an observer on the artificial satellite. After a local sidereal day he will be aware that the earth has made a complete revolution around the satellite. If the plane of the satellite orbit coincides with the plane of the ecliptic, then the earth will move along the belt of the zodiac, passing successfully through the zodiacal constellations of Aries, Taurus, Gemini, Cancer, Leo, Virgo, Libra, Scorpio, Sagittarius, Capricorn, Aquarius, and Pisces, and returning to the constellation Aries (or in the opposite direction, depending on the direction of the satellite's motion). If the satellite overflies the poles, then, during its local sidereal days, the observer will in turn see the Ursa Minor and, close to the Southern Celestial Pole, the constellations of Chamaeleon, Bird of Paradise, Mensa, etc. In this case the earth will successively occult the Pole Star and a number of other stars along the celestial meridian, in the plane of which the orbit of the artificial satellite lies. The earth may periodically pass through the constellations of Andromeda and Cassiopeia along the 15° meridian and then, skirting the celestial pole and proceeding along the opposite 195° meridian (compared with the globe), it may cross the constellations of Canes Venatici and Coma Veronicae. If, however, the plane of the satellite orbit is rotated through 90° about the celestial axis (and the axis of the earth), i.e., so that the satellite continues to move around the pole, then the earth will periodically pass through entirely different constellations, namely through the constellations of Aquila, Unicornus, Canis Major, Canis Minor, and Sagittarius.

If the orbit is circular, then the apparent motion of the earth in the celestial sphere, as seen from the satellite, will be uniform. In the case of an elliptical orbit, however, because of the irregular motion of the satellite itself as well as the variation of the distance to the earth, it will seem to an observer that the earth now accelerates its motion in the celestial vault and now slows it down. If, for example, the apogee of the satellite is two or three times as far from the center of the earth as the perigee, then at the time when the satellite passes through the most distant point of its orbit the apparent angular motion of the earth in the celestial vault will be decreased to one fourth or one ninth the angular motion at perigee during the same period of time.

The angular diameter of the earth will of course continuously vary when the satellite moves in an ellipse, since the greater the distance between an observer and an object observed, the smaller will be the angle subtended by that object.

Apparent Motion of the Moon in the Celestial Vault

To an observer on an artificial satellite, the moon will seem to move constantly through the sky. This motion will be partly due to the proper motion of the satellite in space. However, while the apparent motion of the earth on a great circle of the celestial sphere is always rectilinear (which is explained by the fact that the plane of the satellite orbit passes through the center of the earth), the path of the moon may also appear to be circular or elliptic. Assume, for example, that the plane of a circular orbit of an artificial satellite is perpendicular to the line earth-moon. As the satellite moves, the observer will see the moon against a changing background of stars, as we see a telegraph pole, from the window of a moving train, being displaced against the background of the landscape. During the course of one revolution of the satellite around the earth, the moon will describe a circle which will be greater, the greater the orbit of the artificial satellite. A simple calculation will show, for instance, that with an orbit having a radius ten times the equatorial radius of the earth, the moon will describe a circle with a radius subtending an angle of 9-10° at the satellite (this value will vary depending on whether the moon is at apogee of its orbit or at perigee).[1]

If the plane of the circular orbit of the satellite is inclined relative to the line earth-moon, then the moon will appear to describe an ellipse. If the artificial satellite itself is moving in an ellipse, the apparent motion of the moon will, as a rule, be elliptical but, at a certain definite angle of inclination of the orbit, may also appear circular.

As for the apparent size of the moon, it is only when the satellite moves in a circle whose plane is perpendicular to the line passing through the centers of the earth and the moon that the apparent size will not vary. In all other cases, the apparent size of the moon's disk will vary. The greatest fluctuations of the apparent diameter of the moon will occur when the plane of the satellite orbit passes through the center of the moon. Thus, if the diameter of the circular orbit of the satellite is 20 earth radii, then, at opposition (i.e., when the artificial satellite is closest to the moon), the moon will appear twice as large to the observer as in the position of conjunction (i.e., when the moon is farthest away from the satellite). If, however, the radius of the orbit is increased 2.75 times, then at opposition the disk of the moon will appear to be 22 times as large as at conjunction and 11-odd times as large as when observed from the surface of the earth.[2]

Against the background of the starry sky, the moon will oscillate along a straight line, and will change its size constantly. After opposition, it will move to the right, waning continuously and moving ever slower in the celestial sphere. Then it will begin moving to the left, and its disk will decrease in size as before, until its size reaches a minimum at the position of opposition. Continuing its motion to the left, the disk of the moon will begin to wax and will increase, already turning to the right, until it reaches its maximum size at opposition.

[1] In our discussions we assume that only the artificial satellite is moving in space, while all the other heavenly bodies are at rest.

[2] Strictly speaking, at conjunction the moon is not visible at all, since in that case it is hidden behind the disk of the earth. Here we have in mind its apparent size at the instant the occultation by the earth begins (in practice, they are the same).

FIG. 41.—Apparent Motion of the Moon from the Artificial Satellite and Change in Its Size, with a Radius of the Circular Satellite Orbit Equal to 55 Earth Radii (the Motion of the Moon and the Change of Its Size Are Shown on Different Scales).

Figure 41 shows how the variation in the apparent size and position of the moon appears in the celestial vault as the artificial satellite moves around the earth. It is assumed here that the system earth-moon is at rest, and that the radius of the artificial satellite orbit is equal to 55 equatorial earth radii. For greater clarity the motion of the moon is shown on the sketch not as oscillating along a straight line, which motion will in fact be observed, but as moving in a flattened ellipse. This is how the motion of the moon will appear to an observer on a satellite moving in a circular orbit in a plane inclined at a small angle to the line passing through the centers of the earth and the moon.

We note likewise that the apparent motion of the sun in the heavenly sphere, due to the motion of the satellite as seen from the satellite, will be of the same character as the apparent motion of the moon. Owing to the greater distance of the sun, however, this motion will be far less marked.

Influence of Aberration on the Apparent Position of the Stars

It is well known that the position of the stars observed by us in the sky differs somewhat from their true position. This phenomenon is explained by the interaction between the velocity of light and the velocity of motion of the earth around the sun and is called the aberration of light. Let us now consider the phenomenon of aberration on the observation of the heavenly bodies from an artificial satellite. It is obvious that the velocity of the satellite relative to the sun will differ from the velocity of the earth and that, therefore, the aberration, in observations from the satellite, will not be the same as in observations of the sky from the earth.

In fact, the velocity of the satellite relative to the sun is equal to the geometric sum of the orbital velocities of the earth and the satellite (i.e., it is obtained from these velocities by a construction according to the parallelogram rule). Consequently, according to the angle between the orbital velocities of the earth and the satellite, the aberrations will be intensified or attenuated.

■ **TABLE 32**

Maximum Apparent Change of Position of Stars in the Sky (Owing to the Aberration of Light) Due to the Motion of the Artificial Satellite Relative to the Sun

Radius of Orbit of Satellite, in Equatorial Earth Radii	Maximum Apparent Change of Position of Star, in Seconds of Arc	Per Cent by which the Maximum Apparent Shift of the Star for an Observer from the Satellite is Greater than for an Observer from the Earth	Radius of Orbit of Satellite, in Equatorial Earth Radii	Maximum Apparent Change of Position of Star, in Seconds of Arc	Per Cent by which the Maximum Apparent Shift of the Star for an Observer from the Satellite is Greater than for an Observer from the Earth
1	25.92	26.6	5	22.91	11.9
1.5	24.92	21.7	15	21.89	6.9
2.5	23.92	16.8	200	20.86	1.9

Let us consider the simplest case, when the star is on the line sun-earth. In this case, the shift of the star due to aberration, as observed from the earth, will be maximum, and equal to 20.48 seconds of arc. Table 32 shows the degree to which this shift is intensified at the moment when the satellite, moving in the plane of the ecliptic, crosses the line sun-earth-star and the composition of orbital velocities of the earth and the satellite is arithmetical. As we see, the closer to the earth's surface the satellite moves, the greater will be the shift of the star, which is explained by the greater velocity of flight of the satellite. Whereas, for circular orbits, the "additional" shift may theoretically be as much as 26.6 per cent, for elliptical orbits it may reach 37.7 per cent.

The motion of the artificial satellite, as already stated, may also attenuate the phenomenon of aberration. Such attenuation will reach a maximum when the direction of motion of the earth around the sun is opposite to that of the satellite around the earth.

At the moments when the orbital velocities of the earth and

satellite form some angle with each other, the aberration will be increased or decreased to one extent or another. Table 33 shows the variation in the position, on the celestial sphere, of a star on the line earth-sun as a result of aberration, when observed from a zero artificial satellite of the earth at different moments.

■ **TABLE 33**

Change in Maximum Shift of Stars Due to Aberration when a Zero Artificial Satellite Moves Around the Earth

Angle between Lines Earth-Satellite and Earth-Star	Apparent Shift of Star, in Seconds of Arc	Ratio between Apparent Shift of Star, for an Observer on the Satellite, and Maximum Shift, for an Observer on the Earth's Surface, in Per Cent	Angle between Lines Earth-Satellite and Earth-Star	Apparent Shift of Star, in Seconds of Arc	Ratio between Apparent Shift of Star, for an Observer on the Satellite, and Maximum Shift, for an Observer on the Earth's Surface, in Per Cent
0	25.92	126.6	100	19.53	95.4
20	25.60	125.0	120	17.76	86.7
40	24.65	120.4	140	16.31	79.6
60	23.20	113.3	160	15.36	75.0
80	21.42	104.6	180	15.04	73.4
90	20.48	100.0			

Influence of Rotation of an Artificial Satellite on the Apparent Motion of the Heavenly Bodies

Up to now we have been speaking of the effect exerted by the orbital motion of an artificial satellite around the earth on the apparent motion of the heavenly bodies. Let us now imagine that we are on board an artificial satellite which is placed in rotation with the object of producing artificial gravity. How will the motion of the celestial sphere appear to us in this case? First of all it will seem that the celestial vault, together with the earth, moon, sun, and stars, is rotating about the satellite. One such complete revolution of the celestial sphere will be accomplished during the time in which the artificial satellite executes one revolution around its own axis of rotation, i.e., during the course of several minutes, or even of a fraction of a minute.

At the moment when the axis of rotation of the artificial satellite is horizontal (perpendicular to the radius vector), it will seem to the astronauts that the earth is first overturning above their heads and is then disappearing from beneath their feet. If, however, the axis of rotation of the satellite at some moment coincides with the axis of rotation of our planet,[3] then it will seem that the earth is rotating about its axis at an incredible speed (hundreds of times the actual speed) and that the sun and stars are rotating about the satellite at the same immense speed. The rotation of the earth may appear to be direct or retrograde, depending on the direction of rotation of the artificial satellite.

If the axis of rotation of the artificial satellite (which, as we know already, must pass through its center of mass), does not coincide with the axis of the earth, but in spite of that still passes through the center of the earth, then the earth will appear to be rotating not about its actual axis but about the axis of rotation of the satellite. It will seem to the astronauts that the earth's pole is that point on its surface from which the artificial satellite is visible in the zenith. Consequently, for astronauts moving around the earth, this imaginary terrestrial pole will seem to wander; but during the course of one apparent revolution of the earth about its axis the earth can be displaced only very slightly. If, for example, a polar artificial satellite is moving at an altitude of three earth radii, then the period of its revolution around the earth will be 7 hours 17 minutes, i.e., 437 minutes. Let us imagine that on a toroidal artificial satellite 100 meters in diameter, a normal force of gravity (the same as on earth) is created by means of rotation. For this, the time of one of its rotations about its own axis would have to be 14.2 seconds, i.e., 0.237 minutes. In this way, during this time (which is at the same time also the time of rotation of the earth about its apparent axis), the "pole of rotation" is shifted along the meridian by only $360° \times \frac{0.237}{437} = 0.195°$. Strictly speaking, one should also take account of the effect of the diurnal rotation of the earth, but as a practical matter this would have almost no effect, since, during this same interval of time, the globe would rotate by not more than $360° \times \frac{0.237}{60 \times 24} = 0.059°$.

In a special case, the apparent pole of rotation of the earth may

[3] Since the artificial satellite cannot "stand still" above a pole, this coincidence will last for only an instant.

also be motionless. This will occur when the earth is observed from a stationary artificial satellite rotating about its own axis which passes through the center of mass of the satellite and the center of the earth. Such a pole, for instance, might be the mountain range of Kenya in equatorial Africa, with its plantations of banana and coffee trees. From the point of view of extraterrestrial observers in this case, the Kola Peninsula, which lies beyond the Arctic Circle, and the Island of Sumatra, which is intersected by the equator, will be on the same apparent "parallel of latitude."

As we have seen, astronauts on an artificial satellite will have to make certain efforts to master the art of cosmic navigation and to utilize practical astronomy, for example, to correct the satellite orbit.

■ The Microatmosphere and Its Conditioning

In certain respects, a space vehicle, and in particular an artificial satellite, resembles a submarine: In both cases the crew must live in a hermetically sealed cabin completely isolated from the external medium. The composition, pressure, temperature and humidity of the air within the cabin will be regulated by special equipment. However, the space ship, in comparison with a submarine, will have the advantage that the difference between the pressures inside and outside the cabin will be less. For a space vehicle, this difference will be only one atmosphere (the pressure outside being zero), while for a submarine it is often many atmospheres.

The question of maintaining the necessary pressure in the cabin of a space vehicle is very important. It is possible that at a certain composition of the air the astronaut will be able to breathe normally, even at a cabin pressure below one atmosphere. The lower the pressure in the cabin of an artificial satellite, the thinner may the walls of its shell be built, the simpler will be the design of the cabin and pressure suits, and the less will be the danger of leakage of air into space in the case of insufficiently tight connections of the shell or puncture of the skin (shell) by the impact of a meteorite.

In the earth's atmosphere the lack of oxygen generally makes itself felt at a pressure of 430 millimeters Hg, corresponding to an elevation of 4.5 kilometers above sea level. The experiments of Behag, Garceau, and Richet (France) have established that, when the pressure of the inhaled air is reduced, its oxygen content must be increased, since otherwise asphyxia may supervene. For example, in one of their experiments, a subject tolerated a reduction in pressure of the gas mixture inhaled to values as low as 100 millimeters Hg, with symptoms of only slight discomfort; however, this mixture had an oxygen content of about 75 per cent. The same investigators, on the basis of experiments on rabbits, came to the conclusion that the human organism is capable of tolerating a reduction in the external pressure to 65 millimeters Hg, but under the condition that oxygen constitutes 90 per cent of the gas mixture inhaled.[4] At a gas pressure lower than 47 millimeters Hg, the human organism, like any other organism, cannot exist even in pure oxygen, since at this pressure (which corresponds to the pressure at an altitude of 19 kilometers), the water in the human organism (at 37° C.) begins to boil. This phenomenon, of course, involves danger to life: the skin, the cells, etc., begin to burst (the bends). At low pressure, moreover, the functioning of the organs of hearing is impaired and toothache is felt (especially with filled teeth, since the internal pressure of the air bubbles is not balanced by the ambient pressure). To reduce the rate of evaporation from the surface of the body, as well, a rise in pressure is needed. A solution for the question of the most expedient choice of pressure can be obtained only by experiment.

The microatmosphere of the cabin of a space ship must never consist of pure or almost pure oxygen.

It has been established by experiment that pure oxygen at a pressure of 190 millimeters Hg induces the same physiological reactions as air at sea level. If inhaled for a long time, however, pure oxygen has a depressing effect on the organism. It is considered that a reduction in the partial pressure[5] of oxygen to 150 millimeters Hg cannot cause physiological disorders if the total pressure is not below 190 millimeters Hg. Grant (United States) has therefore proposed, for the cabin of a space vehicle, a microatmosphere with a pressure of 190 millimeters Hg in which the partial pressure of oxygen is 160

---

[4] These indices of pressure and oxygen content are of rather theoretical interest, since, under the extreme conditions we are considering, the endurance of the human organism is stretched to the uttermost limit. For the normal functioning of the various organs of the body, however, a far higher pressure is essential.

[5] The partial pressure of a gas in a mixture is the pressure that the gas would have if it alone occupied the entire volume of the mixture.

millimeters Hg; that of water vapor, 20 millimeters Hg; and that of carbon dioxide, 10 millimeters Hg. It is usually considered that other gases are not necessary for the functioning of the human organism, but this hypothesis still requires confirmation, the more so since, as has been recently found, nitrogen in small doses does play a certain role in the metabolism.

It should be noted that with a high amount of oxygen the danger of fire increases, and food products rapidly oxidize and spoil; for this reason the microatmosphere must also contain a certain amount of other gases. In this connection, the possibility of replacing nitrogen in the microatmosphere of a space ship or artificial satellite by some other lighter inert gas has been repeatedly discussed. In particular, helium has often been proposed as a component of the microatmosphere of a space ship, since it is considerably lighter than nitrogen (by a factor of 7.4). Actually, however, it is not very suitable for this purpose.

In fact, the choice of an inert gas for a microatmosphere could be effectively based on the degree to which the gas is capable of diffusing through small orifices, which depends not only on the pressure but also on the nature of the gas. It is assumed that the rate of diffusion of a gas through a seam of the cabin hull to outside would obey the D'Arcy law, according to which this rate is inversely proportional to the square root of the density of the gas. The rapid leakage of gas from the cabin, however, would produce aeroembolism or "the bends" in astronauts, and the process of formation of subcutaneous bubbles would be more rapid the higher the solubility of the given gas in the organism. The rate of diffusion for neon is somewhat higher, and for helium considerably higher, than for nitrogen; conversely, for argon and krypton it is considerably lower than for nitrogen.

The little studied question of the influence of the velocity of propagation of sound in a gas on the intelligibility of human speech is also of importance. In this respect, among the inert gases, only argon could replace nitrogen as a component of the microatmosphere.

The ability of inert gases to transmit heat is also important. The replacement of nitrogen by helium would increase the heat loss.

Considering the question from all points of view, Haviland (United States) considers nitrogen to be superior in its properties to all other gases and believes, therefore, that the microatmosphere on a space ship should consist of a mixture of oxygen and nitrogen. This question, however, cannot be considered as finally solved, and new studies are necessary.

In flight, it would be expedient to have a certain supply of ozone available. This gas, which is an oxidant and has a sterilizing action, is a good air freshener, a point which is particularly important for a hermetically sealed cabin. It is, however, exceedingly difficult to prepare liquid ozone in a stable form (cf. above). The air in the cabin could be continuously purified by cooling in a special condenser to the temperature of liquefaction of carbon dioxide, i.e., to $-78°$ C. In this case, water would first be liberated, followed by liquid carbon dioxide. The necessary amounts of oxygen and water vapor would have to be added to the purified air, and the water content of the fresh air, as a result, should be lower than in the air entering the regenerator plant. The mixture would then have to be heated to normal temperature.

Obviously, smoking would be undesirable on board an artificial satellite: it would not only involve an unnecessary consumption of oxygen but also greatly complicate the process of purifying the air. The smoke formed by smoking and the gases formed in preparing food could be condensed on cold surfaces (Green, Canada).

Since in air-conditioning we have to do with alternating processes of heating and cooling, their skillful regulation would allow a considerable saving of thermal energy.

The conditioning of air in the cabins of a satellite would be made more difficult by the fact that the process of respiration and elimination of water vapor by a human being is very irregular. As shown by experiments, during strenuous work for one hour a subject may excrete as much as one kilogram of water, in vapor form, in an hour (during a parachute jump, half a kilogram of water vapor is given off by the body).

It could hardly be considered advisable to send a heavy air-regeneration plant, intended for renewal of the composition of air, up to a short-lived artificial satellite. It would be simpler, evidently, to replace the vitiated microatmosphere with a fresh one by "airing" the cabin in the following manner: After going into an adjoining cabin (or putting on pressure suits), the astronauts would turn a cock releasing the air from the cabin they just left into space. This operation would last only a short time, since the air would rush out at the speed of sound. The cock would then be closed and the cabin filled with fresh air. The carbon dioxide might also be removed from the microatmosphere by the aid of chemicals. For example, in a submerged submarine, the carbon dioxide can be eliminated for many days by means of absorbers. This method of air regeneration was also used in the first biosatellite (i.e., on the second Soviet artificial satellite): special compounds, absorbing carbon dioxide and the excess of water vapor, also gave off the necessary oxygen for respiration of the animal. In this case, the quantity of matter participating in these chemical reactions was automatically regulated. Figure XVIII shows the pressurized cabin of the biosatellite with its air-conditioning plant.

The necessary supply of oxygen is conveniently taken along in liquid form. In this case, the weight and volume of the tanks will be less than that of gas cylinders. The design of tanks for the storage of liquid oxygen may follow the principle of the Dewar vessel (as the thermos flask does), thus assuring a rather long storage of liquid gases. The oxygen could also be shipped in the solid state from the earth to the artificial satellite. Such oxygen would need the lightest containers of all. Oxygen for respiration might also be stored in the form of sodium peroxide, which absorbs carbon dioxide and excess moisture and gives off oxygen. Hydrogen peroxide in the solid form would be still more suitable.

Under the condition of weightlessness, the phenomenon of convection (air exchange between the lower and upper layers) is absent in the microatmosphere of an artificial satellite, which might, in particular, lead to suffocation: The air would become stagnant and carbon dioxide "pockets" would form, making the process of respiration impossible (as well as the process of burning of a flame). The air would therefore have to be constantly mixed in the cabins by means of fans or other methods, thus also effecting a forced one-way circulation of the air. It was this method that was used on the second Soviet artificial satellite.

During stratosphere flights, special apparatus is used to produce an artificial microatmosphere for aircraft crews. Such apparatus, with suitable improvements, could also be used on board an artificial satellite.

■ Solar Engineering on an Artificial Satellite

To maintain the temperature in an artificial satellite, artificial heating would be used. It will be necessary in this case to take measures against the loss of heat through the walls of the cabin, for instance by means of a skin of heat-insulating material. However, artificial heating involving the consumption of fuel would hardly be useful. Normal temperature could be maintained in the rooms of an artificial satellite, without any fuel consumption, by utilizing the energy of the sun's rays.

In the popular literature we rather often come across the erroneous idea of the "temperature of interplanetary space." The point is that the matter filling interplanetary space can be ignored for all practical purposes, in view of its absolutely negligible density. Consequently, the concept of temperature of interplanetary space is meaningless; this space, in contrast to the atmospheric medium surrounding us on earth, does not heat and does not cool.

In airless space, the transmission of heat from one body to another can be accomplished only by radiation. A body subjected to the action of solar rays is heated or cooled until the quantity of heat absorbed by it becomes equal to the quantity of heat radiated, after which the temperature of the body becomes established at a definite and constant level, termed the equilibrium temperature.

The equilibrium temperature of a body depends on the substance of which it is composed, on the shape of the body, on the position of the illuminated surface of the body with respect to the rays of the sun, and, finally, on the distance from the sun. For example, on the orbit of an artificial satellite, the temperature of an ideal black sphere, rapidly rotating about an axis perpendicular to the solar rays, will be about 3°. The temperature of an ideal black cylinder of a height five times its diameter will fluctuate from −93 to +130° C., depending on the position of the cylinder relative to the sun's rays.[6]

As for the distance of the artificial satellite from the sun, it may in practice be considered equal to the distance of the earth from the

[6] The quantity of heat received by the body is proportional to the area of its shadow thrown on the plane perpendicular to the solar rays, while the quantity of heat lost by the body, as a result of radiation, is proportional to the total area of the body. The maximum size of the shadow of our cylinder, however, is over six times as great as its minimum shadow.

sun and will vary only slightly during the course of a year. In January it is 3.3 per cent less than in July, after which the intensity of the solar radiation on the satellite will increase by 7 per cent. To study the solar radiation, these data should be calculated in advance for any moment of time.

It is easy to calculate that, in passing in half a year from aphelion to perihelion, the earth will approach the sun on the average at a velocity of 317 meters per second, and during the course of the following half-year it will recede from it at the same velocity. For this reason, for each 3.4 seconds, the temperature of a black body, moving in the orbit of the earth, should increase or decrease by one millionth of a degree.

In the earth's shadow the equilibrium temperature of a satellite is considerably lower than in the rays of the sun. Because of the shortness of the night on an artificial satellite, however, it is possible that this temperature will be established only shortly before the satellite leaves the earth's shadow or, perhaps, will not have time to become established at all. It is more probable that the satellite will have time to warm up to the equilibrium temperature corresponding to the solar illumination (we know that the day on a satellite, as a rule, is considerably longer than the night). In any case, at the moment the artificial satellite sinks into the earth's shadow, its temperature must drop sharply, and when it emerges from the shadow, its temperature must rise. Therefore, even on the first satellites, it will be necessary in some way or other to attenuate these sharp temperature fluctuations for normal functioning of the various instrumentation (to say nothing of the living organisms, such as small animals).

The maximum and minimum temperatures of the satellite, according to its size, its heat capacity, and the optical characteristics of its surface, for a given power of the external sources have been considered by A. G. Karpenko and M. L. Lidov (U.S.S.R.). For a circular orbit, these authors reached the following conclusion: In the absence of internal heat sources, the mean temperature of the satellite will differ somewhat from zero, but its temperature fluctuations (in the solar rays and in the earth's shadow) will be very considerable and, other conditions being equal, will be smaller the higher the total heat capacity of the satellite. If, for example, for a total heat capacity of a definite value, the deviation from the mean temperature varies from

−25° C. to +25° C., then, if the heat capacity of the satellite is multiplied by five, its temperature fluctuations will now cover a more narrow range from −5° C. to +5° C. The heat capacity of a satellite can be increased by increasing its mass (making it necessary to use a more powerful orbital rocket) or by properly selecting the structural materials (this is usually dictated, in practice, by other considerations). The range of fluctuation of the satellite temperature can also be narrowed by increasing the reflectivity of the outer surface of the satellite.

Such a solution, however, leads to an increase in the mean temperature of the artificial satellite.

There may also be a sharp temperature differential between the sides of an artificial satellite—the side illuminated by the sun's rays and the shadow side. A more or less constant temperature on the entire satellite can be attained by its rapid rotation about the center of gravity.

In the rooms of the artificial satellite it will be easily possible to regulate the temperature over a wide range. Indeed, it is well known that an ideal black body absorbs the solar rays completely, while bodies of other colors reflect a part of the solar rays, to some extent.

It would be sufficient to cover the outer walls of one part of the satellite with a shell of a material strongly absorbing the solar rays, and the other part with a shell that was a good reflector of those rays, and then to rotate these shells in the proper manner relative to the sun (it would be more convenient to rotate the shells together with the satellite).

The supplies of liquid oxygen and other liquefied gases on an interplanetary station would of course be stored at a definite low temperature; however, the human organism demands a relatively high temperature. These conflicting demands lead to a considerable complication of the design of an interplanetary station. To solve this problem it will be possible, for instance, to separate the tanks with liquid fuel from the passenger cabin and to maintain them artificially at a low temperature. If it is impossible to maintain a low temperature on the side facing the sun by the use of heat insulation, then the contents of the tanks would have to be cooled mechanically.

The existence of an atmosphere on the earth's surface introduces an appreciable correction to the value of the equilibrium temperature due to solar radiation. This takes place as a result of convection, which removes heat from a heated body. For this reason, the data on the heating of a body obtained in everyday experience cannot be extended to a case where the bodies are in space; some bodies, which in the air are heated more strongly than others, would have a lower temperature in the void.

The energy of the solar rays can also be used on an artificial satellite for practical purposes, in particular, for the production of mechanical and electrical energy. On the satellite (or near it) one might, for example, install a type of solar steam engine, which has long been in use and in which the boiler is heated by a concentrated beam of solar rays reflected from a large mirror (Fig. XIX). In space outside the atmosphere it will also be easy to condense steam on the shadow side of the plant. We note that the temperature differential between the illuminated and shadow sides on an artificial satellite is considerably greater than on earth, and thanks to this fact the efficiency of a solar power plant on the satellite can be higher.

Under ground conditions, to obtain a power of one horsepower, a solar power plant with a mirror 17 square meters in area is required today. On artificial satellites of the earth, owing to the absence of atmosphere, it would be theoretically possible to obtain somewhat better results. But, practically speaking, the conditions of operation on an artificial satellite are of course incomparably more complex. It is well known that even on the solid earth solar power engineering has not yet attained sufficiently good results.

The weight of solar power plants is very high. The use of new methods of transforming solar energy into electric energy will perhaps yield better results. One might, for instance, use semiconductor thermal batteries to transform the solar energy into electric energy, or photo-electric semiconductor batteries. The former type of battery weighs considerably more than the latter type and can therefore be used only on large artificial satellites. The efforts of scientists (V. S. Vavilov, V. M. Malovetskaya, G. N. Galkin, A. P. Landsman in the U.S.S.R., and others) are directed toward the development of high-efficiency silicon photocells, which could be used for feeding the instrumentation on small artificial satellites.

The efficiency of the best experimental designs of photoelectric semiconductor batteries today ranges from 6 to 11 per cent, but this efficiency could theoretically be doubled. Since the power of the perpendicular flux of the sun's rays beyond the limits of the atmosphere is 1350 watts per square meter it is already practically possible to obtain an electric current of over one watt from each square decimeter.

We may also cite the considerations of Stuhlinger (United States) on the power supply for automatic artificial satellites.

A silicon photocell installed on the artificial satellite is automatically held perpendicular to the sun's rays. But the photoelectric generator of current cannot operate for an indefinite period. It is not even known today whether it can serve for several months.

A thermocouple battery has a longer service life. A special automatic device directs the mirror perpendicular to the sun's rays. The thermocouples are heated on one end by the concentrated solar rays, and are cooled on the other end. The thermocouples can be cooled by means of an oil radiator operating on the principle of radiation. To radiate one kilowatt of thermal energy by a black body (radiator) at a temperature of 100° C., placed in shadow, requires a radiator of 0.93 square meter. At a temperature of 20° C., however, the radiating surface must already be 2.7 times as large, since the intensity of radiation increases to the fourth power of the absolute temperature of the body. The cooling device will weigh over half as much as the total weight of the generator plant.

During the time of passage of the satellite in the solar rays, part of the electric power produced will be consumed for charging storage batteries, which will begin to operate at the moment the satellite enters the earth's shadow.

The thermocouples may also be heated by radioactive isotopes, the kinetic energy of beta-disintegration, when the disintegration particles are absorbed by the mass of the isotope itself and by the walls of the chamber, being converted into thermal energy. For this purpose, the use of strontium-90 is proposed. Its half-life is 20 years. However, 25 kilograms of uranium or plutonium must be used to produce 1 kilogram of this isotope. The quantity of raw material necessary is considerably decreased if one is satisfied with strontium-89, whose half-life is only 53 days. For an output of 100 watts, 18.1 kilograms of strontium-90 would be necessary.

If isotopes are used, the charged-particle counters and other instruments sensitive to radioactive radiations would have to be shielded from the gamma-rays and X-rays by a protective shield. If the instrumentation with the recording instruments weighs 27 kilograms, and the radio transmitters weigh 14 kilograms, the total weight of an artificial satellite with a photoelectric power supply would be 159 kilograms, and with a thermal battery heated by the sun or an isotope it would be about 206 kilograms. The efficiency of the proposed electric power sources is about 5 per cent, and they weigh from 0.7 to 1.1 kilograms per watt. There is reason to suppose that the efficiency of semiconductor cells can be considerably improved. Photoelectric current generators may prove to be more advantageous than electric machines as generators.

Possessing a power as high as several hundred watts, and an operating period of several days, ordinary batteries today are preferable over all other sources of electric power. The best sources of this type yield 0.11 kilowatt-hour per kilogram of battery weight. In particular, mercury batteries not only yield the most powerful current per unit weight but also last the longest.

A steam engine with an electric generator of a total power of 100 watts would have a lower efficiency than the above-considered power sources, but for that, at a power of 20 kilowatts, its efficiency could already be greater than these sources, and, with increasing plant power, it would gradually rise.

For large manned artificial satellites, powerful power stations will obviously be necessary. For the movement of the electric space ships of the future, starting out from the interplanetary stations—attempts to project these space ships are already on the way—electric power plants ten times as powerful will be required.

■ Measuring Equipment and Instruments for Observation and Control

The scientific-measurement, navigation, and other instruments and units with which artificial satellites and supply rockets will be equipped must be adapted for operation both under the conditions of weightlessness and under the conditions of increased gravity.

All the equipment of the satellite must be capable of withstanding not only sharp fluctuations of temperature and pressure but also variations in the acceleration of the thrust of the rocket engine.

To transmit to the earth the readings of the measuring instrumentation installed on the artificial satellite, the method used is analogous to that developed for radiosondes as far back as 1930 (P. A. Molchanov, U.S.S.R.), which consists in the use of automatic radio-telegraphy.

The first and second Soviet artificial satellites were each equipped with two radio transmitters operating on frequencies of 20.005 and 40.002 megacycles (15-meter and 7.5-meter waves). The temperature of the first satellite and other data were transmitted to the earth by means of a certain variation in the duration of the signals and the pauses between them.

On the second Soviet satellite the instrumentation for investigating the solar radiation shown in Figure XX was used. In this instrumentation, the radiation pickups were three special photoelectron-multipliers, spaced 120° apart. Each photomultiplier is successively covered by several filters of thin metal and organic films and also of special optical materials, allowing the separation of various bands in the X-ray region of the solar spectrum and the hydrogen line in the far ultraviolet region. The electric signals emitted by the photomultiplier pointed at the sun were amplified by radio circuits and transmitted to the earth by means of a telemetering system.

As a result of the fact that the satellite was continuously changing its orientation relative to the sun, and also spent part of the time on the part of its orbit that was not illuminated by the sun, in order to save electric power, the instrumentation circuits were turned on only when the sun fell in the field of view of one of the three light pickups. Photoresistances, illuminated by the sun at the same time as the photomultipliers, and systems of automatic devices were used to turn on these circuits.

To study the cosmic rays, the instrumentation shown in Figure XXI was used on the second Soviet artificial satellite.

The particles composing the cosmic radiation are recorded in this apparatus by the aid of charged-particle counters. When an electrically charged particle passes through a counter, there is a scintillation, which sends an impulse to a radio circuit using semiconductor triodes, designed to count the number of cosmic-ray particles and emit a signal when a predetermined number of particles has been counted. After the transmission by radio of a signal indicating that a predetermined number of particles has been counted, the recording of cosmic-ray particles is resumed, and after the same number of particles has been counted, a new signal is emitted. On dividing the number of particles recorded by the counting time, the number of particles passing through the counter per second, or the intensity of the cosmic rays, can be found.

Two identical instruments for recording charged particles were installed on the satellite. The axes of the counters of the instruments were mutually perpendicular.

The body of the final stage of the rocket was equipped with radiotelemetric instrumentation and with sources of electric power feeding the scientific and measurement instrumentation. The temperature on the outside surface and the inside of the cabin housing the animal, as well as the temperature of individual instrument and structural elements, were determined by the aid of temperature pickups installed on them. The radiotelemetric equipment ensured the transmission to the ground of all measurements made on the satellite. This equipment was turned on periodically, according to a special program, to transmit the data of the measurements.

For the purpose of studying a number of medico-biological questions, instrumentation for recording the pulse and respiration rates and the arterial blood pressure, and for making electrocardiograms, as well as sensitive elements for measuring a number of parameters characterizing the conditions in the cabin (temperature, pressure) were placed in the pressurized animal cabin on the second satellite.

To measure the electrostatic fields in the upper layers of the atmosphere crossed by the artificial satellite, I. M. Imyanitov (U.S.S.R.) proposed building an apparatus whose operating principle is as follows:

A measuring plate (the receiving electrode) is placed in the electrostatic field to be examined, but is alternately shielded from this field by means of a special rotating slotted electrode. The resulting variation of the field of the measuring plate leads to the appearance of an electric current whose intensity is proportional to the intensity of the electric field to be measured. It is expected that with relatively small over-all dimensions of the instrument (the area of the measuring plate is 10 square centimeters) an alternating current of 0.000001 microampere and a voltage of 0.1 microvolt will flow from the receiving electrode. This voltage is amplified by means of a vacuum-tube amplifier and is then measured. Thus from the voltage of the current one may judge the intensity of the electrostatic field and its variations along the satellite orbit.

K. I. Gringauz and M. Kh. Zelikman (U.S.S.R.) have proposed instrumentation for measuring the concentration of positive ions along the satellite's orbit, using mainly one or several traps for capturing such ions. The ion traps are spherical screens attached to the satellite's surface by the aid of shielding tubes. A fine rod passes along the axis of the tube and connects the inner apparatus in the satellite with the center of the spherical screen trap, which constitutes a small spherical collector. Both positive and negative ions enter the trap through the openings of the screen. The negative ions, however, are repulsed and thrown back beyond the limits of the trap by the electric field produced by imposing on the central collector a suitable voltage with respect to the outer sphere. It is in this way that the positive ions whose concentration is being measured are collected, and the results of the measurements are transmitted to the ground by means of the radiotelemetric system.

Let us now discuss briefly certain instruments which have been designed for the American artificial satellites that have not yet been launched.

To study the effect of the impact of micrometeorites on the skin of an artificial satellite, it is proposed to place on its surface a nichrome strip having a considerable electric resistance, one ten-thousandth of a millimeter in thickness and connected in an electric circuit.[7] As the strip is "eroded" by micrometeorites, its electric resistance increases, which fact is reflected in the character of the radio signals received at the ground observation station.

An instrument signaling the drop in air pressure when the skin of the satellite is punctured by a meteoric body, together with its potentiometer, weighs only 43 grams. It is also proposed to place an acoustic instrument on the satellite to register the impact of micrometeorites. This instrument is provided with a click amplifier and a recording device.

The miniature thermistors intended for installation on artificial satellites constitute a tiny "grain of sand" to which a pair of extremely

[7] The strip is manufactured by condensation of nichrome vapor on a glass surface. Nichrome is an alloy of nickel, chromium, and iron, with small additions of silicon, aluminum, and other elements.

■ FIG. XX.—Instrumentation for Investigating the Solar Radiation, Installed on the Second Soviet Artificial Satellite of the Earth.

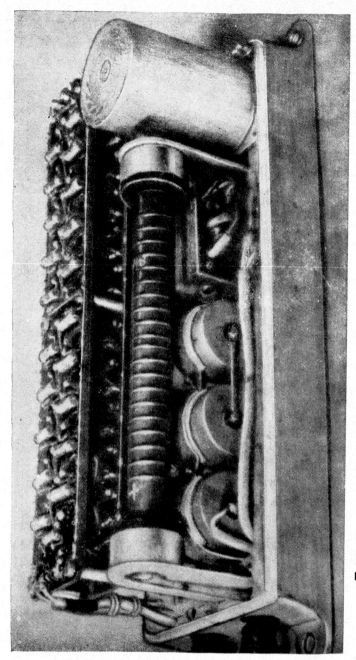

FIG. XXI.—Instrumentation for Studying the Cosmic Rays, Installed on the Second Soviet Artificial Satellite.

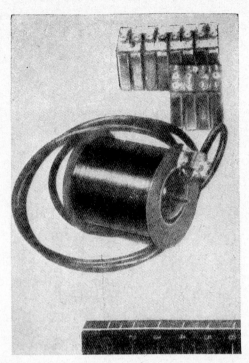

■ FIG. XXII.—Apparatus for Measuring the Magnetic Field of the Earth on the Artificial Satellite: Packard Magnetometer *(United States)*. The ruler shown is graduated in inches.

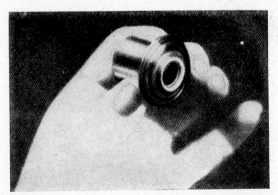

■ FIG. XXIII.—Ionization Chamber for Measuring the Intensity of the Ultraviolet Radiation of the Sun *(United States)*.

■ FIG. XXIV.—Instrumentation for Recording the Intensity of the Ultraviolet Radiation of the Sun along the Path Traveled by the Artificial Satellite *(United States).*

fine "whiskers" are soldered. These thermistors are able to measure temperatures from −90 to +150° C. By their aid it is possible to check whether the temperature inside the satellite, when heated by the solar rays, rises (in spite of the thermal insulation) above the limits of normal semiconductor operation (4-5° C.).

To study the temperature balance of the earth, the American satellites will be provided with four bolometers, three of them spherical. One will be white but will absorb infrared rays; the second will be absolutely black, i.e., it will absorb the invisible rays as well; and the third, developed by Tibor, will reflect infrared rays but will absorb the visible radiation, thus remaining black for the human eye. The fourth bolometer will have a protective screen, stopping all radiations, on one side. The instant of the satellite's entrance into the earth's shadow and of its departure from the shadow will be automatically recorded.

The earth's magnetic field will be measured by Packard proton-precessional magnetometers, which have already been used in high-altitude rockets (Fig. XXII). A Geiger counter in the form of a tube 14 centimeters long has been designed for investigation of the cosmic rays.

The intensity of the Lyman alpha line, of wavelength 1216 Å, in the ultraviolet part of the spectrum is of interest for studies by astrophysicists of the ionizing power of the solar rays. How is this line identified? For artificial satellites, tiny ionization chambers (Fig. XXIII) have been built, filled with nitrogen oxide; this gas is ionized by waves of wavelengths not over 1340 Å (Angstroms). The solar rays are allowed to penetrate into the chamber only through a window made of lithium fluoride, which absorbs waves shorter than 1100Å.

In the 1100-1340 Å range of the ultraviolet part of the solar spectrum, waves of about 1216 Å predominate. An ionization chamber with measuring instrumentation for determining the intensity of the ultraviolet radiation is provided with an amplifier and a memory device. Figure XXIV shows the instrumentation for recording the intensity of the ultraviolet solar radiation along the paths traveled by the artificial satellite. A disk with photocells serves to record the instant of entrance of the satellite into the earth's shadow and of its emergence into sunlight.

We note that the optical instruments designed for various observations may fail rapidly due to clouding of the transparent parts, as a result of the frequent impact of extremely minute micrometeorites. For this reason it is preferable for the observations, if possible, to use instruments of the type (for example) used in radioastronomy. In general, the radio facilities will be of great importance in the equipment of an artificial satellite.

The "Minitrack" telemetric radio transmitter, which is scheduled for installation on a future American artificial satellite, has the outward appearance of a cylinder 76 millimeters in diameter, 127 millimeters high, and weighing 370 grams (Fig. XXV). The four antennas of the satellite are mutually arranged at a 90° angle. The length of each antenna is about 1 meter. Current is supplied by a battery of seven 1.2-volt mercury cells; their output is 20 milliwatts; their life is 350 hours (two weeks); the wavelength is 3.05 meters. The radius of action of the instrument is slightly more than 6400 kilometers. To obtain the necessary measurements, highly improved instrumentation, of the type already used on high-altitude rockets, must mainly be employed.

During ten launchings of the V-2 high-altitude rockets, records of the various parameters could be received on 28-60 channels, with an accuracy of ± 2 per cent. A transmitter emitting a wave of 30 centimeters length was used. When the power was trippled, the instrument error decreased to ± 1 per cent (the weight of the radio apparatus was 61 kilograms). The Aerobee high-altitude rocket was equipped with a 19-kilogram 15-channel transmitter operating on a wavelength of 133 centimeters.

The instrumentation for an artificial satellite must naturally be exceptionally light in weight. In this direction, much has been accomplished during the last decade. For instance, measuring and radio transmission equipment weighing only 12 kilograms has been created to replace the heavy instrumentation of the V-2 (907 kilograms). All instrument readings can now be recorded on magnetic tapes by the aid of a miniature apparatus, although only a little while ago very heavy apparatus would have been required for this purpose; at that time, it was even considered that, for the initial period, one would have to be content merely with a record of a few parameters, recorded from time to time. Figure XXVI shows the external appearance of this apparatus.

It will apparently be possible, for use in airless space, to build all radio equipment demanding a high vacuum without any outer casing at all. It is not impossible that both astronomical and other optical instruments will rapidly fail because of erosion of the glass surfaces. This is an argument in favor of using radio methods. It is likewise not excluded that the primary cosmic rays may put the semiconductors out of commission. It is planned to make wide use of semiconductors in space-flight engineering. These rays may also cause a new kind of radio interference. The sharp difference between the equilibrium temperatures on the side of the satellite illuminated by the sun and the shadow side may likewise damage the radio equipment. The principle of the thermos flask would therefore have to be used for each thermal insulation.

The orbital velocity of a low-flying satellite many times exceeds the velocity of the kinetic motion of the air molecules. The artificial satellite will therefore leave behind it, during the entire time of its motion, a high vacuum, a "rear cone of molecular shadow." Into this cone, only electrons and very rare molecules of air, at velocities considerably higher than those of the other molecules, will be able to penetrate. Therefore, if the intake orifice of the analyzer (of the mass spectrometer) for investigating the ionic composition of the ionized layers of the atmosphere through which the satellite is moving is directed backward, then the instrument might fail to operate at all (V. G. Istomin, U.S.S.R., and others). Ways of keeping the axis of the satellite in the direciton of its motion must therefore be found.

For a number of other investigations, such as the measurement of the earth's albedo or the intensity of the cosmic rays, and also for possible utilization of the directional antenna installed on the satellite for purposes of radio communication and television, it is necessary that the axis of rotation of the satellite is constantly directed toward the center of the earth. On the artificial satellite, where the earth's gravitation cannot be felt, there is no possibility of determining the position of the center of the earth by the aid of a plumb line. Stuhlinger has proposed utilizing for this purpose the earth's shielding effect against the cosmic rays.

An automatic device placed on the artificial satellite contains a counter for charged particles, the cosmic rays. Let us isolate, in space, a cone with its vertex at the satellite and its generatrices touching the earth's surface. If the charged-particle counter is placed outside of

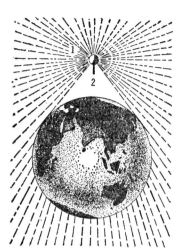

■ FIG. 42.—For Automatic Determination of the Vertical on an Artificial Satellite, the Earth's Shielding Action Against Cosmic Rays May Be Utilized. Such rays impinge on the charged-particle counter from the cosmic space in position 1, but cannot enter the counter when its channel is in position 2.

this cone (position 1 in Fig. 42), it will record a certain number of charged particles; but if it is placed inside the cone (position 2 in Fig. 42), then it will not record particles at all, since its channel, in this position, is shielded from the cosmic rays by the earth. If the counter, rotating in a plane passing through the center of the earth, is located on a generatrix of the cone, then, if it undergoes the slightest shift, the number of particles recorded will either sharply increase or will drop to zero. In this way, the two generatrices lying in this plane will be found easily. It is the bisectrix of the angle between these generatrices (the axis of the cone) that will yield the desired direction of the local vertical. When the axis of the satellite deviates from the vertical, the system of charged-particle counters will actuate rotors by means of servomotors, forcing the satellite to turn and occupy the required position.

If it were possible to prevent the axis of the satellite from deviating more than 10° from the center of the earth, then a directional antenna with a beam spread of 30° could be used on the satellite. In this case, it would need only a fifteenth as much energy for the radio transmission as when a nondirectional antenna is used.

On artificial satellites not entirely covered by artificial gravity it may be necessary to establish gravity in certain "corners" for making some experiments. For instance, during the free flight of an artificial satellite, the force of gravtiy will not manifest itself in the ionization chambers used for measuring the ionizing radiation, and this fact will interfere with formation of the fog zone on passage of a charged particle. In this case, the force of gravity can be replaced by the centrifugal force produced by rotating the ionization chamber about its longitudinal axis. This method is already in use in modern altitude rockets. On the other hand, manned space rockets must also be equipped with a G-force limiter to protect the travelers from excessive acceleration of gravity. Regardless of this, rockets will also have to be equipped with acoustic or light signals for the G-force.

To measure the air pressure in the cabins of a rocket or satellite, an aneroid will have to be used, since the ordinary mercury barometer will be unsuitable for this purpose. The operating principle of the aneroid is based on the elastic deformation of a solid, and this property remains unchanged under increase or disappearance of the acceleration to which the instrument is subjected. A mercury barometer, however, is based on balancing the pressure of the air by the weight of the corresponding column of mercury. While the pressure of the air in the rocket chamber will remain practically unchanged during the operating period of the engine and during the time of flight with engines off, the weight of the mercury column will substantially depend on the value of the thrust of the rocket engine.

For instance, if after the engine is cut in the force of gravity on the rocket is increased by a factor of 4, then the air pressure in the rocket cabin will be balanced by a mercury column only one-fourth of the normal height, which may lead to an error by the observer. In flight with engine off, however (on a rocket or artificial satellite), the mass of mercury will lose its weight entirely; therefore, the mercury in the narrow elbow of the barometer will rise to the very top, and the barometer will cease to detect variations in pressure.

In the case of a slight leak of air from the rooms of the artificial satellite, the air pressure may fall very slowly and remain undetected by an ordinary aneroid. Special leak detectors will therefore be used for checking the cabin pressurization. We note that the constant pressure of the microatmosphere will not be proof of the absence of a leak, since fresh air will at the same time flow into the cabin. Nevertheless, automatic devices must warn the astronauts of any pressure drop in the microatmosphere by means of light or sound signals.

A special apparatus will continuously analyze the microatmosphere on board an artificial satellite, indicating the percentage composition of the air and signaling danger (in case, for instance, of a high concentration of carbon dioxide).

Owing to loss of weight during flight with engine off, a pendulum clock with a weight will be unable to run. Here it will be insufficient to replace the weight by a spring. When the rocket engine develops high acceleration during take-off, the oscillations of the pendulum will take place more often, and the clock will be fast; but after the engine has been cut out, the pendulum will stop swinging altogether, and the clock will stop. Such a clock will not operate, either, on an artificial satellite moving with engine off. It will therefore be necessary to replace the pendulum by a rotor (balance wheel), the operation of whose spring will be independent of the conditions of motion of the rocket or satellite (such a balance wheel is used today in wrist watches and pocket watches).

How will mass be measured on an artificial satellite? Let a kilogram weight be suspended from a spring balance. Up to the moment of take-off of the rocket, the pointer of the balance will point to 1. At the moment the engine is cut in, the pointer will deflect sharply and will indicate as many kilograms as the G-force on the rocket is greater than normal gravity on the surface of the earth. When the acceleration stops, however, the pointer will jump to "zero." Consequently, an ordinary spring balance will not allow the measurement of mass on an artificial satellite or on a supply rocket. Lever scales, likewise, will not operate under the condition of weightlessness. It will be necessary to use a centrifugal balance, in which the force compressing the spring will be generated by rotation and will not depend on the character of motion of the flying vehicle.

A special device of the spring-balance type will prove highly useful on board a rocket in take-off, but for an entirely different purpose. During the period of operation of the engine, the acceleration of its thrust will be determined by means of an accelerograph. This recording instrument indicates the velocity increment of the rocket in every second, but without taking account of the influence of the earth's gravitational field. In other words, it will indicate the acceleration that the rocket would have in free space (the acceleration of reactive thrust). From the readings of the accelerograph, the acceleration of the rocket during take-off, relative to the earth can be calculated (an instrument that would directly indicate this quantity has not yet been invented). The action of the accelerograph is ordinarily based on the principle of operation of the spring balance, as follows: If a certain mass is freely suspended from a spring attached to the rocket, then the distance by which the spring is depressed will be proportional to the acceleration being measured. The accelerograph has a scale in m/sec^{-1}. The instrument could also be calibrated so as to show the factor by which the weight of a body on the rocket during the time of engine operation is greater or smaller than its normal weight on earth.

Miniature accelerographs are already in production. They weigh about 85 grams and measure G-forces from 10 to 40 times as great as normal gravity; they operate perfectly at temperatures from − 50 to +100° C. and withstand up to 2000 vibrations a second (Humphrey Company, United States).

We will finally describe the equipment necessary for giving the artificial satellite a rotation about its axis. Such a rotation may be necessary in many cases. During the time of motion of the satellite, it may, for instance, become necessary to cut in the engine in order to correct an error in direction occurring during takeoff, to compensate deviations from the planned course, to change to a different orbit, etc. In this case, as a rule, the artificial satellite will first have to be turned, so as to give the engine a certain orientation. It may also happen that the satellite must be turned to make some observation or to change the intensity of absorption of the solar rays by the satellite skin for the purpose of regulating its temperature, etc. Finally, it may be necessary to change the orientation of the flying vehicle in order to point the directional antennas toward a certain ground station. How will it be possible to make such a turn?

Several auxiliary jets might be placed along the circumference of the artificial satellite. Their action at the necessary moment would give the satellite a rotary motion. After operation of the jet ceases, the satellite would continue to rotate by inertia. For this reason, if it becomes necessary to change the position of the space vehicle in some definite way so that it will subsequently maintain this new position, then at a precalculated instant retardation must be started with the object of stopping the rotation of the satellite. Naturally enough, this type of maneuver will demand most careful execution and will involve consumption of fuel. There also exists a different, simpler, and more economical method of changing the orientation of a space ship or artificial satellite, which requires no consumption of fuel at all and which is based on the law of conservation of moment of momentum. If an astronaut begins to move inside an artificial satellite in a circle along the walls, in a certain direction, then the satellite will rotate in the opposite direction. In this way, the vehicle may be put into rotation about any desired axis. But since the mass of a person is considerably less than the mass of the satellite, a person would have to make the round of the cabin many times to produce even a minor turn of the satellite. It will therefore be far simpler to put the space vehicle into slow rotation in the desired direction by the rapid rotation of a small disk in the opposite direction. As soon as this rotation stops, the rotation of the satellite itself will also stop.

To turn the artificial satellite about any desired axis, three disks (rotors) with mutually perpendicular axes may also be used, giving these disks different angular velocities of rotation. Instead of three disks, one disk whose axis can rotate in any plane may be used. In this case, it will be necessary to match the axis of the disk with the axis about which the ship is to be turned, and then to begin rotating the disk in a direction opposite to the desired turn of the space vehicle until it assumes the desired position.

To make the turn of an artificial satellite more rapid, the rotors used for this purpose would need, at minimum weight, the maximum possible moment of inertia and the maximum rotational speed.

Attention should be paid to the fact that, during the time of rotation of the space vehicle by this method, no gyroscopic effect will be felt, since the rotation of the vehicle in one direction will be, as it were, "balanced" by the rapid rotation of the flywheel in the opposite direction (the total moment of momentum of the system will remain zero).

We note, finally, that, according to some authors, a number of functions of automatic instruments could be handled more economically, from the point of view of weight economy, by a human subject on the artificial satellite (Green, Canada).

8

Observation of Artificial Satellites and Their Communication with the Ground

■
■
■

■ Conditions of Visibility of a Satellite and Its Light Signals

Vision is the most delicate of all our senses. At the same time, the sensitivity of the eye differs greatly in different persons and varies according to the following conditions: degree of protection from other light sources, time required by the dark adaptation of the eye, etc.

As shown by experiments, persons with good vision who have adapted themselves to the darkness of night for 1-1.5 hours, i.e., with a suitable dilation of the pupil, can see stars of brightness down to the eighth magnitude. The normal human eye, however, can detect a star only of brightness down to the sixth magnitude. A light source of one metric (standard) candle power can be seen from a distance of 11 kilometers as a sixth-magnitude star (Bouisson, France; Drude, Germany, etc.). But in this case the mass of the layers of air between the eye and the point of light will be greater than that of the layers of air between an observer on the earth and an artificial satellite (cf. Chapter 1.

On the other hand, with the sun in the zenith, the illumination of the earth's surface, taking account of the absorption of the rays by the atmosphere, amounts to 0.82 international candle per square centimeter (Russell, United States). A sunbeam 1.22 square centimeters in cross section will have the light power of one candle.

The reflecting power of aluminum or duralumin is at least 0.8. Consequently, a polished aluminum sphere at "full moon" (i.e., when the half of the moon illuminated by the sun is fully visible) can be detected from this distance of 11 kilometers as a sixth-magnitude star, if its cross section is 1.22 : 0.8 = 1.52 square centimeters, and its diameter is 1.39 centimeters.

The farther away a sphere is, the greater must be its diameter if its brightness is not to diminish (direct proportionality). Thus, for visibility at a distance of 1000 kilometers, the diameter of our aluminum sphere must be 1000 : 11 = 90.9 times as great, i.e., it must be 1.27 meters.

Depending on the conditions of observation, an artificial satellite of spherical shape can be visible from the earth in different phases, while its better or poorer visibility depends, in turn, on its phase at the moment of observation. If, for example, at sunset a satellite is on the horizon on the side opposite the sun, it will appear to the eye of the observer like the full moon. The quantity of sunlight reflected by it will then be maximum, and its visibility, other conditions being equal, will be optimum.

At zenith, however, during sunset, it will be visible in the phase of first quarter. The quantity of reflected rays will then be only half, and its visibility will decrease. For the satellite to reflect the same quantity of radiant energy toward the observer as the above-mentioned sphere, its diameter would have to be 1.79 meters. (The area of a semicircle 1.79 meters in diameter equals the area of a circle 1.27 meters in diameter.) For an artificial satellite to be visible as a first-magnitude star, its diameter would have to be ten times as great.

According to data by Ordway, the visibility of a half-meter highly polished sphere at zenith is as follows:

Altitude of flight, in kilometers	322	644	965	1287	1609	1931	2413
Stellar magnitude	5.7	7.2	8.1	8.7	9.2	9.6	10.1

The visibility of an artificial satellite depends not only on its size, reflectivity, distance, etc., but also on its light contrast against the background of the sky. Such a "star" could therefore be observed only at dawn and dusk when the satellite is bathed in the sun's rays, while it is dark on the surface of the earth, where the observations are being made. The Soviet artificial satellite could be observed at this time by the naked eye. The water vapor and dust suspended in the atmosphere considerably impairs the visibility of the satellite. The principal difficulty, however, is that the time interval during which the satellite is visible is very short. We note that the length of the twilight may exceed the period of revolution of a satellite relative to the observer; it is therefore not excluded that in certain cases it will be possible to see the satellite twice during a single twilight; after observing the setting of the satellite, its rise might still be visible (cf. below).

To facilitate observation of an artificial satellite, its surface might be coated with a luminescent substance. The same purpose might be served by illuminating the satellite either from inside or by the aid of searchlights located on the ground. It is believed that to detect the artificial satellite under good atmospheric conditions a zenith searchlight station equipped with four giant searchlights with a total light power of about 4 billion candles would be sufficient.

It should be mentioned that in the case of failure of the radio apparatus on the artificial satellite, visual observations would remain the only means for determining its path, since the theoretical determination of the position of a satellite by Kepler's laws might prove inaccurate in view of the distorting effect of the resistance of the air on the motion of the satellite.

One form of communication between the artificial satellite and the earth is light signaling.

It is easy to calculate that a light source of about 650 candlepower on the artificial satellite will be sufficient to make it visible to the naked eye from an area of 1,000,000 square kilometers on the earth's surface, provided a suitable reflector were used. A one-meter telescope (for instance, a Siemens observatory telescope) could detect a light signal of only 300 candle-power.

To transmit light messages, a code consisting of a combination of dots and dashes, for instance the Morse telegraph code, could be used.

Light telegraphy could be combined with signaling by the use of colored lights. A light of a predetermined color on the artificial satellite might, for example, mean a distress signal. Here, it would have to be taken into consideration that one and the same quantity of luminous energy perceived by the eye will induce entirely different sensations, depending on the color of the rays. The degree of absorption of light by the air also depends on the color of the rays: For violet rays, the coefficient of transparency of the atmosphere amounts to 0.6; it gradually rises as the color passes through blue, green, yellow, and, finally, red (for red light, this coefficient exceeds 0.9)[1]. Moreover, the (glass) filters of searchlights absorb 80-90 per cent of the light flux incident on them. It would ultimately be found, on the whole, that for light signaling from an artificial satellite, only green, yellow, and orange light would be suitable. The use of gas-filled lamps (mercury, sodium, neon, etc.) opens great prospects.

In some cases, mirrors reflecting the sun's rays might also be used for light signaling.[2]

■ Influence of Altitude and Angle of Inclination of the Orbit on the Visibility of a Satellite

In view of the great flight altitude of an artificial satellite, its motion can be tracked from a considerable part of the earth's surface, and, on the other hand, immense spaces of the globe will be visible from the satellite.

The higher the altitude of flight of a satellite, the greater will be the portion of the earth's surface from which it is visible (Fig. 43). For example, a satellite flying at an altitude of 20 kilometers will be visible from a territory 1500 kilometers in radius. At an altitude of flight of 1,000 kilometers, however, the radius of visibility will be doubled (cf. Table 34). Table 34 also shows the minimum linear dimensions of parts of the artificial satellite distinguishable from the earth with the naked eye, through 15 × field glasses and a 500 × telescope.

For an equatorial artificial satellite to be visible from Europe, its

---

[1] The coefficient of transparency of airless space is unity.

[2] For more details, cf. A. Shternfeld, *Introduction to Cosmonautics, op. cit.*, pp. 254-265.

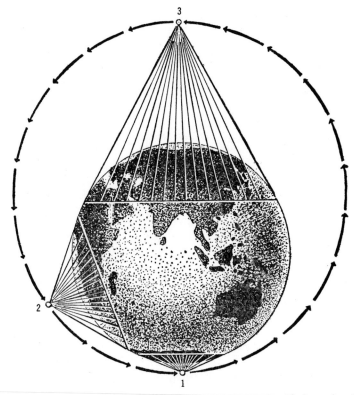

FIG. 43.—Increase in Visible Spherical Segment of the Earth with Increasing Orbital Altitude of the Artificial Satellite. The diameter of a spherical segment visible from an altitude of 500 kilometers is 4900 kilometers (1); and from an altitude of 2000 kilometers, 9000 kilometers (2); from an altitude of 7000 kilometers, it will be as large as 13,700 kilometers (3).

orbit must lie at a minimum altitude of 1948 kilometers. In this case, it will be visible from the southernmost tip of Europe (Cape Tarif on the Pyrennean Peninsula, at the Strait of Gibraltar). For the satellite to be visible from Paris (although only on the horizon), this ceiling would have to be raised to 3312 kilometers, and to be visible by the inhabitants of Moscow, to 4955 kilometers. Since London, Brussels, The Hague, Prague, Berlin, and Warsaw are located north of Paris and south of Moscow, equatorial artificial satellites would be visible from these cities on the horizon line only if their orbits were at altitudes of 3300 to 4950 kilometers.

Equatorial artificial satellites could not be observed from the poles of the earth. But if a tower 638 meters high (0.0001 earth radius)

■ TABLE 34

Conditions of Observation of an Artificial Satellite from the Earth's Surface (and also of the Earth's Surface from the Satellite)

Altitude of Flight of Artificial Satellite, in Kilometers	Diameter* of Area from which Artificial Satellite Is Visible (and which Is Visible from the Satellite), in Kilometers	Minimum Linear Dimensions in Meters, Distinguishable on Observation with:		
		Naked Eye	Fieldglass with 15 × Magnification	Telescope with 500 × Magnification
0	0	—	—	—
200	3,154	58.2	3.88	0.116
300	3,838	87.3	5.82	0.175
400	4,404	116.4	7.76	0.233
500	4,894	145.5	9.70	0.291
1,000	6,719	291.0	19.4	0.582
2,000	8,999	582.0	38.8	1.164
3,000	10,497	873.0	58.2	1.746
4,000	11,595	1164	77.6	2.328
5,000	12,447	1455	97.0	2.910
6,000	13,132	1745	116.4	3.490
6,378	13,358	1855	123.7	3.710
7,000	13,698	2036	135.7	4.072

* More precisely, the length, measured along a great circle, of the arc of the spherical segment from which the satellite is visible.

could be constructed at a pole, then an equatorial satellite moving at an altitude of about 70 earth radii, i.e., beyond the orbit of the moon, could be observed from the top of that tower. If the altitude of the point of observation were made ten times as high, an equatorial satellite flying lower than a third of this altitude could already be seen. From a satellite overflying the pole at an altitude of three earth radii, an equatorial satellite flying very low, at an altitude 210 kilometers, could be observed.

The mutual overlap of the zones of the earth's surface, visible from an artificial satellite on two consecutive crossings of the equator, would depend on the angle of inclination of the satellite's orbit to the plane of the equator. The smaller this inclination, the greater would be the overlap near the equator and the smaller in the high latitudes. Consequently, the smaller the inclination of the satellite orbit to the equator, the more often will it be visible from the equatorial zone, and the less often in places to the north or south of that zone. In this way, one of the advantages of a satellite moving in a plane making a small angle with the plane of the equator lies in the fact that, on consecutive revolutions of the satellite, the overlap of already observed localities is considerably greater than in the case where this angle is large.

■ Duration of Visibility of a Satellite

The period during which an artificial satellite can be observed from any point of the earth's surface will be longer, the higher the orbital altitude of the satellite. During this interval of time, light communication or ultrashort radiowave communication can be established with a satellite (the question of radio communication between a satellite and the earth will be discussed in more detail later in the text).

A satellite revolving at an altitude of about 30 kilometers and making a complete revolution around the earth in 1.5 hours could be linked with any observation point on earth for only 8 minutes. The "conversation time" is lengthened to 17.5 minutes for an artificial satellite flying at an altitude of 1000 kilometers with a period of revolution of 1 hour 45 minutes (Table 35).

■ TABLE 35

Duration of Light Communication and Radio Communication on Ultrashort Waves with Circular Satellites, and Duration of Their Visibiity

Altitude of Artificial Satellite, in Kilometers	Duration of Communication			The Same Duration in Per Cent of Period of Revolution	Period During which Communication is Impossible		
	Hrs.	Min.	Sec.		Hrs.	Min.	Sec.
0	0	0	0	0	1	24	26
200	0	6	57	7.86	1	21	28
300	0	8	40	9.58	1	21	27
400	0	10	10	10.99	1	22	19
500	0	11	33	12.22	1	22	59
1,000	0	17	37	16.77	1	27	25
2,000	0	28	33	22.45	1	38	36
3,000	0	39	25	26.19	1	51	6
4,000	0	50	42	28.92	2	4	35
5,000	1	02	30	31.06	2	18	42
6,000	1	14	49	32.77	2	33	29
6,378	1	19	35	33.33	2	39	12
7,000	1	27	40	34.17	2	48	51

■ Influence of Refraction on the Visibility of a Satellite

The phenomenon of refraction, i.e., the bending of light rays in the earth's atmosphere, has a certain influence on the duration of visibility of an artificial satellite. It is well known that the heavenly bodies, due to this phenomenon, appear to be higher than their actual position in the sky. The observer therefore sees the rise of a heavenly body earlier, and its setting later, than would be the case if there were no atmosphere. In this way, the total duration of visibility of an artificial satellite is increased as a consequence of refraction. As shown below, in the observation of artificial satellites the refraction should play a considerably greater role than in the observation of "ordinary" heavenly bodies.

Let us first consider the influence of refraction on the observation of a satellite whose orbit passes above the poles if the observer himself is at one of the poles. In this case, of course, the rotation of the earth will have no effect. A mathematical calculation shows that the duration of the visibility of a satellite as a result of refraction would be increased by at least 17 seconds. This increase would be greater, the greater the altitude at which the satellite is moving. At an altitude equal to half the earth's radius, it will be 0.5 minutes; at an altitude of 1.5 earth radii, it will be 1 minute; at a distance of 5-6 earth radii from the earth's surface, 4-5 minutes; and at the distance of the moon, over 2 hours. This time increases theoretically and rises to infinity with increasing distance of the satellite (Table 36).

Let us now define the influence of refraction on the period of visibility of an equatorial artificial satellite if the observer is on the equator. In this case, the influence of the earth's rotation must be taken into account. It might seem at first glance that this influence is slight. This, however, is not actually the case.

Let us assume at first that the artificial satellite is revolving around the earth in a direction opposite to that of the earth's rotation. The influence of refraction in this case will be less sensible than in the case of a polar satellite. Thus, at an altitude of flight equal to 5-6 earth radii, the lengthening of the period of visibility of the satellite amounts to only a little more than 2 minutes, while at the distance of the moon it is only a thirtieth of its value in the case of a polar satellite amounting to 4 minutes 32 seconds. With a further increase in satellite dis-

■ **TABLE 36**

Increase in the Period of Visibility of a Polar Artificial Satellite as a Result of the Phenomenon of Refraction

Radius of Orbit, in Equatorial Earth Radii	Increase in Duration of Visibility		
	Hrs.	Min.	Sec.
1.1			19
2			47
3		1	26
5		3	6
10		8	45
20		24	45
30		45	
40	1	10	
50	1	38	
100	4	37	

tance, the influence of refraction slowly increases, but the lengthening of the period of visibility of the satellite can never exceed 4 minutes 42 seconds (which is the theoretical case, at infinity).

We get an entirely different picture when the direction of motion of a satellite is the same as the direction of rotation of the earth. In that case, at all altitudes of flight of the satellite, the influence of refraction will be greater than in the two cases just discussed. Thus, at an altitude of 1.5 earth radii, the increase in the period of visibility will be about 1.5 minutes. The rising of a satellite revolving at a distance of 41,300 kilometers from the center of the earth could be observed 1 hour 12 minutes earlier than if there were no atmosphere, so that the total period of visibility will be increased by 2 hours 24 minutes owing to refraction. If the altitude of flight is still further increased by 800 kilometers, then the effect of refraction would lengthen the period of visibility to 1 day 4 hours and 44 minutes. In addition, this increment would subsequently increase very rapidly, tending toward infinity (for a stationary artificial satellite).[3]

We have seen (cf. above) that satellites with orbits located beyond the stationary orbit would appear to an observer to be moving in a direction opposite their true motion. For such satellites, with in-

[3] As a result of refraction, a stationary satellite would be constantly visible at certain points where, in the absence of atmosphere, it would never appear at all in the sky.

creasing radius of orbit, the influence of refraction would have an ever smaller effect. While at an altitude of flight equal to 6 earth radii, the lengthening of the period of visibility of a satellite due to refraction would still be about an hour, it would be only 10 minutes for an altitude of 9 earth radii. The influence of refraction from then on would continue to decrease, so that for a satellite at infinity (the theoretical case corresponding to the influence of refraction on the period of visibility of the fixed stars) the increase in the period of visibility would amount to 4 minutes 42 seconds (Table 37).

■ **TABLE 37**

Increase in Period of Visibility of an Equatorial Satellite Due to the Phenomenon of Refraction

Radius of Satellite Orbit, in Equatorial Earth Radii	Increase in Period of Visibility of Satellite, in the Case of Direct Motion		Increase in Periods of Visibility of Satellite, in Case of Retrograde Motion	
	Min.	Sec.	Min.	Sec.
1.1	—	20	—	18
2	—	56	—	40
3	2	4	1	6
5	9	2	1	52
6	29	54	2	11
6.61*	Infinity		2	21
7	57	46	2	27
8	18	58	2	41
10	10	11	3	4
20	5	49	3	57
30	5	15	4	16
40	5	3	4	25
50	4	57	4	29
100	4	47	4	38

* Case of the stationary satellite.

We note that, for an observer not on the equator, the influence of refraction on the period of visibility of an equatorial satellite would be still more sensitive, and would be greater the greater the distance of the observer from the equator.

Refraction depends also on the atmospheric pressure and the temperature of the air. The period of visibility of a satellite increases with pressure and with decreasing temperature of the air. The results given above were obtained for an atmospheric pressure of 760 millimeters Hg and an air temperature of 10° C.

■ Training for Visual Observations

For observation of artificial satellites, amateur observers can build telescopes at home with a magnification of 5-6 times and a field of vision of 11-12°. For this purpose a lens of about 50 millimeters in diameter, with a focal length of 180 millimeters, must be used. An aluminum tube of 220 millimeters length can be used for mounting the lenses and eyepiece. If a cross-hair (3 millimeters in diameter) is fixed on the telescope eyepiece on its inner side, the determination of the moment of transit of the satellite will be greatly facilitated. Figure XXVII shows the Soviet standard telescope for artificial satellite observation.

For convenience of the observer, a mirror rotating about its axis in such a way that any desired region of the sky can be observed is placed a short distance in front of the telescope. If the satellite has been detected by the aid of the telescope, the telescope is not shifted to follow the motion of the satellite, but the exact time of appearance of the satellite is noted and then, from memory and orienting himself by the nearest stars, the observer will sketch the path taken by the satellite in the sky. Since the mounting of the optical instruments is fixed, the observer can track the satellite only for some fraction of a minute.

In group observations partly overlapping regions of the sky are observed.

The observation station should be in a location where the sky is particularly open from the northern and southern sides. (One may, for example, set up observation platforms on the roofs of high buildings.) It is also desirable to erect the observation stations in localities where clouds are rare, and the sky is completely transparent. Artificial light sources near the observation platform may disturb the observations of the satellite near the horizon.

Training for visual observation of artificial satellites can be conducted in the following way: An aircraft is sent up to an altitude from which the noise of its engines no longer reaches the surface of the earth. It then picks up a speed such that its angular velocity of displacement relative to the observer will be close to the angular velocity of displacement of the artificial satellite. A signal lamp is installed on the aircraft. The brightness of this signal lamp, for the ground observer, is expressed by the same stellar magnitude as the brightness of the satellite. Training in observation of such a lamp yields favorable results.

It might seem that the largest telescopes in the world could be successfully used for observations of artificial satellites. But this is not the case. The astrograph used in compiling an international photographic atlas of the sky has a relatively long focal length (343 centimeters); in it the image of the satellite would be displaced at a rate of 10 centimeters per second, which would make observation impossible. However, in telescopes on which the size of stars, in fractions of a second of arc, can be measured, the image would move at a speed of tens of centimeters per second.

An astronomical observatory therefore needs telescopes with a short focal length (50-75 centimeters) for the observation of artificial satellites. In such telescopes, the rate of displacement of the satellite image can be reduced to 1 centimeter per second.

■ Photography

Photography will be widely used for observing an artificial satellite. The photographic method permits a determination of the position of an artificial satellite with an accuracy of 9-12 meters.

The determination of the distance of an artificial satellite from the center of the earth with an accuracy of 10 meters is particularly important for refinement of our knowledge of the size and figure of the earth, as well as for other measurements.

To determine the position of a satellite with an accuracy from one to five seconds of arc, the time must be recorded with an accuracy of 0.001 second. When the satellite passes through apogee, its brightness, other conditions being equal, is at a minimum, but for that its angular velocity at this moment will also be minimum, which to a certain extent facilitates photography. As many as 100 photographs a second can be taken by the aid of a rotating shutter. The time indicated by a quartz clock can be recorded on the tape with an accuracy of 0.0001 second. The photographs can be taken by the aid of an astrograph suspended in a triaxial system (gimbals) which permits the camera to be pointed at any desired region of the sky.

The sensitivity of the photographic plates used has greatly increased in recent years. By using various improvements, it will be possible to photograph a spherical satellite 38 centimeters in diameter (i.e., having linear dimensions two-thirds those of the first artificial satellite) from a distance of 1600 kilometers as a tenth-magnitude star (Whipple).

We note that photographs of the two Soviet artificial satellites and of the carrier rocket were made at the Pulkovo Observatory, at the observatories of the Astrophysical Institute, Academy of Sciences Kazakh S.S.R., of the Kharkhov State University, and at other astronomical institutions of the Soviet Union, as well as a number of foreign observatories: "Purple Mountain" (Chinese Peoples Republic), Edinburgh (Great Britain), Dansink (Eire), Potsdam (East Germany), etc. This allows refinement of the orbits of the first artificial heavenly bodies.

■ Calculation of a Satellite Orbit

For the observation of an artificial satellite, it is very important to know the coordinates of its motion. But it is sufficient to establish the coordinates of a satellite at some moment of time and to note, at that same moment, its velocity and direction, in order thereafter to calculate its position at any desired time and to predict the times and places of its future overflights. In particular, it will be possible to determine whether the satellite will appear again over a given place and, if so, at what instant of time. This, of course, involves the assumption that the direction and velocity of the satellite cannot be changed by means of a rocket engine.

It may happen that an artificial satellite, once detected, is afterward lost in the sky. Is it possible to relocate it if only its altitude at the moment of passage through perigee, when the motion proceeds in a horizontal direction, is known?

For this purpose, as will be easily understood, it will be sufficient to confine the search to the volume of the paraboloid of revolution with its vertex at the observed point of perigee (Fig. 44). For example, if it were established that an artificial satellite, which has been lost to

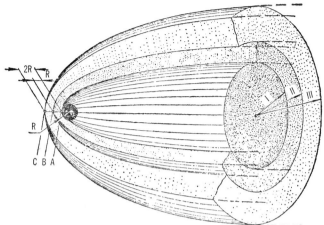

FIG. 44.—If It Is Established that an Artificial Satellite That Has Been Lost from View Has Moved through the Points, A, B, or C (at a Low Altitude or at an Altitude of One or Two Earth Radii) Parallel to the Earth's Surface, then the Search for It Can Be Restricted to the Paraboloids I, II, and III Shown on the Sketch.

view, had been moving at the points A, B, or C (at a low altitude, or at an altitude of one or two earth radii), parallel to the earth's surface, then the search for it might be limited to the paraboloids (I, II, III) shown on the sketch, within which the satellite would necessarily be located. If the orbital plane of the satellite were also known, then the satellite would have to be sought within the limits of the area bounded by the parabola on whose branch it would have gone off into space if the local parabolic velocity had been imparted to it at perigee.

In order completely to determine the orbit of an artificial satellite, it is also sufficient to find its altitude of flight at perigee, and then its altitude at the point of the orbit reached after traveling 90° of elliptical arc.[4] For example, let the altitude of an artificial satellite at perigee be 622 kilometers and, after it has described an arc of 90° on the celestial sphere, let its altitude be 1182 kilometers. Mathematical calculation will permit a determination of the apogee distance from these data (it will be 8218 kilometers from the center of the earth and 1840 kilometers above the equator) as well as other elements of the orbit (for example, the major semiaxis which is 6911 kilometers, the eccentricity which is 0.08, etc.). The sidereal time of revolution of such an orbit would be 1 hour 50 minutes.

[4] I.e., an arc subtending an angle of 90° at the center of the earth.

Table 38 gives the length of the major and minor axes of an elliptical satellite orbit, calculated from the known distance of the satellite from the center of the earth at perigee and after passage through a 90° arc in orbit. Knowing these values, the apogee distance of the satellite can easily be calculated. In Table 38 the perigee distance is taken as the unit of distance.

■ **TABLE 38**

Determination of Orbit of Artificial Satellite, on the Basis of Its Distance from the Center of the Earth at Perigee and After Passage of a 90° Arc

Distance from Center of Earth at Perigee	Distance from Center of Earth after Passage of a 90° Arc	Major Semiaxis of Orbit	Minor Semiaxis of Orbit	Distance from Center of Earth at Apogee
1	1.10	1.111	1.105	1.22
1	1.20	1.25	1.22	1.50
1	1.30	1.43	1.36	1.86
1	1.40	1.67	1.53	2.33
1	1.50	2.00	1.73	3.00
1	1.60	2.50	2.00	4.00
1	1.70	3.33	2.38	5.67
1	1.80	5.00	3.00	9.00
1	1.90	10.00	4.36	19.00

We note that if, after the satellite has passed a 90° arc, its distance from the center of the earth is twice as great as at perigee, this will mean that the body is moving in a parabolic orbit, i.e., that it is essentially no longer a satellite, since it would leave the sphere of the earth's gravitational attraction, never again to return to our planet. In practice, however, it might also be a satellite moving on a very elongated elliptical orbit, since, at a relatively great distance from the earth, the elliptic and parabolic paths almost coincide. For such a satellite, its distance from the center of the earth at any moment can quickly be determined from its direction alone, for example, from the angle formed by this direction and that of the solar rays. The results of such calculations, under the condition that the perigee of the satellite is located on the line earth-sun at a distance of four earth radii from its center, are given in Table 39.

It is also possible to determine the orbit of a satellite, without

■ **TABLE 39**

Determination of Distance Between the Earth and a Satellite with a Very Elongated Orbit, from the Angle Between the Direction of Its Motion and the Solar Rays

Angle Between Direction of Motion of Satellite and the Solar Rays	Distance from Center of the Earth, in Equatorial Earth Radii	Angle Between Direction of Motion of Satellite and the Solar Rays	Distance from Center of the Earth, in Equatorial Earth Radii
90°	4.00	40°	8.77
80°	4.71	30°	10.93
70°	5.46	20°	14.99
60°	6.31	10°	26.69
50°	7.36		

measuring its altitude, after it has traveled a 90° arc on its orbit; for this purpose, it is sufficient merely to note the length of time taken for this passage. If, for example, it took 23 minutes 17 seconds, and the altitude at perigee was a tenth of the equatorial radius, then, as shown by mathematical calculation, the sidereal period of revolution of such a satellite would be 2 hours 29 minutes 17 seconds, the eccentricity of its orbit would be 0.3, the apogee would be at altitude 6656 kilometers, etc.

If the satellite has eluded the eyes of the observers, it can be found again in a few days of "hunting" by observation stations, if the elements of its orbit are known even approximately.

■ **Radio Signaling**

Modern radio engineering is capable of ensuring radio communication between an artificial satellite and the earth, as well as between various satellites traveling in cosmic space.

The advantage of radio signaling over light signaling is that the former can take place at any desired time: even if the satellite is hidden behind a layer of clouds, or in daytime when rays of light would be lost in the ocean of direct and scattered sunlight. Light signaling may therefore be assumed to be inferior to radio signaling as a means of communication between the artificial satellite and the earth. In some cases, however, light signaling may prove to be more convenient than radio signaling, and in particular light signaling may be useful if the radio transmitter or receiver of the satellite fail.

What wavelength will be used for communication between an artificial satellite and the ground? It is well known that radio waves sent out from the earth are, to some degree, reflected or absorbed by the upper layers of the atmosphere. In particular, the ionosphere is an impenetrable screen for waves no longer than 50-100 meters. The radio waves reaching the ionosphere are reflected from it and returned to the earth's surface. The successive reflection of waves from the solid shell of the earth causes multiple repetition of this process, as a result of which radio waves can, as everyone knows, reach a station at the antipodes of the transmitting station. It is, however, precisely these properties of the ionosphere, which make radio communication possible between very distant points on the earth's surface, that will hinder radio communication with an artificial satellite. Even of the shorter waves, about 40 meters long, only a small portion can penetrate beyond the boundaries of the ionosphere. Moreover, the penetration of radio waves through the ionosphere varies sharply with the time of day and season.

For signaling from an artificial satellite flying at an altitude of several thousand kilometers above the earth's surface, nondirectional radio waves or waves somewhat shorter than ultrashort waves may also be used, as was done on the two first artificial satellites.

Nondirectional radio waves involve excessive consumption of electric power. With time, however, when suitable equipment will have been developed for transmission of radio signals through the atmosphere, the utilization of beams of strictly directional ultrashort radio waves will be possible. Waves shorter than 3 centimeters, however, are unsuitable for space signaling, since they are absorbed by the lower layers of the atmosphere. Radio waves shorter than 2 centimeters are strongly absorbed by water vapor and scattered by the ionosphere. Therefore, longer waves must be used for the transmission of radio signals across the atmosphere. Radio communication between an artificial satellite and the earth will apparently be best maintained on directional short waves, ranging in length from one to several meters.

Under terrestrial conditions, shortwave transmission has come into wide use, partly because of the almost complete absence of industrial interference or atmospheric statics on these wavelengths. In cosmic space, however, there are many shortwave radiations arriving from the heavenly bodies. It must be assumed that these radiations will greatly interfere with space radio communication.

Finally, it will be possible to determine the wavelengths suitable for radio transmission from space only after a thorough study of the ranges of the natural radio waves that are constantly being propagated in space. The work-up of the results of the radio observations of the first and second artificial satellites will be of highly valuable service in the selection of radio wavelengths for future satellites.

The radius of operation of ultrashort radio waves is limited, as is well known, to the zone of optical visibility. The duration of the periods of radio communication between artificial satellite and the earth on such waves will therefore be the same as in the case of light signaling. Table 35 (see above) indicates the time during which light signals and ultrashort waves radio signals can be received at a given observation station from artificial satellites flying at various altitudes. (Of course, the same data also apply to transmission from the earth to the satellite.) The table also shows the time during which light communication and radio communication on ultrashort waves cannot be accomplished. We note that radio transmissions from the Soviet satellites have been received beyond the limits of optical visibility (cf. below).

Cosmic Radio Relay Communication

Artificial earth satellites may be used as intermediate receiving and transmitting stations for radio-relay communication between the earth and interplanetary ships. The proper direction of the antenna on an artificial satellite may be set and held by means of gyroscopes for a very prolonged period and with far greater accuracy than on the surface of the earth, since there will be no friction in the rotor bearings because of its relative weightlessness.

The radius of action of parabolic transmitting and receiving antennas will increase with the frequency of the radio waves. The shortest radio wave will, therefore, have to be used for radio communication between satellites flying in airless space. We recall that centimeter waves will be more convenient for the transmission of radio signals from the earth to the artificial satellite (or in the reverse direction) since the water vapor in the atmosphere strongly absorbs high-frequency waves.

If the transmitting antenna is parabolic and the receiving antenna has an isotropic character (a nondirectional antenna), then the radius of action of the equipment will not depend on the wavelength. If, however, both antennas are isotropic, then the radius of action of the radio equipment will increase with decreasing wavelength (Webb, Great Britain). These relations are true for airless space, but as we have seen the choice of the frequency is considerably complicated when radio waves must pass through the entire thickness of the atmosphere.

The lower the frequency, the simpler will be the technique of generating radio waves, but the larger the dimensions of a directional antenna.

If a high-sensitivity receiver (1 : 10^{13} watts) with a nondirectional receiving antenna is used on a rocket-sonde and an astrodirectional companion antenna with a 2° aperture is installed on earth, thus reducing the required power by a factor of 10,000, then for a range of 480,000 kilometers (which is practically the maximum distance to an artificial satellite flying at the same time around the earth and the moon) at a frequency of 500 megacycles, a radio installation with a power of about 1000 watts will be required. If it were possible to set up the same directional antenna on the rocket-sonde as on the earth, then the necessary power for the lunar radio station would be decreased to 100 watts. For this purpose, however, a directional antenna not less than 24 meters in diameter would be required. If the wavelength were increased to 3000 megacycles, when the diameter of the antenna would be reduced to 4.5 meters the radiated power would have to be increased by a factor of 36.

With a 9-meter directional antenna, and a dipole antenna with a receiver having a sensitivity of 1 : 10^{13} watts, the necessary power would be 5 kilowatts. In this case, the transmitting and receiving apparatus on the earth and on the flying vehicle would be identical. It would, however, be useful to simplify and lighten the radio apparatus on the rocket at the price of making the apparatus on the earth's surface more complicated and heavier. For example, the power of the radio waves radiated from the earth might be increased 100 times (to 500 kilowatts), at the same time reducing the sensitivity of the radio receiver on the moon by the same factor (i.e., to $1 : 10^{11}$ watts). The power radiated by the radiosonde, however, could be reduced from 5 to 2 kilowatts, and the sensitivity of the radio receiver on the earth correspondingly increased. The payload of the rocket satellite for investigating the moon would be from 226 to 453 kilograms, of which about 23 kilograms would be radio apparatus.

Three or four earth radio stations would be sufficient for the continuous maintenance of communications with a space radiosonde-satellite flying around the system earth-moon. In the extreme case, a single radio station might be sufficient during the travel of such a space-sonde on the passive segment of its trajectory since, during this period, it would be possible to use the elements of the radiosonde orbit for predicting the time and coordinates of its rise relative to the earth radio station with respect to which the radiosonde had sunk beneath the horizon as a result of the earth's rotation.

Since the operator controlling the space rocket-sonde would be on the earth, the ground apparatus for telemetering and telecontrol would have to be provided with a device to compensate the earth's rotation (Prout, United States).

For radio communication with expeditions on the other side of the moon which is never visible from the earth, an artificial earth satellite permanently located beyond the moon, on the prolongation of the straight line earth-moon at a distance of 64,360 kilometers from the moon, might be used as a relay station (Clarke). However, since such a satellite would never be visible from the earth's surface, still another relay satellite would have to be placed on the relay line in question, at one of the so-called Trojan points[6] on the moon's orbit.

Radio signals from the first Soviet artificial satellite have been transmitted continuously. To save power, some experts believe that the radio transmission of records from a small artificial satellite should be periodic rather than continuous. A radio signal from the earth would turn on a radio transmitter on the artificial satellite which, operating for 1-2 minutes, would report the instrument readings recorded over a period of tens of minutes.

[6] The concept of the Trojan point is explained later in the text.

■ Radio Telemetering of the Parameters of Motion of an Artificial Satellite

It will be possible to determine with great accuracy both the distance of an artificial satellite of the earth and its velocity, by the aid of transmitting and receiving radio stations. As shown by investigations, the velocity can be measured with an accuracy to one ten-thousandth[7], and the distance to one ten-millionth of the quantity being measured. Naturally the radio altimeter will operate at an immense speed. To determine the radial velocities (i.e., the velocity of recession from or approach toward the observer) of artificial satellites and rockets as well as of rockets flying toward an artificial satellite, the Doppler effect[8] can be utilized. Certain data on this point have already been obtained from launchings of guided rockets. For correcting the trajectories of orbital rockets and artificial satellites, as for many other purposes, electronic instruments may be used.

Instrumentation operating in accordance with the following system may be used to detect an artificial satellite and to determine its direction of motion.

Two antennas, spaced at a distance equal to a multiple of the wavelength, receive radio signals transmitted from the artificial satellite and form an interferometer. As a result of the composition of the radio waves, a total signal of a certain intensity is received, depending on the position of the artificial satellite (phenomenon of interference). However, in view of the fact that the satellite is in motion, this signal is at times intensified and at times attenuated. For an artificial satellite, this signal is at times intensified and at times attenuated. For an artificial satellite, moving (for example) at an altitude of 322 kilometers

[7] Modern radio altimeters indicate altitudes up to 15 kilometers with an accuracy of 5 meters, and their weight does not exceed 15 kilograms. The operating principle of a radio altimeter is based on measurement of the transit time of a radio signal to the surface of a heavenly body and back again (radio echo). The instrument automatically indicates the distance, proportional to this time, from the reflecting surface (for instance, the earth's surface).

[8] When a locomotive blowing its whistle approaches the observer, the pitch of the whistle gradually seems to increase, whereas when the locomotive recedes from the observer, the pitch of the sound seems to decrease. This is explained by the fact that, in the former case, the frequency of the vibrations is increasing while in the latter case it is decreasing. This phenomenon is called the Doppler effect, from the name of the physicist who first explained it.

at a velocity of 7.62 kilometers per second, the phenomenon of gradual intensification of the signal followed by its attenuation would be repeated every second if the distance between the two antennas of the interferometer were 50 times the wavelength. The cycle can be shortened by increasing the distance between the receiving antennas.

A chain of ground radar stations can be so arranged that their observations overlap to a greater or smaller degree. This will allow uninterrupted reception of reliable data on the motion of an artificial satellite. All observations will have to be made automatically. This is required in view of the high velocities of an orbital rocket and an artificial satellite. The initial moment of all observations might be the take-off of the orbital rocket from the earth's surface.

Thus, to maintain uninterrupted radio communication would require a series of radio stations spaced at definite distances. The number and distribution of these radio stations depends on the character of the orbit of the artificial satellite.

At the Fourth International Astronautical Congress (1953), Haley (United States) proposed a system of radio control of space rockets from the earth. This system plans the establishment on the earth of about 20 transmitting and receiving stations, six of which would be in permanent contact with the rocket.

The characteristics of the receiving radio stations would determine the minimum number of stations necessary for uninterrupted tracking of the artificial satellite. If the number of receiving stations were increased, not only could signals of higher power be received as a result of the fact that the mean distance between the radio transmitter and receiver would be diminished, but the influence of the ionospheric refraction of radio waves could also be reduced.

To avoid industrial interference, the ground receiving stations could be established far from urban centers, industrial enterprises, and heavy-traffic highways.

■ Determination of the Time of Culmination of the Satellite

Magnetic tape records of the radio signals from the artificial satellite, on which time marks would be simultaneously recorded, will be very important. The maximum intensity of these signals will correspond to the closest approach of the satellite to the receiving station.

The time of transit of the satellite through zenith or of its arrival at the point of maximum distance from the point of reception (culmination of the satellite) may also be determined by the so-called equisignal-zone method which is as follows:

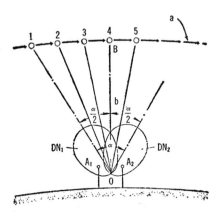

■ FIG. 45.—Determination of Time of Culmination of Satellite by the Equisignal-Zone Method. (a)—Satellite orbit; (b)—equisignal zone.

At the points A_1 and A_2 (Fig. 45), identical antennas are installed, with radiation patterns DN_1 and DN_2, which are symmetric with respect to the vertical axis $0 - 4$ and are displaced relative to each other by the angle α. At the instant of passage of the satellite across the line of the direction of optimum reception $1 - 0$, the level of the signal received by the antenna A_1 will be maximum, and that received by the antenna A_2 considerably lower. As the satellite moves further along its orbit, at the points 2, 3, etc. the signal level will drop in the antenna A_1 will rise in the antenna A_2 until, at the instant of passage through the vertical plane $0 - 4$, the signals received by the two antennas become equal: At this instant the satellite passes through the equisignal zone.

Experiments have been made under field conditions, with a radio transmitter installed on an aircraft, for training in the use of this method (Dubrovin, U.S.S.R.).

■ Determination of the Flight Attitude of the Satellite

The present-day technique of observing artificial satellites permits an experimental determination not only of the coordinates of the satellite for any desired instants of time but also of its orientation with respect to the earth or to the celestial vault. This determination in principle is performed exactly like the determination of the attitude of a rocket in flight. If a photoelectric detector is attached to a rocket so that the axis of its maximum sensitivity is perpendicular to the longitudinal axis of the rocket, then one complete rotation of the rocket about its axis will alternately result in a minimum and maximum of illumination alternately obtained, corresponding to the blackness of the celestial vault and the brightness of the earth's surface. In this case, the instant when the axis of the detector is directed toward the horizon line will also be known. Each time the rocket spins about its longitudinal axis, the rays of the sun might also fall on a less sensitive photocell which would respond to them, but would remain insensitive to the rays reflected by the earth. In addition, pickup elements sensitive to the rays of the moon or to some specific star, or to the earth's magnetic field, could be used. All of this allows obtaining a number of parameters sufficient for determining the position of the body of the rocket. To facilitate the calculations, a mechanical model with a system of recording instruments has been built (Kupperian and Kreplin, United States).

This method gives satisfactory results in practice, despite the fact that the presence of clouds greatly hinders the determination of the horizon line, and the inertia of the instruments as well as the inaccuracy of the apparatus cause certain difficulties.

Data on the rotation of the rocket about its longitudinal axis may also be obtained by the following method:

In the plane perpendicular to the rocket axis, three cameras are mounted, spaced 120° apart. An optical filter is installed on each camera. These filters are red, green, and blue, respectively. All the images are made on one and the same film, which is sensitive to the different colors. After development of the film, the images are superimposed, reconstituting the original color. The position of the sun relative to the horizon on the resultant photograph makes it possible to determine the orientation of the rocket in space.

Finally, the flight attitude of the rocket can also be determined by the aid of radio methods. For example, transmitting rod antennas may be placed in the plane of the "equator" of an artificial satellite rapidly spinning about its axis. At the moment of separation of the artificial satellite from the nose section of the rocket, the plane of its equator (and of its antennas) will usually pass through the center of the earth, i.e., will be perpendicular to its surface. Since this surface remains at rest relative to the fixed stars, its inclination relative to the earth's surface must continuously vary. When it is parallel to the earth's surface, the Faraday effect (maximum rotation of the plane of polarization of radio waves in the ionosphere, under the influence of the earth's magnetic field) will be observed. At this moment, the fidelity of reception will be at its maximum.

The first time that such a position of the antennas will occur after launching of the satellite is when it has passed one fourth the length of its circular orbit, and then again at the antipodal point of the globe. However, because of the earth's rotation and also to some extent because of its oblateness, these points will "drift" over the surface of the globe. However, it is not impossible (in the case of periodic satellites) that, after a certain time has elapsed, the antennas will again occupy their initial position relative to a definite locality. Thus, from the character of the radio signals received on the earth, the degree of inclination of the equatorial plane of the satellite can be estimated.

■ Observations of the First and Second Artificial Satellites

Thanks to the fact that the orbit of the first artificial satellite is inclined at a large angle to the plane of the equator, it will circle almost all the continents and oceans of the globe, except for the polar spaces and narrow zones located south of the Arctic Circle and north of the Antarctic Circle—an area of overflight encompassing about 90 per cent of the earth's surface.

The passage of the first Soviet artificial satellite was recorded in all corners of the globe (Table 40).

On observation of the satellite with the naked eye, it was visible as a star of the fifth to sixth magnitude, and the carrier rocket, as a star of the first magnitude.

Figure 46 shows the track left by the carrier rocket on a photographic plate after a long exposure. This photograph clearly shows how much faster than the stars (in their diurnal motion) the carrier rocket moves in the heavenly vault: The corresponding velocities are proportional to the length of the traces left on the photographic plate (the astrographs used in making these photographs remain stationary). It will be also seen from the photograph that the carrier rocket is moving at an angle to the direction of the diurnal motion of the stars. Only an observer at the 65th parallel of latitude could see the carrier rocket and satellite moving parallel to each other, in a direction retrograde to the motion of the stars, (i.e., toward the east). The break in the track of the carrier rocket is made to determine the time and duration of its passage across the heavenly vault.

▧ TABLE 40

Places and Dates of (First) Overflights of First Soviet Artificial Satellite (in October 1957)

Place	Date	Hr.	Min.	Place	Date	Hr.	Min.
Addis Ababa	9	08	45	Haiti	10	15	04
Alexandria	9	22	37	Guatemala City	8	06	31
Aleutian Islands	7	14	39	Goteborg	10	01	57
Algiers	9	10	14	Glasgow	10	08	32
Alma Ata	5	20	58	Honolulu	7	11	18
Ankara	10	22	37	Damascus	6	08	34
Antarctica	7	06	—	Delhi	8	19	24
Arkhangelsk	8	03	36	Detroit	5	16	30
Askinus, Alaska	10	18	03	Jakarta	8	16	01
Athens	12	22	36	Dublin	13	08	29
Ashkhabad	8	21	02	Yerevan	6	22	36
Bagdad	5	22	32	Johannesburg	10	10	30
Baku	12	21	00	Lisbon	11	10	09
Bangkok	7	17	41	London	6	10	05
Bandung	6	05	35	Los Angeles	9	18	15
Barcelona	13	00	13	Lhasa	12	03	47
Beirut	13	06	59	Madagascar	10	19	08
Belgrade	8	00	14	Madras	6	19	17
Bergen	12	06	48	Madrid	9	10	12
Berlin	13	00	16	Manila	8	16	07
Bermuda	7	15	—	Manchester	6	10	05
Bombay	6	07	03	Marseilles	12	00	12
Boston	7	14	56	Melbourne	8	12	38
Brussels	10	08	34	Mexico City	6	18	16
Budapest	10	00	18	Minsk	10	00	19
Bucharest	13	06	55	Montreal	8	06	39
Buenos Aires	12	01	25	Montevideo	6	16	56
Vancouver	7	18	07	Moscow	5	01	46
Warsaw	12	06	52	Mukden	6	17	50
Washington	5	16	31	Munich	10	08	35
Wellington, New Zealand.	6	11	00	Naples	14	22	34
Vilna	10	06	57	New Guinea	9	14	26
Vladivostok	9	16	15	Novosibirsk	8	03	41
Havana	7	16	39	New Orleans	9	16	40

■ TABLE 40 *(Continued)*

Place	Date	Hr.	Min.	Place	Date	Hr.	Min.
New York	7	06	36	Karachi	5	20	54
Tierra del Fuego	10	18	42	Casablanca, Morocco	11	10	11
Odessa	12	06	54	Quebec	6	14	55
Omsk	10	03	44	Kiev	7	00	15
Oslo	6	03	27	Colombo	12	17	40
Ottawa	8	14	57	Copenhagen	8	01	53
Palermo	12	08	32	Cordova, Spain	10	10	10
Panama	8	16	45	Kurile Islands	9	22	59
Paris	6	10	06	Leningrad	6	06	49
Peiping	7	17	49	Liverpool	12	01	50
Petropavlovsk	6	16	16	Lima, Peru	13	03	09
Pyongyang	11	16	10	Istanbul	11	22	35
Rangoon	6	05	28	Tallin	8	06	59
Rejkjavik	12	05	07	Tashkent	7	21	01
Riga	6	01	51	Teheran	8	07	01
Rome	6	10	09	Tirana	8	00	13
Rio Grande (S.A.)	6	16	56	Tokyo	6	16	11
Rio de Janeiro	8	15	18	Tripoli, Africa	6	10	10
Saigon	6	17	40	Ulan Bator	5	19	23
San Salvador	7	15	14	Frunze	6	21	01
San Francisco	8	18	12	Hanoi	7	17	43
Seoul	10	16	12	Hangchow	11	16	08
Sidney	7	12	39	Hankow	12	02	10
Singapore	11	16	00	Helsinki	8	01	56
Irkutsk	7	19	28	Hiroshima	8	16	12
Kabul	6	20	58	Chicago	6	16	32
Cairo	8	22	35	Chungchin	8	30	50
Calcutta	5	19	16	Shanghai	10	16	10
Canary Islands	7	11	48				

After one complete revolution, the first artificial satellite will be detected at the zenith, not over the former place but over a different point on the same parallel, located about 24° west of the first point. (If this shift were exactly equal to 24°, then after one day the satellite could be observed from the same place and in the same position. In reality, however, there are small deviations.) Figure 23 (see above) is a diagram of the transits of the satellite through the zenith in the course of the day. As will be seen, there remain zones between the territories encircled by the satellite over which the satellite will never appear in the zenith (it can be observed from these zones at a certain angle to the horizon). However, if the life of the satellite is sufficiently long, it will still appear in the zenith over these places. During the first days of the existence of the satellite, certain shifts in the points of its projection were observed, i.e., shifts in its passage through the zenith by comparison with the preceding days. By November 1957, the satellite had already made so many revolutions that the entire map of the globe was dotted by the projection of its path.

In all, 66 visual observation stations and 26 radio observation stations tracked the first artificial satellite immediately after its launching in the Soviet Union. In addition to this, observations were also made by the aid of radar stations and radio direction-finding stations, of astrographs, and other instruments. The aerological stations of the Hydro-Meteorological Service subsequently also participated in the visual observations of the artificial satellites. These stations are equipped with aerological (pilot-balloon) theodolites which, under normal conditions, are used only to track pilot balloons with the object of determining the direction and speed of the wind at various altitudes. (Such theodolites are very convenient for tracking artificial satellites, since the horizontal position of the optical axis of the eye-piece is still preserved when the lens is trained on any point of the celestial vault).

Thirty observatories of other countries participating in the International Geophysical Year also tracked the Soviet satellites.

Observers equipped with optical instruments, "lying in wait" for

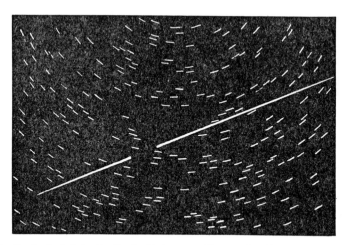

■ FIG. 46.—Tracks Left by the Carrier Rocket on a Photographic Plate after Long Exposure (Photographed by T. P. Kiseleva, Pulkovo Observatory, October 10, 1957). The photograph shows how many times faster than the diurnal motion of the stars the carrier rocket moves through the heavenly vault (compare the length of the lines). The break in the track of the carrier rocket indicates the instant and duration of the time of transit of the carrier rocket on the heavenly vault.

the satellite, were arranged in two groups, one group along the meridian and the other in a plane perpendicular to the apparent orbit of the satellite. In this way, two "optical barriers" were set up.

Ephemerides of the satellite, and later of the carrier rocket, were communicated daily to the press, thus facilitating the work of the observers: to detect the first artificial heavenly bodies on the celestial vault, the astronomic instruments were first pointed at the "points of expectation." The error of the angular measurements performed visually by the observation stations did not exceed 1°. The time was measured with an accuracy of 0.01 second.

During the time of a complete revolution of the satellite, an observation station on the earth's surface was displaced by 1100-2600 kilometers, owing to its diurnal rotation, depending on whether this observation station was located on the 65th parallel of latitude or on the equator. But for an orbital altitude of 200 kilometers, the diameter of the area from which an artificial satellite is visible already exceeds 3000 kilometers. For this reason, after 1.5 hours had elapsed since the setting of the satellite in a given place, it often reappeared in the field of view of the same observer.

The observations showed that the carrier rocket is rotating about an axis passing through its center of gravity (more precisely, through its center of mass).

Radio observations of the first satellites were conducted by many radio amateurs at all corners of the earth. The wavelength selected for the artificial satellite (cf. above) was very convenient for radio amateurs, many of whom do not have receivers able to receive very short waves. The radio transmitters of the satellite emitted signals in the form of telegraph transmissions lasting about 0.3 second, with a pause of the same length. The transmission of signals of one frequency took place during the pause of the signal of the other frequency.

The receiving radio stations had a sensitivity not less than 1-3 microvolts, i.e., many times the sensitivity of radio receivers of the first class. For this purpose, special radio receivers were built capable of detecting the signals at a field intensity at the receiving antenna of not more than several microvolts per meter. These receivers took their power supply from the AC mains and used a power of about 60 watts.

The radio signals of the satellite were received at a distance up to several thousand kilometers and, in exceptional cases, up to 10,000 and even 15,000 kilometers.

After three weeks of uninterrupted operation of the radio transmitters, the sources of electric power on the first satellite were exhausted. Subsequent observations of the satellite and the considerably brighter carrier rocket were mainly by visual methods.

In view of the fact that the second satellite is revolving at a greater altitude than the first one, the radius of the area from which it can be observed has also become greater. A satellite flying at an altitude of 900 kilometers can theoretically be observed from an area of 3200 kilometers radius (along the arc of a great circle); if its altitude is increased to 1700 kilometers, this radius would increase to 4200 kilometers (but a satellite could be actually observed from such distances only by means of improved astronomical instruments).

In some cases, the second satellite has been observed as a first-magnitude star.

As in the case of the first artificial satellite, the signals of the radio transmitter of the second satellite operating on a frequency of 20.005 megacycles were in the form of telegraphic transmissions lasting about 0.3 second, with a pause of the same length. The radio transmitter, on 40.002 megacycles frequency, operated in a state of continuous emission. The installation of two radio transmitters on these frequencies made it possible to study the propagation of the radio waves radiated from the satellite, and to measure the parameters of its orbit. This ensured reception of the signals from the satellite under any conditions of the ionosphere.

After one week, the radio station of the satellite and the airborne instrumentation, in accordance with the test program, ceased to operate. Observations on the motion of the second satellite and predictions of its future motion were made by the aid of optical and radar means, as in the case of the first satellite and its carrier rocket.

9

The Descent to the Earth

■

■

■

■ Methods of Retarding Descending Vehicles

Is it possible to recover an artificial vehicle that has descended to earth and thus to gain access to all records of the automatic instruments, or is the disintegration of the satellite in the dense layers of the atmosphere inevitable? How could the descent of the crew of an artificial satellite be accomplished? These are questions that intrigue investigators.

The descent from an artificial satellite to the earth will obviously take place by means of a special flying vehicle. During the descent it is necessary to retard the motion of the vehicle. This may be done either by the aid of a rocket engine, or by utilizing the resistance of the air.

However, the method of retardation by reversing the thrust of the rocket engine, i.e., by means of a jet of gas ejected in the direction of motion (from an engine turned "rear end forward"), should be used only in cases where utilization of the atmosphere is impossible.

On return from an artificial satellite to the earth, rocket descent will be inapplicable in practice: Such a method would require an immense amount of fuel for checking the velocity of descent and a still greater amount to bring fuel to the artificial satellite—fuel which will afterwards be needed for the landing on earth. In fact, the amount of fuel consumed per unit mass will be the same for the accelerated motion of the rocket during take-off as for its retarded motion during descent to the earth. For this reason, the ratio of the initial mass of the rocket (before take-off from the earth) to its final mass after landing is equal to the square of the ratio of the final mass of the rocket after take-off is completed to the initial mass.

On the other hand, the retardation of a flying vehicle in the atmosphere, utilizing the resistance of the air, demands no consumption of fuel whatever, and therefore the weight of a vehicle for descending will be relatively small. Such a retardation will be of great importance not only for landing after descent of an artificial satellite but also for the landing of superlong-range terrestrial rockets as well as of space ships.

◾ Physical Phenomena on Retardation by the Atmosphere

During retardation, the larger part of the kinetic energy of the landing glider will be coverted into heat, as a result of which both the glider itself and the surrounding air will be heated. We can get an idea as to the magnitude of the kinetic energy that must be absorbed in retarding a descending flying vehicle from the following considerations. If all the kinetic energy of a zero artificial satellite were to be converted into thermal energy, then 74,720 kilocalories could be obtained from each kilogram of weight of the satellite. However, one kilogram of hydrogen-ozone fuel, at best, liberates only 4330 kilocalories, i.e., less than $1/17$ as much. If an artificial satellite were moving at the altitude of one earth radius, its total mechanical energy (kinetic energy plus potential energy) would be exactly 1.5 times as much as the energy of a zero artificial satellite. Not all of the kinetic energy will be converted into heat, however. A small portion will also be expended on imparting vortical motion to the air.

It has today been established that, at a high temperature of the air surrounding a moving missile and as a result of the violent collisions between the molecules, the bonds between the atoms composing the molecules are broken, and the molecules are dissociated (thermal dissociation). Part of the thermal energy is expended on this, so that the glider will evidently be heated to a lesser degree.

In the case of slow retardation, the heating of a landing glider will be only slight, while in the case of abrupt retardation, the vehicle may burn up even if it has a highly streamlined shape.

The burn-up of meteor bodies, i.e., the appearance of "shooting stars," cannot serve as an argument against utilizing the resistance of the air for retarding a space flight vehicle. Meteor bodies usually move at far higher velocities than those that a landing vehicle would have on descending from an artificial satellite; moreover, meteor bodies reach relatively dense layers of the atmosphere faster and, in addition, have an unstreamlined shape. Even under these unfavorable conditions, only the very smallest meteorites completely burn up in the atmosphere (their size runs up to several millimeters in diameter); in larger meteor bodies, the temperature of the core remains considerably below 0° C.

Nevertheless we are still not entirely certain that a space glider will not be destroyed as a result of the high temperature and the destructive action of the external forces. The point is that the physical nature of the combustion of meteor bodies during their retardation in the atmosphere, unfortunately, has been little studied, and the quantitative aspects of this phenomenon are completely unknown. It is possible that, at such immense speeds of flight, new factors, as yet unknown, may manifest themselves. The existing theories of this phenomenon are contradictory and are far from complete. Application of calculation methods valid for ordinary velocities to cosmic velocities may lead to entirely false results.

We note that even when bodies move through the air at considerably lower velocities, phenomena similar to those taking place during the fall of meteor bodies are observed. For example, in one experiment, an aluminum missile left a luminous train 6 meters long in the air, during flight at a velocity of only 5 kilometers per second. Such a train is created by the abrupt parting of the surrounding air of the missile by hurled-off incandescent particles of aluminum. In this case the surface of the missile is heated far more strongly than the combustion chamber of a rocket engine or the chamber of an electric furnace. The extent of the train and its brightness depend on the material of which the missile is made. Observations have shown, for example, that steel becomes incandescent and is hurled off far less than aluminum. It would be still better to coat the missile with beryllium oxide, which has a low thermal conductivity and absorbs an immense amount of heat on sublimation[1] (about 5900 kilocalories per kilogram which would protect its interior from overheating.

It is possible that even on landing from an artificial satellite, the effects would be limited to the abrupt parting of the surrounding air near the nose of the missile by hurled-off incandescent particles of metal (or of ceramic). Heat insulation might also help.

The problem of protecting a space vehicle from excessive heating on retardation by the atmosphere is still not amenable either to comprehensive experimental studies, or to exact mathematical calculation, although several attempts have been made in this direction. For example, the Lockheed Co. (United States) has constructed a three-stage rocket burning solid fuel, for studying the aerodynamic phenomena during invasion of the earth's atmosphere by supersonic rockets.

It may be expedient at first to study the influence of aerodynamic heating at great altitudes, where this effect, because of the rarefaction of the air, is insignificant. Then it might be possible to cause the flight vehicle at high speeds to descend gradually into increasingly denser layers of the atmosphere.

These questions are also being studied by other methods. The National Advisory Committee on Aeronautics (United States), for example, disposes of an installation that uses compressed helium to project a 6.35 millimeter caliber missile at a speed of about 3 kilometers per second. Under normal atmospheric pressure these missiles become white-hot and burn up in the air. At the present time a similar installation is being built for missiles of three times the caliber, which will be fired in an altitude chamber in which the pressure of the air can be varied, simulating the conditions at any altitude. Information has been given out that in an airtight steel tube velocities of about 4.5 kilometers per second have already been obtained for test missiles, and that the pattern of flow around these missiles has been photographed at an exposure of one ten-millionth of a second.

A number of questions must first be solved before a safe method of descent of a space glider to the earth can be worked out: What

[1] Sublimation is the transition of a substance from the solid state directly to the vapor state, without passing through the liquid state.

part of the kinetic and potential energies of the vehicle will be transformed into thermal energy and what part into other forms of energy? What part of this energy will be absorbed by the external medium and what part by the landing vehicle itself?

It is very probable that the temperature in the cabin of a space glider will rise above 100-200° C. This, however, is not disastrous in itself. There are suits in existence for firemen, made of heat-insulating material and cooled by liquid gases, which offer protection from an external temperature of 250° C. and make it possible even to cross through a wall of flame. The rescue means for various types of accident, however, have still not been sufficiently developed at the present time. In this field, much will be borrowed from aviation, with the appropriate modifications demanded by the high velocities of orbital rockets.

■ Design of a Descending Space Flight Vehicle

From the above, certain conclusions may be drawn as to the design of a vehicle for descent from an artificial satellite to the earth, and on the technique of the descent itself. The necessity of protecting the vehicle from excessive heating and stresses as well as physiological considerations demand that the period of retardation be as long as possible. Therefore parachutes of any kind are out of the question for the descent. At the immense speed of the vehicle, these would burn up instantly, and the cosmonauts would not survive the extremely abrupt retardation in the dense layers of the atmosphere. The principal concern of designers should be to reduce to the utmost limits the resistance of the air during descent. The landing vehicle would have to be an ideally streamlined glider. Certain experiments would seem to indicate that a blunt nose is heated considerably less than a sharply pointed head for the same braking effect, but these conclusions require further confirmation.

The astronaut would have to avoid an incorrect plunge into the atmosphere, more specifically, at too great an angle to the horizon. In this case, a fatal G-force might develop, due to the sharp deceleration in the dense layers of the atmosphere, or there would be a violent impact on the earth's surface. For this reason, the velocity of the vehicle would have to be dissipated in the rarefied layers of the atmosphere over a very long segment of the path, which demands an almost horizontal descent.

Even a low-flying artificial satellite would still be moving in practically airless space. For this reason, the glider would have to be "ejected" by the aid of a miniature rocket engine from the satellite at a relatively low speed in a direction opposite to the orbital motion (Fig. 47, point A). Then the velocity of the glider would drop below the circular velocity, and the glider would begin to approach the earth's surface on a semielliptical orbit (Fig. 47, semiellipse AB). At perigee of this orbit, the glider would enter the dense layers of the atmosphere (point B on the sketch). As the velocity was dissipated, the lift on the vehicle wings would decrease; therefore, to prevent the glider from going into a steeper descent, its wing area would have to be gradually increased.

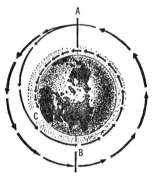

FIG. 47.—Descent to the Earth from an Artificial Satellite Flying at a Low Altitude. At the point A the glider is ejected from the Satellite and descends in the upper layers of the atmosphere on the semiellipse AB. At the point B the retardation of the glider by the atmosphere begins. The glider lands at the point C at a low landing speed.

The glider would slowly begin to enter increasingly denser layers of the atmosphere; the descent to the surface of the earth might even last for several hours. In this way, the retardation in gliding flight would be gradual, which would preserve the vehicle from overheating, and therefore the temperature in the cabin would not rise excessively (if necessary, the glider could be equipped with a cooling plant). When, finally, the velocity of the space glider was almost entirely dissipated and would decrease to about 100 kilometers per hour near the earth's surface, the glider could land like an ordinary glider (Point C on Fig. 47). On this final stage of the descent, it would perhaps be necessary to use a brief rocket braking. According to calculations by Kueme, in the 27 minutes from the beginning of this retardation (at an altitude of 50 kilometers, where the velocity of the vehicle is about

8 kilometers per second) to the instant of landing, the vehicle will cover a distance of 7900 kilometers.

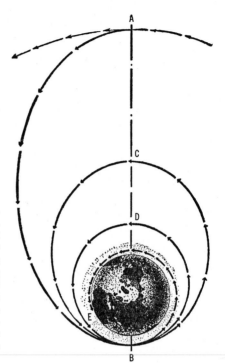

■ FIG. 48.—Descent to Earth from an Artificial Satellite Flying at a Very Great Altitude. At the point A the glider is ejected from the satellite and descends to the upper layers of the atmosphere on the semiellipse AB. From the atmosphere, the glider again breaks away into airless space at reduced velocity. On returning once more on the ellipse BCB into the Earth's atmosphere, the glider again slows down its velocity. Further motion takes place along the ellipse BDB. Finally, traveling along the spiral BE, the glider lands at the point E.

Other conditions being equal, it will be easier to descend from an artificial satellite moving in the direction of the earth's rotation than from a satellite moving in the retrograde direction, since in the former case the velocity of the satellite relative to the earth's surface will be lower.

At the symposium held in 1956 at the Franklin Institute at Philadelphia on questions of the program of the peaceful use of rockets, Porter proposed a method of ejection from an artificial satellite to the earth of film carrying the records of the measuring instruments. The film would automatically be placed in a cartridge, after which a small rocket would go into operation, decreasing the orbital velocity of the cartridge to 1.5 kilometers per second. A spherical shell of stainless steel, 0.08 millimeter in thickness and 0.9-1.8 meters in diameter, would be used as a parachute. The empty shell would be brought to the artificial satellite in a collapsed state and would then be auto-matically filled with helium, giving it the rigidity necessary to over-come the resistance of the air. To protect the sphere from aerodynamic heating, it could be covered with a layer of polytetrafluoroethylene. The cartridge would be provided with a small transmitter, sending out radio signals during the descent and for a short time after landing. With a total satellite weight of about 9 kilograms the safe landing on the earth of a cartridge with film weighing 450 grams would be possible.

The descent from an artificial satellite (or the descent of the satellite itself) will apparently proceed somewhat differently in the case where its circular orbit or apogee is located far from the earth's surface (Fig. 48). In this case, the vehicle must enter the atmosphere (point B in the sketch) at a velocity considerably exceeding the mean circular velocity. Thus, on descending from a stationary artificial satellite, this velocity of submergence will exceed 10 kilometers per second. To facilitate the task, the retardation process may be divided into several stages (Hohmann, Germany). The space glider, circling around the earth in highly rarefied layers of the atmosphere, returns into interplanetary space. Traveling a path on an ellipse (Fig. 48, BCB), the vehicle will again be submerged in the earth's atmosphere. Here it will once again partially retard its motion and will fly out of the atmosphere at a velocity lower than that at which it had entered it. Its stay in airless space will result each time in a cooling of the overheated parts of the glider structure by radiation. Making use of such repeated submergence into the atmosphere for a few times in succession will considerably decrease the velocity of the vehicle, with-out subjecting it to overheating.

It is quite possible that the practical application of retardation of an orbital glider will show that the heating of the vehicle is not as great as expected; in that case, repeated flights outside the atmosphere will no longer be necessary. Landing may be accomplished on the very first plunge into the earth's atmosphere; in order to hold the glider within the limits of the atmospheric envelope of the earth, the wings will have to be set so that their lift is no longer directed upward, but downward toward the earth. It will seem to the pas-sengers of space glider, however, that the sky is beneath them and the earth above them, but otherwise their sensations will be normal, i.e., they will stand on the floor of the glider. In exactly the same way, a pilot making a dead-man's loop on an aircraft has the impression that the earth is overturning and is above his head.

After the velocity has dropped to a value equal to the circular velocity, further descent of the ship may take place by means of an ordinary glide. Now the wings on the glider must be set so that their lift is directed upward from the earth. For this purpose, for example, the glider must be rotated through 180° about its longitudinal axis. Further descent for the astronauts will take place "feet downward," i.e., they will already see the sky above their head and the earth beneath their feet, as usual.

The force of inertia during engine operation on take-off forces the pilot against his seat, but when the vehicle, on descending is retarded by the reaction of the gas jet or the resistance of the air, the force of inertia should instead tend to throw the pilot out of his seat, since it now acts in the opposite direction (assuming that the position of the seat relative to the flight vehicle has not been changed).

In this way, on retardation of a wingless flight vehicle, the force of gravity sensed by the pilot will point in the direction of motion of the vehicle. For this reason, if the pilot wants to look forward, with his head in its normal position relative to his body (the head not thrown back and not inclined forward), he will have to lie on his stomach to prevent himself from falling. If there are wings, however, the force of gravity perceived by astronauts, which force will arise as a result of the resistance of the medium, will be inclined at a certain angle to the direction of motion, which will require a special layout for the seat.

It will be possible to track the return path of the space glider from the earth by means of radar and other installations. Moreover, an artificial "star shower" can also be utilized, which would permit tracking the landing of the glider by naked eye. Such a shower may be produced by ejecting certain small objects from the glider at the instant of its plunge into the more or less dense layers of the atmosphere. For instance, a strip of metal weighing several grams, if thrown out of the glider, will be seen from the earth as a meteor of great brightness. Even objects of the size of a pin will form conspicuous meteors. Larger parts of the glider, now expendable, will (if thrown out) cause the effect of a flash of bolides. The bright train along the path of fall of the bolide will be observed for several minutes, which will permit a more exact determination of the direction of landing of the glider. It is obvious that the size and weight of released objects must be such that they will burn up completely (or almost completely) in the atmosphere, since otherwise they would constitute a hazard for the population and structures.

With proper handling, the glider will be able to land at any desired point on earth, regardless of the point of entry into the atmosphere. On the last stage of the descent, the glider might also be intercepted by a supersonic aircraft, on whose "back" it could land.

It is possible that landing can be accomplished in gliding flight even in the case of an automatic artificial satellite.

■ Landing of an Artificial Satellite on an Indirect Trajectory

Above (Chapter 4), we discussed the method of launching an artificial satellite on an indirect trajectory, involving a preliminary detour. A satellite can return to earth (or leave another satellite) by means of a rocket engine (following an indirect trajectory which is symmetrical with respect to the trajectory on which the satellite was launched).[2]

Naturally, if we neglect the resistance of the atmosphere, then the descent from a satellite on an indirect trajectory will have an advantage over a semielliptical trajectory under the conditions that held true for the launching of the artificial satellite, namely, for circular satellite orbits whose radius exceeds 11.9 earth radii.

At the instant the flight vehicle plunges into the earth's atmosphere, however, the resistance of the air may be utilized instead of braking by rocket. Taking this possibility into account, the descent from the artificial satellite to the earth on an indirect trajectory will have an advantage over a descent on a semiellipse, even if the radius of the circular satellite orbit is only 4.8 earth radii. The advantage in total velocity imparted to the rocket during braking, in comparison with launching on a semielliptical trajectory, may theoretically reach 58 per cent. The saving of fuel will be considerably greater.

[2] Calculated on the basis of a paper by A. Shternfeld, "Trajectories of Flight to a Central Heavenly Body with Take-off from a Given Kepler Orbit," *Comptes Rendus,* Acad. Sci., Paris, Feb. 12, 1934.

■ FIG. XXV.—The Minitrack Radio Transmitter *(United States)* Viewed from the Outside, Is a Cylinder 7.6 Centimeters in Diameter and 12.7 Centimeters in Height. The battery consists of seven 1.2-volt mercury cells.

■ FIG. XXVI.—Instrument with Magnetic Tape for Recording the Measurements of Cosmic-Ray Intensity, Solar Radiation, and Radiations of the Earth *(United States)*.

■ FIG. XXVII.—Standard Soviet Telescope for Observation of Artificial Satellites.

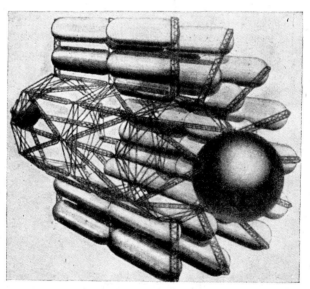

■ FIG. XXVIII.—Assembly of Ship for Circling the Moon on a Circular Orbit Near the Earth. In front, the spherical cabin; in back, the engine room with rocket engine. The sketch shows only some of the capsules with fuel which are mounted in the framework of the ship. (From a project by Gatland, Kunesch, and Dixon.)

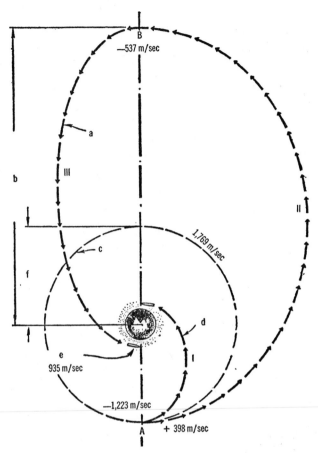

FIG. 49.—Descent from an Artificial Satellite to the Earth on an Indirect Trajectory with a Preliminary Detour May Considerably Reduce the Consumption of Necessary Fuel. (a)—Indirect trajectory with preliminary detour; (b)—60 earth radii; (c)—satellite orbit; (d)—semielliptical trajectory; (e)—total velocity; (f)—20 earth radii.

Let us compare these two methods of descent from an artificial satellite, for a concrete example.

Assume that it is required to make a descent from an artificial satellite in a circular orbit 20 earth radii in diameter, moving at the orbital velocity of 1769 meters per second.

Let us first consider the descent to the earth on a semielliptical trajectory with the perigee in the dense layers of the atmosphere, i.e., close to the earth's surface (curve I in Fig. 49). For transition to such an orbit, the space glider on the satellite (at point A) must be ejected in a direction opposite to the orbital motion at a velocity of 1223 meters per second relative to the satellite, i.e., the velocity of the glider relative to the earth must be brought up to $1769 - 1223 = 546$ meters per second.

The velocity of the glider at perigee, which is equal to 10,919 meters per second, is "dissipated" completely by the resistance of the atmosphere.

It is easy to calculate from the Tsiolkovskiy formula that, at an exhaust velocity of 3 kilometers per second, 0.504 kilogram of fuel would be necessary to eject 1 kilogram of dry glider structure from the satellite in a semiellipse. Let us see now what fuel saving can be obtained if the descent from the satellite takes place on an indirect trajectory with a preliminary detour or recession. To attain this trajectory, on departure from the artificial satellite at point A, the velocity of the glider relative to the earth must not be decreased, as in the former case, but actually increased. If the point B, located at a distance of 60 earth radii from the center of the earth, is selected as the apogee of the indirect trajectory, then the velocity of departure of the space glider from the artificial satellite must be 398 meters per second (i.e., $1769 + 398 = 2167$ meters per second relative to the earth). After leaving the orbit of the satellite on the semiellipse II, the glider gradually retards its motion and arrives at the apogee B with a velocity of 722 meters per second. Here the rocket engine is again turned on and dissipates part of the velocity of the vehicle, more specifically, reduces it to 537 meters per second. As a result, the glider begins its motion on the new semiellipse III at a velocity in apogee equal to $722 - 537 = 185$ meters per second. Moving on this semiellipse, the vehicle will gradually accelerate its motion and will enter the earth's atmosphere at a velocity of 11,097 meters per second (such is its velocity in perigee, which we assumed to be located near the earth's surface). This velocity will be "dissipated" by the resistance of the atmosphere.

In this way, the total velocity imparted to the glider by the rocket engine during the descent on an indirect trajectory will amount to $398 + 537 = 935$ meters per second. Under these conditions, the amount of fuel necessary for the descent from the satellite on the trajectory selected, for each kilogram of dry structural weight of the glider, would be 0.366 kilogram (if, as before, we take the exhaust velocity of the rocket as 3 kilometers per second.

In the last analysis the net gain with respect to the total velocity imparted by the rocket engine on descent along an indirect trajectory would amount to 288 meters per second by comparison with the corresponding value for the descent along a semiellipse, i.e., a saving of 23.6 per cent. The corresponding gain in fuel will be found to be somewhat greater, 27.4 per cent.

We note that the velocity of re-entry of the space glider into the earth's atmosphere on descent along an indirect trajectory, in our example, is 1.6 per cent greater than in the case of descent on a semiellipse (11,097 instead of 10,919 meters per second), but this circumstance is of negligible importance, since this velocity is dissipated, without fuel consumption, by the resistance of the air alone.

10

Artificial Satellites of Bodies of the Solar System

■ Artificial Satellites of the Moon

The first artificial satellites were created in connection with the program of the International Geophysical Year for the study of the earth and of the space surrounding it. Just as soon as satellites have proved suitable for studying the plane on which we ourselves live, they may prove useful for an investigation of such distant heavenly bodies as the moon, the sun, and other planets. Artificial satellites may also serve as interplanetary stations (cf. later in text). Thus, for the conquest of interplanetary space, artificial satellites that revolve not only around the earth but also around the moon and the planets must be created.

Rockets launched from an interplanetary station or from an orbital ship may become artificial satellites of the moon and be utilized for a detailed investigation of its surface. A satellite of the moon, revolving in the plane passing through the lunar poles, would be very convenient. As we know, the plane of motion of a satellite maintains constant orientation relative to the fixed stars. This circumstance will make it possible in four weeks (the time of rotation of the moon about its axis) to photograph from the satellite the entire lunar surface lit by the sun's rays. But even the lunar hemisphere which is illuminated by the solar rays reflected by the earth (what is called the ashen light) will be excellently visible from a space ship, since this light (with a greenish-gray tinge) on the satellite of the moon will be ten times as bright as the moonlight on earth at full moon. If this illumination is also utilized, then the entire surface of the moon can be photographed in only two weeks.

To prevent the sun and the planets from perturbing the motion of the artificial satellite, it must revolve in immediate proximity to the moon, where the gravitational field of the moon is practically the only one in effect.

The period of revolution of a satellite around the moon at an altitude of 30 kilometers will be 1 hour 51 minutes 13 seconds; at an altitude of 100 kilometers, the time of revolution will increase by 6.5 minutes. The orbital velocities of artificial satellites of the moon flying at altitudes of up to several hundred kilometers will be hardly more than a fifth of the velocities of artificial satellites flying at the same altitudes above the earth's surface. This fact will considerably facilitate observation of the surface of the moon. From an altitude of 30 kilometers, objects of 3.8 to 8.7 meters in size can be distinguished on the lunar surface, even with the naked eye (depending on the visual acuity). But at the velocity corresponding to this altitude (over 1600 meters per second), and with the relatively small diameter of the field of vision (about 650 kilometers), an observed object will rapidly disappear from view. A satellite revolving at a greater distance, for instance 150 kilometers from the moon, will therefore be more convenient for observation. In that case, at a somewhat lower orbital velocity, the diameter of the moon's area in the field of view of the eye would be considerably greater (up to 1400 kilometers). Objects on the lunar surface would remain longer in the field of view of the observer. In this case, however, only objects having a diameter of 19-44 meters could be observed by the naked eye. We note, incidentally, that since such an expedition would have powerful optical installations, even the smallest details could be observed. The maximum time of visibility of any point on the lunar surface from the satellite ship at an altitude of 30 kilometers would be about 6.4 minutes, and at altitude 150 kilometers, 15.7 minutes.

If it were required to study from a short distance a certain detail of the lunar surface, then, at consumption of a small amount of fuel, the artificial satellite, revolving in a circular orbit at an altitude of 30 kilometers, could go into an elliptical orbit with a periastron[1] located at the desired altitude. In order to bring the periastron down to the very surface of the moon, the velocity would have to be reduced only by 7.14 meters per second. However, the artificial satellite could approach the locality marked for study only after the lapse of 54 minutes 3 seconds, after first completely encircling one lunar hemisphere. The satellite would then automatically return to its former altitude of flight at 30 kilometers, where the increase in velocity by the same 7.14 meters per second would lead to the transition of the satellite into its former circular orbit. In general, the transition of an artificial satellite of the moon into another, higher or lower, circular orbit would require only minor changes in velocity and thus only a small consumption of fuel. For example, for transition to the zero circular orbit at the moment of passage through periastron, the velocity would have to be reduced by only 7 meters per second.

When the satellite enters the shadow of the moon, night will fall on the satellite; this night, as in the case of the artificial satellite of the earth, would always be shorter than the local day. The "day" on a satellite at an altitude of 122 kilometers above the moon would last exactly 2 hours. A further increase in height would lengthen the "day" by about 1 minute for each 10 kilometers, while a decrease in altitude would cause the same shortening of the day.

In order to accelerate the viewing of the entire surface of the moon, one would not have to wait passively until the moon had made a half revolution (or a full revolution) about its axis. After only a single revolution around the moon with engine off and viewing a zone of definite width, the cosmonauts would then, flying above the pole, turn on the rocket engine in order to rotate the plane of the satellite orbit about the axis of the moon through a definite angle relative to the fixed stars. In this way, on the next revolution of the satellite around the moon on a new orbit, the astronauts will see completely new terri-

---

[1] The point of an orbit that is closest to the heavenly body about which the body in question is revolving is called the periastron.

tories. The higher the altitude of motion of the satellite, the wider will be the visible zone and the less often will it be necessary to change the plane of the satellite orbit. Thus, at a flight altitude of 10 kilometers, this operation would have to be performed 14 times, while at an altitude of 50 kilometers it would be needed only 6 times (Table 41). By using this method it will be possible, instead of a passive two-week wait, to view from altitude 10 kilometers the entire surface of the moon in 1 day 3 hours 20 minutes, and from an altitude of 50 kilometers, almost twice as fast. Naturally, this would not be inexpensive. In the former case, for each rotation of the plane of the orbit it would be necessary to spend as much fuel as would be required to give the rocket a velocity of 350 meters per second, and in the latter case, 736 meters per second. In this case, the thrust of the rocket engine would be so directed each time as to change only the orientation of the plane of the orbit, leaving the orbital velocity of the moon satellite unchanged, as before.

With such a method of flying around the moon, a certain portion of its surface could be viewed even twice, three times, etc. Figure 50 illustrates this method of accelerated viewing of the moon from an artificial moon satellite flying at an altitude equal to the radius of the moon. In this case, it would be sufficient to change the plane of the orbit of the artificial satellite only twice. The numerals on the drawing indicate how many times a given surface could be viewed from the satellite with a single flight around each orbit.

In 1957, at the Astronautical Congress at Rome, the opinion was expressed that artificial satellites of the moon would be created even before a manned artificial satellite of the moon could be launched.

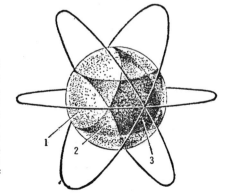

■ FIG. 50.—Accelerated Method of Viewing the Surface of the Moon. After making one revolution around the moon, the cosmonauts, over the pole, would change the plane of revolution of the orbit of the satellite. The numerals indicate how many times a given area can be viewed from the satellite after two changes in the plane of an orbit located at an altitude equal to the radius of the moon.

■ **TABLE 41**

Characteristics of Two Artificial Satellites of the Moon

Characteristics	Altitude of Flight Above Surface of Moon, in Kilometers	
	10	50
1. Circular velocity, in meters per second	1,674	1,655
2. Ratio of circular velocity to zero circular velocity, in per cent	99.71	98.59
3. Increase in circular velocity on decrease in flight altitude by 1 kilometer in meters per second	0.479	0.463
4. Radius of orbit, in kilometers	1,748	1,788
5. Ratio of radius of orbit to radius of moon, in per cent	100.6	102.9
6. Length of orbit, in kilometers	10,983	11,234
7. Angular velocity, in arc seconds per second	198	191
8. Ratio of angular velocity to zero angular velocity, in per cent	99.1	95.8
9. Period of revolution	1 hour 49 minutes 20 seconds	1 hour 53 minutes 7 seconds
10. Minimum length of day	58 minutes 24 seconds	1 hour 5 minutes 5 seconds
11. Ratio of length of day to period of revolution, in per cent	53.4	57.5
12. Maximum length of night	50 minutes 56 seconds	48 minutes 1 second
13. Ratio of maximum length of night to period of revolution, in percent	46.6	42.4
14. Minimum arc of orbit traced by satellite in the shadow of the moon	192°16'	207°10'
15. Maximum arc of orbit traced by satellite in the rays of the sun	167°44'	152°50'
16. Arc described by satellite in the heavenly vault, as seen by an observer on the moon in the plane of the orbit (the center of the arc is at the center of the orbit)	12°16'	27°10'
17. Length of arc of spherical segment of moon (along great circle), visible from artificial satellite, in kilometers	372	824
18. Ratio of area of visible spherical segment to surface of moon, in per cent	0.286	1.398
19. Maximum period of observation of a point on the surface of the moon	3 minutes 42 seconds	8 minutes 32 seconds
20. Minimum linear dimension of objects distinguishable in binoculars with 15 × magnification, in meters		
(a) for average vision	2.91	14.54
(b) for acute vision	2.26	6.30

■ **TABLE 41 (Continued)**

Characteristics of Two Artificial Satellites of the Moon

Characteristics	Altitude of Flight Above Surface of Moon, in Kilometers	
	10	50
21. Acceleration of free fall on orbit of artificial satellite, in meters per second squared	1.60	1.53
22. Ratio of above quantity to acceleration of free fall on lunar surface, in per cent	98.9	94.5
23. Minimum number of rotations of plane of orbit, necessary for complete viewing of the moon	15	7
24. Angle between consecutive positions of plane of orbit	12°0′	25°42′
25. Minimum arc of overlap observations	0°16′	1°28′
26. Necessary velocity for rotation of orbital plane, in meters per second	350	736
27. Total velocity necessary for effecting all rotations of the orbital plane, in meters per second	4,900	4,418
28. Minimum duration of viewing entire surface of moon	1 day 3 hours 20 minutes	14 hours 57 minutes
29. Ratio of surface viewed to surface of moon, in per cent	160	169
30. Velocity of departure from artificial satellite to moon, in meters per second	3	12
31. Velocity of landing on moon, in meters per second	1,681	1,691
32. Total velocity on descent to the moon from artificial satellite, in meters per second	1,683	1,703
33. Length of flight from satellite to moon	53 minutes 30 seconds	54 minutes 31 seconds

■ **Artificial Satellites of the Planets and the Sun**

As already mentioned, artificial satellites revolving about other bodies of the solar system will be of great importance for interplanetary flights. The orbital velocities and periods of revolution of these satellites will vary over a very wide range. These quantities are characterized, on the one hand, by the degree of difficulty of their launching, and on the other hand, by the degree of their suitability as an observation station.

Let us compare the values of the circular velocity and sidereal period of revolution of a zero artificial satellite of the earth with the analogous data for zero satellites of other planets and of the sun.

If a uniform gravitational force acts on the surfaces of various heavenly bodies (which is approximately true, for example, for Earth, Uranus, and Neptune, and also for the second and third satellites of Jupiter: Europa and Ganymede), then the circular velocity will be greater on that one of the heavenly bodies which has the greatest size. On the other hand, in the case where two heavenly bodies are of the same size (for example, approximately, Earth and Venus, or Moon and the first satellite of Jupiter: Io), the circular velocity will be greater on the heavenly body where the force of gravitation is greater.

As will be seen from Table 42, the zero circular velocity for the earth is greater than for the other three inner planets (Mercury, Venus, and Mars), but is only half as great as for Uranus and Neptune, and only a fifth as great as for Jupiter. For the sun, the zero circular velocity is 55 times as great as the zero circular velocity for the earth, and over 10 times as great as for Jupiter.

▨ TABLE 42

Zero Circular and Parabolic Velocities for the Planets and the Sun

Name of Heavenly Body	Zero Circular Velocity, in Kilometers Per Second	Zero Parabolic Velocity, in Kilometers Per Second	Ratio of Zero Circular Velocity and Parabolic Velocity to Corresponding Velocities for the Earth
Sun	437,535	618,753	55.300
Mercury	3,028	4,282	0.383
Venus	7,319	10,351	0.925
Earth	7,912	11,189	1.000
Mars	3,562	5,038	0.450
Jupiter	42,205	59,686	5.334
Saturn	25,100	35,495	3.172
Uranus	15,308	21,648	1.935
Neptune	15,129	22,810	2.039

The sidereal period of revolution of a zero artificial satellite of the earth and the corresponding period for Mercury are the shortest of those for all the bodies of the solar system (Table 43). For Venus and Mars, this period is slightly longer than for the Earth, while for the Sun, Uranus, Neptune, and Jupiter it is twice as long. The longest sidereal period of revolution (three times as long as for the earth), is that of the zero artificial satellite of Saturn.

What is the explanation for the different lengths of the sidereal period of revolution for the different planets? It can be shown that the period of revolution of an artificial satellite near the surface of a heavenly body depends only on the mean density of that body. The lower the density, the longer will be the period of revolution, which is inversely proportional to the square root of the density. If the density of a heavenly body, for example, is a fourth that of the earth (the Sun, Jupiter, Uranus, and Neptune have about that density), then the period of revolution of a satellite at the surface will be twice as long. For a ninefold density, the period of revolution will be a third, etc.

■ **TABLE 43**

Sidereal (Stellar) Periods of Revolution of Zero Artificial Satellites of the Planets and the Sun

Name of Heavenly Body	Sidereal Period of Revolution of the Zero Satellite		Ratio of this Period to the Sidereal Period of the Zero Satellite of the Earth
	Hours	Minutes	
Sun	2	46	1.98
Mercury	1	24	1.00
Venus	1	27	1.04
Earth	1	24	1.00
Mars	1	40	1.19
Jupiter	2	57	2.11
Saturn	3	45	2.68
Uranus	2	50	1.90
Neptune	2	62	2.02

With respect to the mean density, the planets of the solar system may on the whole be divided into two groups, with the densities in each group fairly close together. The first group includes Mercury, Venus, Earth, Mars, and, apparently, Pluto; the second includes the Sun, Jupiter, Saturn, Uranus, and Neptune, the density of Saturn being only half that of the Sun. The zero period of revolution for Saturn is the longest of the solar system.

Thus the periods of revolution of zero artificial satellites for Mercury and the Earth, i.e., for planets of about the same density, are almost the same despite the fact that the diameter of Mercury is only

1/2.63 the diameter of the earth. The period of revolution of an artificial satellite at the surface of the moon whose density is lower than that of the earth, will be longer than the period of revolution of the zero satellite of our own planet, in spite of the smaller size of the moon.

We note that the question as to the density of Mercury has not yet been answered. According to the American astronomer S. Newcomb (1835-1909), the density of Mercury is about the same as that of Earth. According to calculations by the Russian astronomer O. A. Baklund (1846-1916), however, it is only two-thirds as great. This question might be answered if an artificial satellite of Mercury were created. From its period of revolution, the density of the planet could be established (Mercury has no natural satellite of its own).

As will be seen from Table 43, a zero artificial satellite of the sun (it would be better to say a zero artificial planet) would make a complete revolution around the sun in 2 hours 46 minutes. This, in other words, would be the length of the year on such a satellite. With a radius of the orbit of an artificial satellite equal to 100 astronomical units,[2] the year on it would last a thousand terrestrial years, and with a radius 10 times as great, 31,623 years.[3]

Table 44 gives the characteristics of stationary satellites of the planets and of the sun.

Artificial satellites of the planets, like satellites of the earth, would in fact not be able to revolve at any arbitrary distance from their central heavenly body. At a very great distance from the planet, such satellites might be captured by the powerful gravitational field of the sun. The existing natural satellites likewise might more or less strongly distort the orbits of the artificial satellites, and in exceptional cases even capture those satellites.

Table 45 gives the radii of the spheres of attraction of the planets, according to Tisserand (France). Here we note at once the outstanding fact that Mars, with a mass only half the mass of Venus, has the

[2] The mean distance between earth and sun, being 149.5 million kilometers, is taken as the astronomical unit.

[3] It is well known that there are giant stars consisting of exceptionally rarefied matter: their density ranges from one thousandth to one hundred-millionth of the density of the sun. The period of revolution of satellites at the surfaces of these stars would range from 4 days to over 3 years. Conversely, the so-called white dwarfs have a density 7000 times that of the earth, or even greater. The period of revolution of a zero artificial satellite around such a star would be only 1 minute.

■ **TABLE 44**

Characteristics of Stationary Satellites of the Planets and of the Sun

Heavenly Body	Sidereal Day* and Sidereal Period of Revolution of Satellite			Radius of Satellite Orbit, in Radii of Heavenly Body	Radius of Satellite Orbit, in Thousands of Kilometers
	Days	Hours	Minutes		
Sun	25.38			36.45	25.350
Mercury	87.97			131.5	318.4
Venus		68		2.802	17.08
Earth		23	56	6.614	42.19
Mars		24	37	6.020	20.42
Jupiter		9	50	2.231	159.2
Saturn		10	14	1.952	117.9
Uranus		10	42	2.425	60.25
Neptune		15		3.014	79.87

* For Jupiter and Saturn, the sidereal day for the equator is shown, since the surface of either of these planets does not participate as a single unit in the diurnal rotation.

same sphere of attraction as Venus, while Uranus, whose mass is hardly more than 1/22 that of Jupiter, still has a sphere of attraction somewhat greater than that of Jupiter. This is explained by the fact that Mars is farther from the Sun than Venus, and Uranus is farther than Jupiter, so that the gravitational force of the Sun near Mars (or Uranus) is considerably less than it is near Venus (or Jupiter).

As for the launching of artificial planets, scientists of today give preference to launching them on a semielliptic trajectory. In this

■ **TABLE 45**

Spheres of Attraction of Planets (According to Tisserand)

Name of Planet	Radius of Sphere of Attraction, in Astronomical Units	Radius of Sphere of Attraction, in Millions of Kilometers	Name of Planet	Radius of Sphere of Attraction, in Astronomical Units	Radius of Sphere of Attraction, in Millions of Kilometers
Mercury	0.001	0.15	Jupiter	0.322	48.1
Venus	0.004	0.6	Saturn	0.363	54.3
Earth	0.006	0.9	Uranus	0.339	50.7
Mars	0.004	0.6	Neptune	0.576	86.1

connection, we may call the reader's attention to certain peculiarities of the launching of artificial planets by this method.

We have seen above that, to launch an artificial satellite on a semiellipse, for instance to an altitude of 15 earth radii (measured from the center of the earth), a smaller total velocity would be needed than for an altitude several times greater. A similar picture is obtained in the launching of artificial planets.

Naturally, the launching of an artificial planet to revolve around the sun on the orbit of Jupiter, in view of the distance of this orbit, would require a higher total velocity than the launching of an artificial planet on the orbit of the earth's neighbor, Mars. But to create an artificial planet that would move in a circular orbit of greater dimensions that the orbit of Saturn would require a lower total velocity than to launch a planet on the orbit of Saturn. Table 46 gives more detailed data.

■ **TABLE 46**

Launching of Artificial Planets on a Semielliptical Trajectory

	Saturn	Uranus	Neptune	Pluto
Mean distance from the sun, in astronomical units	9.54	19.19	30.07	39.46
Escape velocity from surface of earth, in kilometers per second	15.213	15.897	16.164	16.279
Additional velocity imparted to rocket at moment of arrival in orbit, in kilometers per second	5.441	4.661	4.054	3.685
Total velocity imparted to rocket to transform it into an artificial planet, in kilometers per second	20.654	20.558	20.218	19.964
Amount by which total velocity is less than corresponding velocity for orbit of Saturn, in kilometers per second	—	0.096	0.436	0.690

Imagine that a rocket-sonde has been launched from the earth on a semiellipse and was to be converted into an artificial planet revolving around the sun on the orbit of Saturn. During take-off, there was an accidental leakage of fuel and a velocity equal to 400 meters per second was lost. Then, by radio command from the earth, the pumps began to supply the combustion chamber with the fuel that had been previously reserved for the additional increase of velocity at the instant the rocket reached a point at the distance of Saturn from the Sun. This not only compensated the loss of velocity, but instead of the planned escape velocity from the earth of 15.21 kilometers per second the rocket developed a velocity of 0.95 kilometer per second higher than that. As a result, the rocket crossed the orbit of Uranus, moving at twice the distance of Saturn from the Sun, and reached the orbit of Neptune whose radius is over three times the radius of the orbit of Saturn. At this moment, the rocket engine was automatically turned on again. Almost all the remaining fuel that had been reserved for the additional push on transition into the orbit of Saturn was consumed, and the rocket was converted into an artificial planet moving on the orbit of Neptune. Thus, it actually took less fuel to launch an artificial planet on the orbit of distant Neptune than to create an artificial planet moving on the orbit of Saturn, which is considerably closer.

■ Artificial Satellites of Comets

Artificial satellites built for the study of comets are obviously of considerable interest.

Comets usually consist of a head composed of a nucleus surrounded by a hazy envelope, and of a long tail. Exceptional comets with several heads or several tails are also encountered. The nucleus is a conglomerate of solid bodies of more or less large dimensions, surrounded by an envelope of dust which has a considerably greater density than the matter in the tail.

As a comet approaches the sun, its head is compressed while its gaseous tail is elongated. This tail consists of matter so rarefied that a space ship flying through it would not feel any resistance at all. "A visible nothing," "a bag of emptiness"—this is how astronomers speak of the tail.

Comets are exceedingly "short-lived" bodies. At each approach to the sun, an immense amount of gas is evaporated from their head, thus forming the tail. This gas is afterwards dispersed into space; therefore, at each successive approach to the sun, a comet's tail becomes increasingly dimmer until it finally disappears altogether. All comets whose bright and expansive tails often shine against the black velvet background of the sky were born in recent centuries and millenia.

There are quite a few unsolved problems relating to the structure, life, and death of comets which could be solved by observing a comet from close by during even a single complete revolution of that comet about the sun. There can be no doubt that such an expedition will, some time or other, be accomplished by astronauts.

Only when comets are close to the sun can they be observed from the earth. Astronauts, however, will be able to observe all changes that take place in a comet, even at its maximum distance from the sun, and will be able to follow all stages of the variations in the shape of its tail and head.

It is still too early today to talk about a landing of astronauts on the large blocks that may be contained in the head of a comet. The very approach to the head part of a comet might not be without danger for a space ship. Here the probability of collision with a meteorite would be particularly great. For this reason, we can speak only of accompanying a comet at a safe distance. By equalizing the velocity of the ship to that of the comet and then turning off the rocket engine, astronauts will be able to accompany this heavenly body at a distance convenient for observation.

The most convenient time of studying the nucleus of a comet would be after converting a rocket into its artificial satellite. In view of the low gravitational force of a comet, such a satellite would revolve at a very low velocity about the nucleus, which would favor observation. The artificial satellite could move in the "densest part" of the matter of the comet's head almost without encountering any resistance of the medium (if we disregard the above-mentioned danger of meteorite collisions).

The comet observed in 1818 was the largest in dimensions and mass of all known comets. Its nucleus was 20 kilometers in diameter, and its mass was 2×10^{13} tons. An artificial satellite moving at the "surface" of the nucleus of this comet would have a velocity of 10 meters per second (about the speed of a passenger train). Under such conditions, it would take only 1 hour 45 minutes to view the comet during a single satellite revolution around the nucleus. (Of course, a certain altitude of flight would have to be selected for photographing the comet nucleus.)

If it were found that the nucleus of a comet rotates around its own axis (a still unknown fact), then, on continuing the flight in the former orbit, the nucleus could be viewed from all sides from the artificial satellite. In the opposite case, it will be possible after each revolution of the artificial satellite (or after several such revolutions) to rotate the plane of the satellite orbit by the aid of a rocket engine. In this case, for all revolutions and for complete viewing of the comet nucleus, the same fuel consumption would be required as for a rocket velocity of 31 meters per second.

In studying the matter in the head of the comet, surrounding the nucleus, the rocket might make a "jump" to a certain altitude and then pass into an elliptical orbit, so that the period of revolution would (for example) last several days or weeks. For this maneuver, it would be sufficient to give the artificial satellite an additional velocity of less than 5 meters per second.

◾ Orbital Ships

As stated above, not all artificial satellites will be able to revolve around the earth in its immediate proximity. Theoretical calculations show that it will also be possible to build powered artificial satellites of the earth and powered artificial planets (i.e., artificial satellites of the sun) which, moving on an elongated elliptical orbit, will regularly cruise in the universe as transportation means by suitable correction of the orbit by the aid of a rocket engine (to eliminate the perturbing influences of other heavenly bodies). They will move on their orbits like the planets and their satellites, and will thus periodically pass close to the earth.

We will designate such artificial heavenly bodies as orbital ships, since they could be utilized for the purposes of space transportation. An expedition proceeding, for example, from the earth to the moon might utilize an orbital ship as a transfer facility. After flying on a small rocket to such a ship, the astronauts would transfer to it and continue their journey. Then, after approaching the moon, the travelers would again transfer to a small rocket, which would land them on the surface of the moon.

Living quarters, workshops, and observatories will be set up on orbital ships. Here the astronauts will find everything necessary for further flight.

Let us first talk about orbital ship-satellites flying at the same time around the earth and the moon (Fig. XXVIII). Such ships will regularly cruise on orbits passing close to the surfaces of these two heavenly bodies. The orbit of the ship can be so calculated that during each sidereal month (the interval of time during which the moon, after encircling the earth, returns to its former position relative to the celestial vault), it will fly past the lunar hemisphere that is invisible from the earth. If, for example, the major axis of the orbit is 484,318 kilometers, then the orbital ship will make two revolutions relative to the fixed stars while the moon is making only one revolution. The trajectory can be planned in such a way that the artificial satellites will cross the orbit of the moon at the desired distance from its surface. It will be possible to leave the earth or an interplanetary station revolving at a low altitude[4] (at a velocity somewhat exceeding 3 kilometers per second) at a moment such that the orbital ship will cross the lunar orbit before the moon arrives at this point. In this way, observers will be able to investigate the wide zone of the lunar hemisphere hidden from human eyes, at a short distance (Fig. 51).

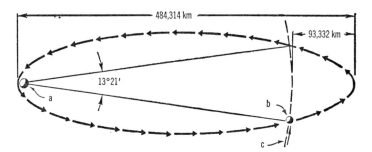

■ FIG. 51.—Trajectory of an Orbital Ship Which Will Allow Observation of a Wide Zone of the Hemisphere of the Moon Hidden from Human Eyes. The investigators will encounter the moon at intervals of one sidereal month. (a)—Earth; (b)—moon; (c)—orbit of moon.

If this orbital ship at its perigee flies at an altitude of 200 kilometers above the earth's equator, then its flight to the moon will take 3 hours 20 minutes. After crossing the lunar orbit, the ship will still recede 93,337 kilometers from the moon and will then begin to return to earth; after 7 days 9 hours 11 minutes have passed it will again cross the moon's orbit at a distance of 13°21' from the first point of

[4] Here and below, when we speak of a start from an interplanetary station, the calculations will be made under the assumption that the artificial satellite is moving in a circular orbit at an altitude of 200 kilometers at the velocity of 7,791 meters per second corresponding to this altitude.

crossing. On a flattened ellipse with a minor axis of 112,120 kilometers, the orbital ship will return to the earth, will make one "idling" revolution without meeting the moon, and then, 27 days 7 hours 43 minutes after take-off, the entire cycle will repeat, with the only difference that now the phase of the moon will be different for the observers. On such a ship, the astronauts, during the course of a year, will fly 13 times (sometimes 14 times) to the moon, which will be in a different phase each time. Every two weeks the astronauts will be able to descend to the earth from the orbital ship. At the same time, various types of cargo, particularly provisions, can also be sent up to the ship from the earth.

Such an orbital ship, however, will have one shortcoming: It will recede too far from the moon and will pass it at a very high velocity. From this point of view, an orbital ship moving on a different orbit will be preferable. It will fly only 3,600 kilometers above the moon during its passage through the point of its orbit most remote from the earth (Fig. 52). This type of orbital ship, however, will have

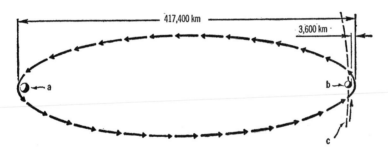

FIG. 52.—Type of Orbit on Which the Orbital Ship Will Pass Close to the Moon, at a Distance of 3,600 Kilometers. This will take place only once every two sidereal months; during this same period the ship will pass close to the earth 5 times. (a)—Earth; (b)—moon; (c)—orbit of moon.

another shortcoming: It will fly near the moon only once every other month, although it is true that during this time it will encircle the earth five times.

To explore the lunar hemisphere visible from the earth from a relatively low altitude, a ship-satellite making three revolutions a month around the earth can be launched. With a perigee at an altitude of 200 kilometers above the earth, such a satellite would fly for 4 days 13 hours 17 minutes to apogee, 363,026 kilometers away. Owing to the eccentricity of the lunar orbit, such an orbital ship could fly very close to the moon.

Figures 51 and 52 show the trajectories of "lunar" orbital ships. They will have this appearance only when the ship makes an "idling" flight without encountering the moon on its path. On approaching apogee, the velocity will gradually decrease, dropping to 150-200 meters per second on reaching apogee. After passing apogee, the ship will again pick up speed. When the orbital ship re-enters the field of attraction of the moon after one or several "idling" revolutions, its velocity will not decrease on its approach to apogee but rather will begin to increase owing to the moon's attraction. After passing through apogee, when the ship again begins to approach the earth, the field of lunar gravitation will retard its motion, and it is only at a great distance from the moon, finally, that the earth's attraction, accelerating the motion of the satellite, will at length begin to be felt. Naturally, during this process, the elliptical shape of the ship's orbit will be considerably distorted (cf. Chapter 4).

As already stated, the oblateness of the earth will also have some effect on the motion of the satellite. As a result of this oblateness, the perigee and apogee of the orbit will be displaced and the orientation of the plane of that orbit will be changed. The so-called inequalities of the lunar motion (deviations from the Kepler law) will also exert a certain influence. As a result of all this, an orbital ship which has been flying for a number of months past the moon, even at a great distance from it, might even collide with it after a certain length of time. It is therefore absolutely necessary to correct constantly the orbits of such orbital satellite ships by means of a rocket engine (cf. Chapter 4).

Let us now pass to orbital ships that can move around the sun as artificial planets. Their orbits will differ from the orbits of natural planets in that their eccentricity will be greater: the distance of the orbital ships from the sun will vary sharply, thanks to which they will be able to serve as a means of transportation between the planets.

Let us consider one of the possible versions of the trajectories of an orbital ship flying the route Earth-Venus (Fig. 53).

An orbital ship with an expedition for the study of Venus on board takes off from the earth's surface or from an interplanetary station (at a velocity somewhat greater than 4 kilometers per second) on a planned orbit, tangent to the earth's orbit. After 81 days it will

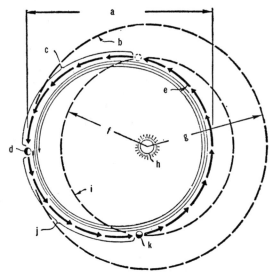

■ FIG. 53.—Orbital Ships Can Also Circle the Sun. The sketch shows one of the possible versions of the trajectory of an orbital ship moving on the route Earth-Venus. (a)—1.54 Astronomical units; (b)—orbit of the earth; (c)—route Venus-Earth; (d)—earth; (e)—orbit of ship; (f)—0.72 astronomical unit; (g)—1 astronomical unit; (h)—sun; (i)—orbit of Venus; (j)—route Earth-Venus; (k)—venus.

fly close to Venus. By the aid of a space glider, a landing party will be put down on the surface of the planet, while the ship, continuing on its orbit, will approach the sun at a distance of 0.54 astronomical unit and will return to its starting point on the earth's orbit after eight months have passed. During this time, the earth will still not have arrived at this point. When the orbital ship, eight months thereafter, again returns to its point of departure, it will again not reach the earth, since the earth will have passed this point four months earlier. . . . And it will only be after two years have elapsed from the moment of take-off, after making three complete revolutions around the sun, that the orbital ship will finally meet the earth.

The landing party on Venus had been occupied, during the year and a half that has passed, with studying the planet and making all preparations for departure at a time calculated in advance, when the orbital ship again passes close to Venus. In our case, the duration of the stay of the expedition on Venus will be two years minus 162 days, the time of the flight to there and return. Thus, 568 days after the descent of the landing party of the expedition, it will return to the orbital ship, which flies past it at exactly that moment, and will again deliver it to the earth. The astronauts will descend to the earth, while their ship continues its endless motion in space.

After the lapse of a certain time, the same orbital ship can be used by a second expedition. For this purpose it will be necessary that, at the moment of take-off of the expedition from the earth, Venus and Earth are in the same position with respect to each other as at the time of the first flight. The moment of departure from the earth can be calculated so that the ship will meet Venus at its very first crossing of the orbit (which is what we assumed when we described the first flight).

It will be easily understood that the next such departure for Venus could take place when the whole number of Venusian years elapsed is equal to a whole number of Earth years. Venus makes a complete revolution around the sun in 0.6152 terrestrial year. For this reason, of course, complete coincidence between the number of revolutions of the orbital ship and that of the earth cannot be expected. But if a not quite exact coincidence is considered sufficient, the next trip could be made six years after the return of the Venus expedition, i.e., eight years after the departure of that expedition from the earth. During

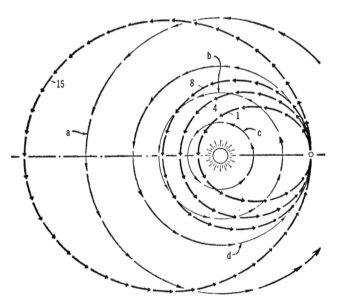

■ FIG. 54.—Routes of Orbital Ships—Artificial Planets, Returning Automatically to the Earth after One Year (Orbit 1), Two Years (Orbit 15) and Three Years (Orbits 4 and 8). (The numbers of the orbits correspond to Table 47.) (a)—orbit of Mars; (b) orbit of Venus; (c)—orbit of Mercury; (d)—orbit of Earth.

these eight years, Venus will make 13 complete revolutions around the sun, and its position relative to the earth will almost precisely recur.[5] The only difference will be about 1° of arc of the earth's orbit, which can easily be adjusted by a suitable correction of the trajectory. The "work timetable" of our new expedition will of course be exactly the same as that of the first expedition.

We have here been speaking only about a few versions of cosmic trips on artificial satellites and artificial planets. Other trajectories will also be possible for the orbital ships from which exploration of the universe will take place. Figure 54 shows the routes of orbital ships or artificial planets returning automatically to the earth after one year (1), two years (15), and three years (4 and 8).

As we have calculated, there are 24 elliptical trajectories for or-

■ **TABLE 47**

Principal Characteristics of Orbits of Orbital Ships and Artificial Planets, Returning from Space to the Earth at Intervals not Exceeding Five Years

Orbit Number	Distance from Sun in Perihelion, in Astronomical Units	Distance from Sun in Aphelion, in Astronomical Units	Major Semiaxis of Orbit, in Astronomical Units	Period of Revolution, in Years	Number of Ellipses Traveled between Two Consecutive Encounters with the Earth
1	0.260	1	0.630	0.500	2
2	0.352	1	0.676	0.556	9
3	0.377	1	0.689	0.571	7
4	0.423	1	0.711	0.600	5
5	0.462	1	0.731	0.625	8
6	0.526	1	0.763	0.667	3
7	0.598	1	0.799	0.714	7
8	0.651	1	0.825	0.750	4
9	0.724	1	0.862	0.800	5
10	0.711	1	0.886	0.833	6
11	1	1.321	1.160	1.250	4
12	1	1.423	1.211	1.333	3
13	1	1.621	1.310	1.500	2
14	1	1.811	1.406	1.667	3
15	1	2.175	1.587	2.000	1
16	1	2.684	1.842	2.500	2
17	1	3.160	2.080	3.000	1
18	1	4.040	2.520	4.000	1
19	1	4.848	2.924	5.000	1

[5] The year on Venus will last about 8/13 of a terrestrial year (8/13 = 0.6154).

■ **TABLE 47** *(Continued)*

Orbit Number	Interval of Time Elapsed between Two Consecutive Encounters with the Earth, in Years	Escape Velocity from Pole of Earth, in Kilometers Per Second	Escape Velocity from Interplanetary Station of Earth, in Kilometers Per Second	Escape Velocity Relative to Sun, from Sphere of Attraction of Earth, in Kilometers Per Second	Ratio of Initial Mass of Rocket Flying from Interplanetary Station to its Final Mass at Exhaust Velocity of 4 Kilometers Per Second
1	1	15.458	7.529	10.646	6.568
2	5	13.944	6.000	8.296	4.482
3	4	13.617	5.670	7.735	4.727
4	3	13.119	5.166	6.820	3.638
5	5	12.761	4.803	6.102	3.323
6	2	12.291	4.327	5.047	2.950
7	5	11.904	3.934	4.013	2.674
8	3	11.693	3.719	3.333	2.534
9	4	11.481	3.506	2.492	2.402
10	5	11.383	3.405	1.990	2.343
11	5	11.383	3.405	1.991	2.343
12	4	11.481	3.506	2.493	2.402
13	3	11.694	3.721	3.338	2.535
14	5	11.908	3.938	4.024	2.676
15	2	12.311	4.338	5.075	2.958
16	5	12.791	4.834	6.165	3.348
17	3	13.174	5.299	6.923	3.755
18	4	13.723	5.778	7.929	4.240
19	5	14.104	6.162	8.562	4.667

bital ship-planets ranging inside the earth's orbit as far as the very surface of the sun and passing close to our planet at intervals of time expressed in a whole number of years ranging from 1 to 5. In this same space there also exist 39 orbits on which the ship could pass the earth every 6, 7, 8, 9, and 10 years. For studying the space between the orbits of the earth and Jupiter, there are 27 trajectories passing outside the orbit of our planet. Moving on these trajectories, the travelers could return to the earth after 2, 3, 4, 5, or 6 years have passed.

Table 47 gives the characteristics of several orbital ships and artificial planets, returning to the earth at intervals from 1 to 5 years. For orbital ships revolving inside the earth's orbit, we confine ourselves here only to those orbits (Numbers 1-10) which do not go closer than 0.260 astronomical unit to the sun.

11

The Utilization
of Artificial Satellites

■
■
■

■ Flying Observatories and Laboratories

The artificial satellite combines the properties of balloons capable of hovering above the earth for a long time, and of rockets capable of rising to high altitudes. According to one apt expression, an artificial satellite is essentially a long-lived rocket. But while the studies conducted by the aid of altitude rockets are limited both in time (several minutes) and in space, unlimited spaces can be investigated for a long period of time by means of artificial satellites.

Artificial satellites will be useful primarily as flying observatories for observation of the earth's surface. Precision instruments can be installed on an artificial satellite for automatic observations of natural phenomena taking place in the upper layers of the atmosphere and in the universe. The results will be automatically recorded and transmitted to the earth by radio. Our knowledge of space will then be enriched by many data which cannot be obtained by the aid of instruments launched on altitude rockets.

Investigation of the Earth and its Surface

In speaking of the conditions of visibility of an artificial satellite from the earth, we indicated the minimum linear dimensions of certain parts of the satellite that would be visible to observers with the naked eye, with binoculars, and with a telescope (cf. Table 34). Naturally, exactly the same relations are obtained for observations of the earth's surface from an artificial satellite. For example, from an artificial satellite flying at an altitude of 200 kilometers, ground objects 4 meters in diameter will be visible in prism binoculars of 15 × magnification. Because of the rapid motion of the satellite, however, the image will have to be held motionless by the aid of a special mechanism. It will also be very difficult to distinguish details of the earth's surface on the horizon. In this way, the practical radius of visibility from a satellite will be considerably less than indicated in Table 34.

From an artificial satellite, man for the first time will be able to see the earth suspended in space. But we already know what the earth will look like from the altitude of flight of a satellite. Figure XXIX shows a photograph of a part of the earth's surface taken by the aid of an altitude rocket. The photograph was made by preliminary mounting of two separate photographs taken from an altitude of 255 and 222 kilometers (the photographs were reduced to a common scale and matched by means of common points). In view of the fact that the photographs were made through almost the entire thickness of the atmosphere, an infrared filter was used. The various details of the earth's surface, the pile-up of clouds, the layers of the atmosphere on the horizon, the earth's convexity, all are reflected with great accuracy on the photographs. An observer from an orbital observatory will see about the same thing.

At the present time, high precision cartography of the continents has covered only 7 per cent of the land surface of the earth. From an artificial satellite, however, it will be rather readily possible to map, by photosurvey, many of the almost inaccessible localities and to revise maps that have become obsolete as a result of the changes produced by the construction of airfields, roads, dams, etc. It is true that this would require an automatic descent of the exposed film to the earth, without damaging it, and we still do not know how to solve this problem.

The number of aerial photographs necessary for mapping the entire earth decreases with increasing altitude of flight of the satellite. From a satellite flying at various altitudes in the range of several thousand kilometers, the entire surface of the earth could be photographed in full daylight in less than 24 hours.

It is true that large areas will always be covered by clouds, but in this case the photographic survey can be made by means of invisible infrared rays as well as by means of radar installations. It is well known that even in the case of total cloudlessness, with a perfectly clear sky, the air still remains hazy. However, in spite of this fact, photographs of the earth's surface taken from an artificial satellite will be distinguished by high accuracy, and distortions due to the atmosphere and visible in telescopic observations will have practically no effect. This gives an effect like reading a printed text through wax paper. The words are easily read through wax paper pressed tightly to the print, while the outlines of the letters are completely blurred if the wax paper is brought closer to the eye (Braun). It should be mentioned, however, that the existence of cosmic rays, and also of X-rays, in the space beyond the atmosphere greatly complicates the technique of photography from an artificial satellite, since ordinary magazines give no guarantee against the premature spoilage of the photographic plates.

Television transmitters installed on artificial satellites of the earth (or of the moon) will be able to transmit, to the observation stations, simple and stereoscopic views of the surface of the earth (or the moon) visible from the altitude of the satellite orbit. To obtain stereoscopic images, two transmitting television cameras (in view of the small size of artificial satellites) will have to be placed on two separate satellites and the distance between them maintained approximately constant during their motion. It is, of course, possible to obtain stereoscopic photographs of the earth's surface by means of only one satellite, if photographs made by a single camera at different moments of time are used.

It will also be possible to measure the albedo[1] of the earth by the aid of an artificial satellite. The latter fluctuates over a very great range, mainly owing to the variability of the cloud cover of the earth.

---

[1] The albedo is the number indicating what part of the light received from the sun is reflected by a planet (or satellite).

From the artificial satellite it will be easy to determine this value for various latitudes and seasons.

Some specialists consider that exact observations of the motion of artificial satellites, even of very small size, will permit various measurements, such as, for example, triangulation of the earth's surface[2] (especially of water bodies), measurement of the distances between the continents, etc. By means of the artificial satellite, for example, the width of the Atlantic Ocean will be measurable with an accuracy of 30 meters (Levitt, United States).

In this way, the artificial satellite will make it finally possible to confirm or refute the hypothesis of the relative shift of the continents.

During observations of the motion of satellites, it will be possible to detect gravity anomalies (deviations of the value of gravity from the normal), connected with the nonuniform structure of the earth's crust, which, possibly, may permit the discovery of petroleum deposits and other useful minerals.

It is believed that, on the basis of the anomalies in the motion of the artificial satellite, it will be possible to refine the position and size even of the third axis of the terrestrial ellipsoid. The "transverse" oblateness of the earth at the equator is very slight (much less than in the direction of the poles) and it has not yet been possible to measure it with high accuracy. It will be far easier to determine the exact degree of the earth's oblateness along the axis of rotation. But this would require long-term observations of the movement of a series of satellites with orbital planes inclined at different angles to the plane of the equator (I. M. Yatsunskiy, U.S.S.R.).

It is well known that the depressions on the surface of the oceans (the depression of the true level of the body of water below the theoretical level) amount to several hundred meters. There are also grounds for supposing that the figure of the earth itself is continuously varying. All these variations could be noted from satellite observatories.

Although polar aviation is making constant observations of the movement of the floating ice in the Arctic seas and oceans, and fire wardens of the forest-fire protection service are patrolling the forest expanses by aircraft, such observations will be considerably more efficient from artificial satellites. The instruments installed on them will

[2] Triangulation is the method of measuring the earth's surface by construction of a system of triangles.

warn navigators of ice packs. All icebergs of more or less extensive proportions will be "tracked" and will no longer cause shipwrecks by collision. The orbital observatories will be able to report back to the earth on forest fires in the depths of the forests, with precise indication of the location of the focus of the fire.

In the opinion of some workers, future oceanographic, glaciological, and seismological (relating to the oscillations of the earth's crust) investigations may be conducted with the aid of an artificial satellite. Glaciologists, for example, hope that observations from an artificial satellite will confirm the hypothesis that the earth's climate is gradually becoming milder and that, in this connection, the ice cover of our planet is gradually thawing. At present, 1 per cent of the water mass of the earth is in the solid state of aggregation (ice), which covers 1/10 of the earth's surface. However, in the more or less distant future, the ice seas may become navigable, and the fresh streams of water from melting ice will raise the level of the world oceans and submerge some of the ports existing today.

From the earth's surface we cannot solve the question of whether our planet, together with its atmosphere, is a charged or neutral heavenly body. This can be elucidated only on an artificial satellite flying beyond the boundaries of the atmospheric envelope of our planet. At the same time it will be possible to measure the radiation of the earth from the satellite.

Investigation of the Atmosphere

Before considering the question of investigation of the atmosphere by the aid of artificial satellites, we will briefly discuss the other methods used for this purpose.

The study of the atmosphere may be conducted by direct or indirect methods.

For a direct investigation of the atmosphere near the earth's surface, aircraft, captive balloons, free balloons, balloon sondes, and even kites are used; recording instruments on such equipment are often used to record the temperature, pressure, and humidity of the air at various altitudes, etc.

Modern altitude rockets, piercing the atmosphere, leave beneath them layers representing over 99 per cent of the entire mass of the atmosphere and furnish readings not only on the character of the stratosphere but even on the properties of the ionosphere. By means of such rockets, the temperature, pressure, and density of the air at great altitudes are determined, air samples are taken for chemical analysis, and both solar and cosmic radiations are investigated. The flights of altitude rockets yield abundant materials for projects of artificial satellites, which will often move below the ceilings already attained by the rockets of today.

For measuring low atmospheric pressures by the aid of altitude rockets, Pirani hot wire gauges are used (Pirani is a German physicist). The principle of operation of these manometers is based on the relation between the thermal conductivity of a gas and its pressure. In addition, inertialess alphatrons, used in vacuum engineering, are also employed for this purpose. These instruments allow measurement of a pressure of one ten-millionth of a millimeter of mercury at altitudes of 200 kilometers. The density of the air is sometimes determined by the aid of a sphere ejected from a rocket at great altitude, which then goes into a free fall. In practice a sphere about 20 centimeters in diameter is used, equipped with an accelerometer and a radio transmitter sending out the signals necessary for telemetering at definite intervals of time. The sphere is usually ejected on the ascending branch of the trajectory at altitudes above 50 kilometers. The wind velocity at altitudes of 20-70 kilometers is determined, for example, by radar study of the motion of strips of aluminum foil (windows) ejected from the rocket. The temperature and pressure of the atmosphere (as well as the wind velocity) may be determined by ground-station recording of the sound waves created by the explosion of shells ejected from the rocket at predetermined altitudes.

Additional material for the study of temperature conditions in the atmosphere is provided by the character and distribution of the "zones of silence" created on the earth's surface as a result of the refraction of sound waves, especially those produced by rockets exploding at altitudes of 30 to 50 kilometers.

The composition of the upper layers of the atmosphere is also studied by spectral analysis of the radiation of the sun and stars. On passage through the atmosphere, a portion of the rays of the sun is absorbed, so that dark lines, due to the presence of various elements in the atmosphere, appear in the solar spectrum (telluric lines). The more distinct the lines, the thicker the layer of air through which the rays pass.

Observations of the atmosphere at dawn and twilight show that the air layers are illuminated by the sun up to altitudes of 75 kilometers. Meteors and auroras, radio waves and sound waves, furnish information about still higher layers. It has been possible to determine the density of the air up to an altitude of 220 kilometers, by indirect methods.

Finally, the percentage content of various gases at any altitude in the ionosphere, still inaccessible to flying vehicles, can be calculated theoretically as soon as the composition of the lowest layer is known.

Until recently, atmospheric layers higher than 40 kilometers could be studied only by indirect methods. It is not surprising that contradictory results have sometimes been obtained. For example, some scientists, on the basis of spectroscopic studies of the aurora as well as on the basis of observations of the spectra of shooting stars, have asserted that a layer of solid nitrogen in the finely-divided state must exist at an altitude of 120-600 kilometers. Other scientists have questioned this assertion; they have proved that an analogous spectrum could be obtained from a mixture of helium and oxygen subjected to the action of an electric discharge. Rocket studies of the upper layers of the atmosphere have shown the unsoundness of the hypothesis of the existence of a layer of solid nitrogen.

Thus we see that our knowledge of the upper layers of the atmosphere is still incomplete and demands fundamental deepening; some of the information obtained, which now appears to be trustworthy, may prove inaccurate on further experimental checking. Artificial satellites will be used in solving all these questions. In particular, the attention of a number of scientists is attracted by the problem of measuring the pressure and density of the high layers of the atmosphere by the aid of earth satellites. Methods based on the utilization of the ionization of a gas have been worked out, by means of which it will be possible to measure a pressure of the order of one billionth of a millimeter of mercury. This will also make it possible to determine the density of the gases (B. S. Daniline, A. I. Repnev, Ye. G. Shvidkovskiy, in U.S.S.R., and others).

By the aid of artificial satellites it will be possible to determine indirectly the density of the upper layers of the atmosphere. Visual or radar observations of an artificial satellite, equipped with no instrumentation whatever, will be sufficient for this purpose. In fact, let a satellite be launched in an elliptical orbit with the perigee located in the upper layers of the atmosphere. Because of the resistance of the air, the apogee of the satellite orbit will constantly descend, and, after a definite number of revolutions, the satellite trajectory will become circular; the satellite will then begin to fall rapidly in a spiral toward the earth's surface. Observations on the variation in the elements of the orbit of a satellite launched by this method will permit an accurate determination of the degree to which its motion is decelerated. Knowing the mass, dimensions, and shape of the satellite, however, it will be possible to calculate the value of the drag experienced by the satellite in its motion and, finally, to determine the density of the air from these data. The fluctuations of the orbital velocity of the satellite will allow us to judge the distribution of the molecules on its path. In particular, the processing of the data obtained on the motion of the Soviet artificial satellites (and of the carrier rocket) will refine our concepts on the structure of the atmosphere.

Artificial satellites will also be useful for meteorological observations. Even on dry land, which occupies less than 30 per cent of the earth's surface, the lack of meteorological stations is felt: Tens of thousands of these stations are still unable to form a complete picture, for example, of the cloud cover of the earth not only over the immense water surfaces of the globe but even over the continents. Just as meteorological stations, equipped with automatic instrumentation, make it possible to measure the various meteorological data at a distance (so-called robot meteorological stations), artificial satellites will permit determination of the temperature, pressure, and density of the air at various altitudes. For example, a low-flying polar satellite, especially a powered satellite, permits rapid determination of the parameters characterizing the state of the atmosphere at a constant high altitude along the meridians (as for small radiations of the satellite orbit from the plane of the earth's meridian, see Chapter 2).

The satellite could periodically eject sodium vapor, which becomes strongly luminiscent in the rays of the sun (Singer, United States). From the degree of dispersion of the sodium train it will be possible to judge the temperature of the upper layers of the atmosphere, while the change in the shape of the sodium "cloud" will serve

■ FIG. XXIX.—View of the Earth's Surface from an Altitude of 255 Kilometers. This combined photograph was made automatically from the Viking No. 11 Rocket.

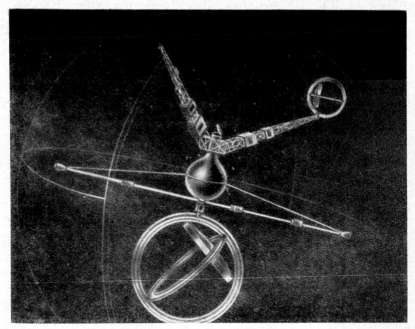

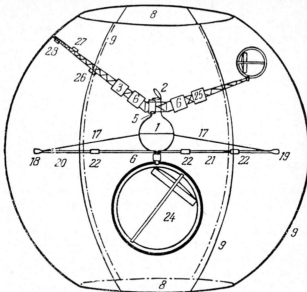

■ FIG. XXX.—Artificial Satellite According to Oberth. 1—Assembly shop; 2—air lock; 3 and 23—supply stockrooms; 4—arm of structure; 5—reflector shielding air lock from solar rays; 6—refuse storage compartment; 7, 8, 9—wires to hold "guard" bombs; 17—tension cables; 18, 19—living quarters; 20, 21—tubes for connecting passages; 22—buoyancy chambers; 24, 25—telescopes for observation; 26, 27, 28—special-purpose rooms.

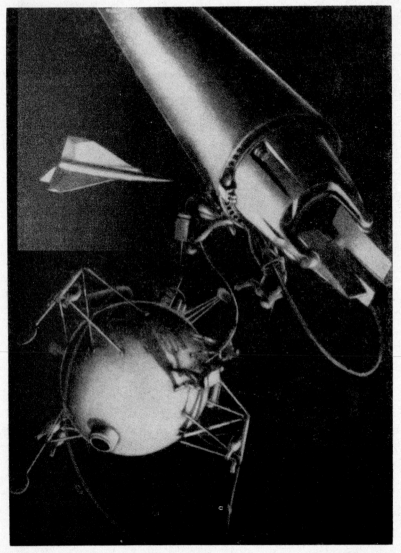

■ FIG. XXXI.—An Automatic Rocket, Revolving Around the Earth, Is Refueled before Its Departure for the Moon. *(According to Clarke.)*

■ FIG. XXXII.—A Space Ship Flies Out into Space from an Artificial Earth Satellite (According to A. Shternfeld; Artist N. Kolchintskiy.)

as a basis for determining the wind velocity at the given altitude. The satellites will make it possible to track the spread and movement of clouds, to determine the character of the earth's cloud cover, to define the boundaries of warm and cold air masses, and to measure the spread of storms.

All this shows the great importance of the artificial satellite for correct weather forecasting.

We note, however, that in the opinion of some specialists it will still be difficult to determine the motion of large cloud masses from the altitude of an artificial satellite, since the outlines of the continents, which must be known for this purpose, will not be visible through the clouds; it will also be difficult to establish the accurate displacement of the cloud masses and the extent of change in their dimensions during the time of a single satellite revolution. Meteorological observations from an artificial satellite will be somewhat more complicated because of the fact that, as we know, a satellite will be able to fly over any specific territory only at one and the same time of the sidereal day, not of the mean solar day.

It will obviously be preferable to have an artificial satellite of a specific shape for this purpose—one in the form of an inflated sphere ejected by a satellite or by an orbital rocket. In view of the considerably greater volume and smaller mass of such a satellite, its motion would prove far more sensitive to the resistance of the air.

It has been established that the earth's atmosphere is luminescent at high altitudes. By day, even at an altitude of 120 kilometers, the heavenly vault does not appear black. At such an altitude the sky glow amounts to 4 per cent of the corresponding value at sea level, in the zenith. The sky glow does not cease even at night, when the molecules of oxygen, nitrogen and other gases, dissociated during the day, recombine, liberating a definite amount of energy.

From a satellite revolving around the earth, the changes in the radiation of the earth's atmosphere itself, with the season and the geographic coordinates, will be amenable to study.

An artificial satellite will permit detailed investigation of the so-called gaseous tail of the earth, a long projection of the uppermost layers of the atmosphere on the side of the earth approximately opposite the sun. In the opinion of Faust (West Germany) artificial satellites will make it possible to test the hypothesis that atmospheric oxygen is the result of the decomposition of water vapor under the action of the solar rays into its constituent chemical elements, with the hydrogen, owing to the relatively high velocity of its molecules, flying off into space while the oxygen remains on the earth.

By the aid of artificial satellites it will be possible to study the ionization of the atmosphere (the distribution of ions and electrons) at various altitudes, which will play a highly important role in forecasting the conditions of radio communications.

In view of the fact that the distance between an artificial satellite and the receiving station on the earth will continuously vary and that the thickness of the intervening layer of air will increase and decrease periodically, the number of ions between the radio transmitter and the radio receiver will also vary. The character of the radio signal received from an artificial satellite at different positions relative to the receiving station will vary accordingly, permitting an estimate of the state of the ionosphere.

During periods of increased solar activity (for instance, during the International Geophysical Year) with the associated intensification of ultraviolet radiation the upper layers of the atmosphere from the day side of the earth strongly absorb the short radio waves, which is the cause of their fading. An artificial satellite may be useful in studying such phenomena, especially during strong magnetic storms and bright aurora displays.

Investigation of the Earth's Magnetic Field

The magnetic field of our planet has been rather well investigated at the surface of the earth, and the results of these investigations have long been used in navigation, aviation, geodesy, and other fields. The earth's magnetic field is composed of a permanent field due to sources inside the earth, and a variable field due to the electric currents circulating in the ionosphere and in space outside the atmosphere. The periodic smooth fluctuations of the earth's magnetic field have a diurnal, 27-day (connected with the period of rotation of the sun about its axis), annual, and 11-year (connected with the period of solar activity) cycle. The variations in the earth's magnetic field assume a pronounced character in certain regions. Sharp fluctuations of the earth's magnetic field are also observed (magnetic storms). It is believed that the earth's magnetic field exerts a repulsive action on the charged particles moving around the earth. On the other hand, it is considered that, owing to the penetration into the atmosphere of charged particles coming from the sun, fluctuations of the earth's magnetic field take place.

Artificial satellites, especially satellites revolving in elliptical orbits, would permit making a three-dimensional magnetic survey of the space surrounding the earth; studying the causes of magnetic anomalies, which are manifested in a deviation of the intensity of the horizontal and vertical component of the earth's magnetic field from their mean ("normal") values for a given place; investigating the effect on the earth's magnetic field of the electric currents generated at very great altitudes; studying the influence of the variation in cosmic-ray intensity on the course of magnetic storms; and other things. The investigation of the earth's magnetic field by means of artificial satellites will be not only of scientific interest but also of practical importance. Such studies will, for example, permit the discovery of mineral deposits and the determination of their ore reserves.

Study of Micrometeorites and "Cosmic Dust"

It is believed that micrometeorites, to some degree, affect the state of the ionosphere and thereby also the propagation of radio waves. In particular, the meteoric matter penetrating the upper layers of the atmosphere is to a great extent "involved" in the formation of the sporadic (nonuniform) E layer of the ionosphere, in the air glow, and in the formation of the silvery noctilucent clouds. The opinion has also been expressed that there is a direct relation between the number of micrometeorites entering the earth's atmosphere and the rainfall.

Up to now, micrometeorites have been studied directly only during the flight of certain experimental rockets. With this object, the tracks from the impacts of micrometeorites made on polished metal plates carried aloft by altitude rockets into the rarefied layers of the atmosphere, have been examined under the microscope. The crackling from the impact of micrometeorites against the rocket shell is detected by a crystal microphone and transmitted to the earth. But the smaller micrometeorites, of about one micron in size, still elude investigation.

The most sensitive instrument for use as a micrometeorite counter is an instrument consisting of a Plexiglas cone, covered by an extremely thin layer of aluminum (1/12500 millimeters), and a photomultiplier. The impact of a micrometeorite on the receiving cone causes a flash which is recorded by the photomultiplier.

However, the impact of large cosmic alpha-particles on the micrometeorite counter will not be recorded, since these counters are "transparent" for such rays (the receiving membranes of the instruments are penetrated without impact).

By means of artificial satellites it will be possible to establish the distribution of micrometeorites, and also the variation of their impulses and electric charges with geographic latitude.

The study of the impact energy of meteorites is a rather simple problem. More complex is the question of the individual determination of the mass of a meteorite and its velocity. The energy may be the same for a meteor body of small mass and high velocity as for a meteor body of large mass and low velocity.

The highly polished skin of an artificial satellite will gradually become dull from the impact of micrometeorites. This phenomenon may be of substantial help in studying the peculiarities of micrometeorites. The skin of a satellite might also be coated with a radioactive substance, and by telemetering the radioactivity of the satellite, the abrasion of this substance by meteoric dust and micrometeorites could be judged from the gradual decrease in its intensity.

An artificial satellite may be made completely airtight and filled with gas under pressure before launching. This will give it the rigidity necessary under the high G-forces that arise in launching. During flight with engine off, however, a drop in gas pressure will indirectly indicate a puncture of the satellite skin by a meteorite. The duration of accident-free flight will give an indication of the possible frequency of meteoric impacts, and the curve of decrease in pressure as a function of time will indirectly indicate the size of the meteorite and its velocity.

Meteorites will be visible from an artificial satellite, not against the background of the sky but against the background of the earth, submerged in the darkness of night. Perhaps these new conditions of observations of meteors will expand the possibilities for studying them. It would be possible to collect samples of meteoric dust on the satellite and investigate the influence of that dust on the weather (Wechsler, United States). Artificial satellites may also be used for studying the "cosmic dust" originating in interplanetary space as a result of the comminution of matter on the collision of meteorites with small planets (V. G. Fesenkov). It is only near the sun that there is no cosmic dust, since it vaporizes under the action of the solar rays. This phenomenon is observed during total eclipses of the sun. Cosmic dust, which scatters the sunlight, is also visible in the region of the zodiacal constellations. It is sometimes possible to detect such dust even on the earth's surface (this dust falls on the earth in August more than at any other time). We note that, although the particles of interplanetary dust are of larger size than the particles of interstellar dust ("cosmic smoke"), they will also be no practical obstacle to the motion of an artificial satellite.

The study of the concentration of interplanetary dust on the earth's orbit by direct methods, with the aid of an artificial satellite, is of great interest. The studies staged by various authors (S. M. Poloskov, T. N. Nazarova, U.S.S.R.) have demonstrated the unreliability of presently available data. For example, some investigators consider the density of the interplanetary dust to be 0.005 grams per cubic kilometer, while others estimate it at only 1/500,000 of that value.

Artificial meteoric bodies of known shape and composition can be ejected from the satellite, thus yielding abundant material for the study of natural meteors and of the conditions of retardation of space ships by the atmosphere. If a meteor body is launched at a velocity of 50-250 meters per second from an artificial satellite at an altitude of 200 to 1000 kilometers, in a direction opposite to the satellite motion, it will be sufficient for that body to plummet into the atmosphere at a velocity of about 8 kilometers per second. A point of great importance is the fact that, in each individual case, we will know not only the velocity of entry of the meteor body into the atmosphere but also its path from the instant of launching to the penetration of the atmosphere. All these data, together with the time of launching the meteor body, will be reported in proper time to the observatories on earth.

Repeated attempts have been made to produce photographic records of the path traveled by artificial meteors produced by ejecting metal spheres from altitude rockets.

Astronomical Observations

It is well known that the atmosphere interferes with the photography of very faint heavenly objects by night, and makes it completely impossible to observe the starry sky by day. However, at the altitude of flight of an artificial satellite, the atmosphere will no longer distort astronomical observations.

The space outside the atmosphere, in the shadow of any dark body, for instance of an artificial satellite, will be plunged almost in total darkness, while the untwinkling stars will be distinctly visible. This will create particularly favorable conditions for astronomical observations. It is considerably easier to observe and photograph stars that do not twinkle. Under such conditions, photographs of the planets and their satellites can be taken at any desired magnification, while in earth observatories a 100 × magnification already causes trouble, because of the optical "vorticity" caused by the atmosphere. Moreover, the astronomical optical observations on an artificial satellite will not depend on the caprices of the weather.

Beyond the boundaries of the atmosphere it will be easier to study the aurora, as well as the zodiacal light,[3] since the luminescence of the high layers of the atmosphere will not distort the normal picture of this phenomenon. In particular, from an artificial satellite it will be possible to determine the brightness of the metagalaxy, which, in the opinion of many scientists (V. L. Ginzburg, U.S.S.R.; Baum, United States), is of great importance for cosmology.

The opportunities for radio-astronomy will also be considerably expanded, since it will be possible to detect radio waves from space, which have not reached the earth's surface, before their penetration into the atmosphere.

Whereas the visible radiation of the sun is almost constant, its ultraviolet radiation varies over a wide range; from this point of view

[3] The zodiacal light is observed in the form of a faintly luminescent cone against the background of the night sky at a certain season before sunrise or sunset in the region of the zodiacal constellations, i.e., along the ecliptic.

the sun resembles a variable star. And, while no solar rays of wavelength shorter than 3,000 Å can reach the surface of the earth, X-rays from the sun of wavelengths from 0.06 to 20 Å can be photographically detected at an altitude as low as 100 kilometers. The difference between the spectra of the solar radiation at the earth's surface and beyond the exosphere indicates the range of waves absorbed by the earth's atmosphere.

Iron, magnesium, and calcium have been detected in the solar spectrum beyond the atmosphere. However, these studies are still in their infancy. A profound study of this question will be possible with the aid of artificial satellites.

Because of the fact that glass absorbs the greater part of the ultraviolet spectrum, ordinary spectrographs carried aloft on altitude rockets have not been able to record the solar radiation of wavelengths shorter than 2300 Å. The replacement of glass by lithium fluoride, which is the substance most transparent to ultraviolet rays, has made it possible to photograph the solar spectrum of wavelengths down to 1,000 Å. A wavelength of 1700 Å can already be detected at an altitude of 30 kilometers. For the study of the ultraviolet and X-rays of the sun, Geiger photon counters or photosensitive plates with the proper filters can be used successfully.

Altitude rockets which remain only a few minutes in the upper layers of the atmosphere have recently made it possible to establish that the solar constant, i.e., the intensity of solar radiation before its penetration into the earth's atmosphere, is about 3 per cent greater than had previously been assumed, amounting to 2 calories per square centimeter per minute. The continuous determination of the solar radiation, by the aid of instrumentation installed on an artificial satellite, and the comparison of the resultant data with the radiation of the earth will permit a periodic establishment of a radiant energy balance for our planet, and define the causes of the fall and rise in the intensity of various radiations. The ultraviolet radiation of the sun may be studied indirectly from the changes in the state of the ionosphere. An artificial satellite, however, will permit a direct determination of the relation between solar activity and ionization of the atmosphere.

For studying the short-wave ultraviolet radiation of the sun, the instrumentation described in the paper by S. L. Mandelshtam and A. I. Yefremov will be installed on one of the Soviet artificial satellites. A disk with a set of filters consisting of films of beryllium, aluminum, and polyethylene of various thickness is placed in front of the X-ray received. The filters are changed by means of a step mechanism. Signals from the receiver are fed to a radio counting and integrating circuit whose output is connected to a transmitting radio telemetric system. There is an automatic device, controlled by means of two photoresistors, for switching on the instrument.

The artificial satellite can also be useful for studying the cosmic rays in the space beyond the atmosphere (for example, their content of atomic nuclei of lithium, beryllium, boron, etc.).

Soviet scientists (S. N. Vernov, V. L. Ginzburg, L. V. Kurnosova, L. A. Razorenov, M. I. Fradkin) are studying the composition of the primary cosmic radiation mainly by the aid of Cherenkov counters. These counters are based on what is known as the Vavilov-Cherenkov effect, which is the occurrence of luminescence in a transparent material under the action of a charged particle moving at a velocity exceeding the velocity of light in this substance.

Studies of cosmic-ray variation (and of the variation in the ionization due to this radiation) as functions of time, altitude, and geographic coordinates are highly important. The special instrumentation developed for this purpose consists primarily of a charged-particle counter and an ionization chamber (Yu. I. Logachev, A. Ye. Chudakov, Yu. G. Shafer, U.S.S.R.).

We note that the work-up of the data on cosmic rays transmitted from the second Soviet artificial satellite distinctly showed the dependence of the number of particles of cosmic radiation on the geomagnetic latitude (the latitude with reference to the magnetic poles).

In Whipple's opinion, it will be possible to install a "telescope" sensitive to the entire spectrum of electromagnetic waves, from 1 Å to 10,000 kilometers, in an extraterrestrial observatory.

Some scientists (Kenny, Ordway, and others) advise placing extraterrestrial observers on what is known as "Trojan points," i.e., points possessing the property that a body placed on them would remain at constant distances from the earth and the moon, in spite of the motion and attraction of these bodies. As early as 1772, the famous French mathematician Lagrange proved (of course, without thinking of artificial satellites) that the "Trojan points" are on the orbit of the moon (in front of the moon and behind it) equidistant from the moon and the earth (each such point is a vertex of an equilateral triangle, the other two vertices being the earth and the moon).

The opinion has been expressed that, instead of constructing a giant new observatory on the earth (like the observatory on Mt. Palomar in the United States) it would be better to make use of an artificial satellite for this purpose. It would be cheaper to construct such a flying observatory, and more important discoveries could evidently be made from this.

In the future, artificial satellites will be equipped with electronic devices and with television transmitters which will permit observers on the earth to "view" the sky in telescopes set up on the satellite (Criquis, France).

Artificial satellites with large circular oribts, included within the orbit of the moon, will permit viewing and studying a certain portion of the inner (rear) hemisphere of the moon, invisible from the earth. Observation of this hemisphere will be possible at times when the satellite is at a great distance from the line earth-moon (Fig. 55). Before an observer on an artificial satellite at this moment an additional zone will unfold which will be wider, the greater the radius of the orbit of the earth satellite. (We observe a similar phenomenon in everyday life when, on walking past a portal with columns, we see part of the rear side of these columns). This effect is perceptible even

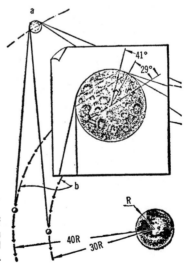

■ FIG. 55.—Widening of Visible Area of Outer Hemisphere of Moon with Increasing Radius of the Circular Orbit of the Artificial Satellite. (a)—Moon; (b)—orbits of satellites.

when the moon is observed from different points of the earth's surface. At one and the same moment, different observers on the earth see somwhat different lunar hemispheres. Let us imagine three such observers. One of them sees the moon at zenith, another on the horizon, and the third, at a point diametrically opposite the second, likewise on the horizon. But those viewing the moon on the horizon also see a little of the far side of the moon: one from the left, the other from the right. By comparison with the first observer, this deviation will be 42 seconds of arc. As will be clear from Table 48, for an artificial

■ **TABLE 48**

Widening of the Visible Area of the Outer Hemisphere of the Moon (Outer with Respect to the Earth) with Increasing Radius of the Circular Orbit of an Artificial Satellite

Radius of Orbit, in Equatorial Earth Radii	Extreme Parallel of Visible Outer Hemisphere of Moon, if the Parallel of the Lunar Circle Visible from the Earth Is Considered the Zero Parallel	Radius of Orbit, in Equatorial Earth Radii	Extreme Parallel of Visible Outer Hemisphere of Moon, If the Parallel of the Lunar Circle Visible from the Earth Is Considered the Zero Parallel
1	42″	50	55°36′
5	4°30′	55	65°15′
10	9°17′	58	73°19′
15	14°8′	59	77°2′
20	19°6′	59.5	79°21′
30	29°33′	59.994	84°33′
40	41°14′		

satellite whose orbit has a radius 5 times that of the earth, the zone revealed on the other side of the moon will already be 4°30′ wide, while if the artificial satellite of the earth were moving in a circular orbit tangent to the surface of the moon visible to us (in practice such an orbit would obviously not be realized), then almost the entire far side of the moon would be disclosed to the observer (see the last row in Table 48). Only a circle 331 kilometers in diameter, or not more than 0.23 per cent of the lunar surface, would remain hidden from his view. But, owing to the libration[4] of the moon, even this blank spot could theoretically be investigated. We say "theoretically" in view of the

---

[4] Libration is the observed oscillatory motion of the lunar disk, attributable in part to the eccentricity of the lunar orbit as well as to certain other causes.

fact that this part of the lunar surface would be on the very horizon and would be difficult to view. We note that those zones of the moon which, when observed from the earth, are located on the horizon of the visible portion of the lunar surface (appearing, as it were, "in profile" to the observer) and whose visibility is therefore poor, would (because of the phenomenon of libration) turn their "face," to a greater or smaller degree, toward an observer on the artificial satellite.

Verification of the Theory of Relativity

It is expected that artificial satellites will permit an experimental verification of the general theory of relativity. Of the planned program, experiments of three kinds may be mentioned.

According to the general theory of relativity, a gravitational field exerts an influence on photons (particles of light), slowing down or accelerating their motion, depending on whether the attracting body emits light or, conversely, is exposed to light directed toward it. As a result of this, the frequency of the electromagnetic oscillations (i.e., of the light rays or radio waves) will respectively decrease or increase.

In particular, if rays of light (or radio waves) from an artificial satellite are received on the earth, then the frequency will be increased. In this case, the frequency variation will be stronger, the higher the level of the satellite orbit. Since, however, no direct proportionality exists between these quantities, there is no need for the satellite participating in the expriment to be very far from the earth.

It is sufficient, for example, for the satellite to move at an altitude equal to the earth's radius; even this altitude would yield half the increase in frequency of the electromagnetic waves that could be observed in the theoretical case of signals transmitted from infinity. However, if radio waves are received from a stationary satellite—and it is just such a satellite that, according to the proposals, is to be utilized as a radio-relay station—the observed increase in wavelength would amount to 84.9 per cent of the maximum increase. Table 49 shows the course of increase in frequency of light waves or radio waves emitted by an artificial satellite, as a function of the orbital altitude.

Thus, if a light ray sent out from a satellite is passed through a prism on the earth, a shift of the lines toward the violet should be

■ TABLE 49

Relative Increase in Frequency of Light and Radio Waves Emitted from an Artificial Satellite, Owing to the Gravitational Shift of Spectral Lines Observed on Earth

Distance from Center of Earth to Satellite, in Earth Radii	Relative Increase of Frequency	Distance from Center of Earth to Satellite, in Earth Radii	Relative Increase of Frequency
1	0	2.5	406×10^{-12}
1.1	63×10^{-12}	3	465×10^{-12}
1.2	116×10^{-12}	4	523×10^{-12}
1.3	161×10^{-12}	5	557×10^{-12}
1.5	232×10^{-12}	10	627×10^{-12}
1.7	287×10^{-12}	50	683×10^{-12}
2	348×10^{-12}	Infinity	697×10^{-12}

detected in the resultant spectrum. However, if such a ray were sent out from the earth to the satellite, a shift of the spectrum lines toward the red would be expected on the satellite. For this reason, the effect described here is called the gravitational shift of the spectral lines. Although such a phenomenon is evidently observed in nature (for instance, in the solar spectrum and in the spectrum of Sirius, where this effect is about 30 times as strong), we are not completely confident that it might not be due to other causes. Astronomers hope that such an experiment can be staged in a purer form by making use of an artificial earth satellite. (In this case, it will be important to take account of the influence of the Doppler effect, which also results in a shift of the spectrum lines, and which distorts the picture.)

A second possible experiment is as follows: According to the theory of relativity, the duration of processes taking place on any body depends on the velocity of motion of that body. In particular, a clock on an artificial satellite should run slower, the higher the velocity of the satellite. But even on a satellite moving close to the boundaries of the atmosphere (at an altitude of some 2,000 kilometers), the lag would be only a thousandth of a second in three months. In the opinion of Winterberg (Germany), this could be checked by means of a so-called atomic clock.

Let us pass now to the third possible experiment. In accordance with the refined law of gravitation resulting from the general theory of relativity, the perihelion of a planet and its satellite is constantly, though very slowly, shifting in the direction of motion of these luminaries. Of all the bodies of the solar system, this motion of the major axis of the orbit is most pronounced in Mercury, amounting to 42.6 seconds of arc per century. The theory of relativity will explain this motion (the formulas derived by Einstein give a value of 43.03 seconds of arc for the shift in the perihelion of Mercury). A verification of this conclusion of the general theory of relativity could also be staged on the basis of the motion of an artificial earth satellite which, by comparison with Mercury, has the advantage that the rotation of the axis of its orbit through a certain angle takes place in a considerably shorter period of time than the rotation of the axis of the orbit of Mercury through the same angle (Fig. 56). Figure 57 shows various

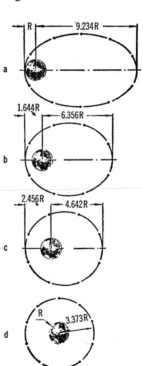

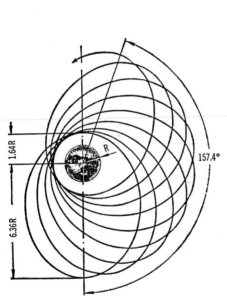

■ FIG. 56.—If an Artificial Satellite Moving in an Ellipse with the Characteristics Indicated in the Sketch Makes 0.5 Billion Revolutions, then, According to the Theory of Relativity, Its Perigee and Apogee Will Be Shifted by 157.4°. To shift the perigee of Mercury by the same angle would take twice as long.

■ FIG. 57.—Various Orbits of Artificial Earth Satellites, Which Would Require Only Half the Period of Observation Necessary for Mercury.

orbits of artificial earth satellites, for which the time of the necessary observations might be shortened to half the time of the observations of Mercury. The circle shown in Fig. 57d represents the theoretical case approached by the ellipses, becoming successively less and less flattened and yielding the same shift in the perigee of the ellipse in unit time as the other orbits shown in Fig. 57a, b, c.

For one and the same length of the major axis of a satellite orbit, this phenomenon will be more remarkable, the closer the perigee is to the earth's surface. On the other hand, at one and the same perigee distance, this phenomenon is intensified with decreasing major axis of the orbit. All this indicates that for conducting the experiment it would be desirable to use artificial satellites with an orbit as close as possible to the earth's surface. Calculations show that, in this case, the time for conducting a certain experiment might be reduced by a factor of more than 40 compared to observations of Mercury, but the resistance of the atmosphere would interfere with the realization of such an experimental test. If, as it is now believed, there are not even the slightest traces of air at altitudes over 2000 kilometers, then in a single year one might perform the same experiment for which 20 years of observations of Mercury are necessary, and at altitudes of 4900 or 8500 kilometers, the observations would be respectively 10 and 5 times as fast as observations of Mercury.

Biological Research

The artificial satellite is of interest from the point of view of studying the possible accomplishment of manned interplanetary flights. The influence of weightlessness on the physiological and psychic processes could be studied on such a satellite, as well as the action of cosmic, solar, and other radiations on living organisms not protected by the earth's atmosphere. As mentioned above, such experiments were actually staged on the second Soviet artificial satellite.

The opinion has been expressed that therapy on an artificial satellite under conditions of weightlessness might possibly be indicated for certain heart diseases (Clarke). But the flight to such a "sanatorium" would unavoidably involve the necessity for the patient to endure a high G-forces on take-off from the earth.

On an artificial satellite it will be possible to verify the hypothesis expressed by K. E. Tsiolkovskiy that plants and organisms, from the simplest to the most complex, will grow and develop far more rapidly under conditions of weightlessness than in the presence of gravity.

Military Application of Artificial Satellites

Questions related to the construction and utilization of artificial satellites attract the attention not only of scientists and engineers but also of politicians. In the opinion of certain circles in the United States and other capitalist countries, the development of the program of operations for the realization of space flight should proceed along the line of military application of rocket aircraft, guided missiles, etc., and the first stage on this road should be completed by the building of artificial satellites with thermo-chemical rockets (Fig. XXX).

Since an artificial satellite could be of minimum dimensions and thus would be invisible both by day and night, it could be utilized for military inspection of enemy territory. In particular, this would allow detection of preparatory work for testing of atomic weapons, deployment of the enemy navy, construction of industrial plants, etc. (Criquis).

In a paper read before the Fourth International Astronautical Congress (1953), the American specialist Stehling proposed a project for an artificial satellite of the earth, for this very purpose of military reconnaissance. This satellite would move at an altitude of 800 kilometers above the earth's surface, which would allow the detection of military objects 550 meters in diameter. The optical method of observation, however, does not satisfy Stehling, in spite of the relatively light weight and high resolving power of optical instruments. The author of this project considers that if a human observer were placed on board an artificial satellite, its initial weight would be smaller, in spite of the need for supplying food, water, and oxygen. The subsequent descent of the scout-observer to the earth would involve certain complications, because of the immense difficulties of protecting a flying vehicle from excessive heating on traversing the atmosphere.

Von Braun likewise considers that an artificial satellite may be provided with optical instruments for observation of countries inaccessible to aerial reconnaissance. It is believed that, with an artificial satellite, even the take-off of an aircraft from an aircraft carrier could be detected. For a continuous inspection of enemy territory, however, a whole series of artificial satellites would be necessary. From an artificial satellite, bombing could also be conducted with matchless accuracy. In this way, the artificial satellite would be of immense military significance both for reconnaissance and bombing, the more so since, at a suitably selected orbit, it could encircle the whole world in 24 hours. Consequently, the entire surface of the earth would be the constant target of the camera lens on an artificial satellite, and would be within striking distance of death-carrying bombs.

Von Braun expressed himself more specifically on this subject before the Second Congress of American Military Specialists in 1956. In his words, the bombing of enemy objectives could be carried out with extraordinary accuracy from an artificial satellite. The guided missile designed for bombing would be ejected, by the aid of a rocket engine, at a velocity of the order of 400 meters per second, from a satellite orbiting at an altitude of 1730 kilometers. The observers on the satellite would constantly track the missile, which would be only a short distance away from them, since the flight of the satellite over a semicircle would take only a little longer than the flight of the missile from its apogee to its perigee. The instant of ejection of the missile would be so calculated that, when the missile reaches the perigee, the bomb target would be already before the eyes of the observers on the satellite, in their optical or radar telescope. Thereafter, the visibility not only of the object but also of the missile would be improved: The artificial satellite, moving through practically airless space, would rapidly overtake the missile which would already have been subject to the resistance of the air, and would then overfly the missile itself. This would make it possible to guide the missile with an accuracy impossible for ground control. From an artificial satellite, a missile can also be aimed accurately at a flying object, and if the visibility of this object were satisfactory, there might be no need to establish its coordinates.

In Von Braun's opinion, artificial satellites can serve for observation of concentrations of ground forces, ships, and aircraft, of new road and building construction, of the extent of damage caused by military operations, and for a number of other observations. (Von Braun is apparently counting on future new advances in the technology of aerial photosurveying, which has not yet reached so high a degree of perfection.)

At the Symposium on Astronautics held at the beginning of 1957 at San Diego (United States), United States Air Force specialists expressed the opinion that the rockets already in existence were powerful enough to launch a satellite that would permanently revolve around the earth and would transmit the recorded position of light or heat flashes of military nature to predetermined receiving stations on the ground. From an artificial satellite it will become possible to detect the coordinates and the instant of take-off of superlong-range rockets from enemy territory, thus considerably increasing the time interval necessary for taking measures to neutralize its action. The interference due to the transmitter installed on the artificial satellite could frustrate the attempts of the enemy to guide his missiles by means of teleradio equipment.

The adherents of the use of artificial satellite as bomb carriers should bear in mind, however, that such a satellite is very difficult to build and is much easier to shoot down. If a satellite is struck by a missile aimed in its direction, even at the instant when the missile stops for a moment (at the ceiling) the missile will still puncture the satellite's skin, since the relative velocity of impact of satellite and missile (or its fragments if the missile has exploded) is several times as high as the impact velocity of an artillery shell.

The proponents of the military use of artificial satellites consider it invulnerable in view of its high velocity and the insufficient accuracy of fire of a rocket anti-aircraft gun. But a missile of shrapnel type, launched into the orbit of the satellite in a direction opposite to its motion, might destroy a satellite regardless of the moment of launching of the missile. The missiles directed against the military artificial satellite might be provided with a device for correcting their orbits (Kenny, Ordway).

We are still firmly convinced that it will not be necessary to shoot down military artificial satellites, since the public opinion of the world would prevent even their construction. In this connection, it will be useful to mention that the paper read by Romano (Italy) before the Seventh International Astronautical Congress (Rome, 1956) on the possibility of camouflaging large artificial satellites used for military purposes did not meet with the approval of the audience, since the International Astronomical Federation (see below) encourages only the peaceful uses of astronautics.

Other Possibilities of Application of Artificial Satellites

One of the fields in which the creation of artificial satellites will play an important role is that of radio and television.

It is well known that television programs are transmitted over great distances by the aid of radio-relay lines on the earth's surface, which require a very large number of intermediate relay stations. Artificial satellites, however, could be used for long-range relaying of ultrashort radio waves, especially of television transmissions. It is true that, because of the complexity of the instrumentation and the need for strong sources of electric power, such use is not envisaged for the immediate future. Later on, however, artificial satellites may well prove profitable for intercontinental transmission of television programs, etc. In the opinion of Pierce (United States), a stationary spherical artificial satellite for relaying ultrashort waves would be 300 meters in diameter. Three such relay stations would be sufficient to maintain communications over 90 per cent of the earth's surface. Instead of three stationary artificial satellites for relaying ultrashort radio waves, the use of four satellites, but flying considerably lower, has also been proposed.

Ephemerides of artificial satellites may possibly find uses in navigation and aviation for the determination of the coordinates of a ship or aircraft. In fact, on variations in the distance of a radio receiver from an artificial satellite, the frequency of the radio waves received would also vary. In addition, the intensity of the signals would vary. On the basis of these data and of the existing ephemerides, Lorens (United States) has proposed a method for determining the coordinates of ships and aircraft. For this purpose, three polar satellites would be used, revolving at low altitudes in planes mutually intersecting at 60° angles. Satellites 0.6 meters in diameter would be provided with eight 20-centimeter antennas. A half kilogram of strontium-90 and any ytrium isotope would be sufficient to supply power to the radio transmitter for 20 years.

Ship radio stations of relatively short range would be sufficient to maintain communication with the land through an intermediate artificial satellite, that might appear daily above the horizon. We note that in clear weather such communication could also be maintained by the aid of light signals, which penetrate the atmosphere far more easily when they are directed upward, since this would shorten their path in the absorbing medium.

Research workers on board an artificial satellite will have available a high vacuum, so difficult to obtain under ground conditions. This will make it possible to stage a number of experiments demanding a higher vacuum than can be attained in laboratories on the ground. Finally, extreme low temperatures will be more easily established for work on superconductivity and in other experiments.

By means of an artificial satellite it will be possible to determine a number of parameters of interest in gas dynamics, which cannot be determined in wind tunnels because of the fact that the airflow of even the most powerful installations of this kind is too slow.

It is possible that under the conditions of weightlessness on an artificial satellite, crystals will grow more rapidly and even change their structure; in this manner, the range of available piezoelectric crystals will be augmented (Kenny, Ordway; United States).

Unrealistic projects are also being advanced, alongside the serious projects for utilization of artificial satellites. For example, it has been proposed to set up immense mirrors near artificial satellites to reflect solar rays onto the earth. This type of reflector, it is claimed, could heat large area of the globe, melt the ice, and change the climate of the Arctic and Antarctic and thus exert an influence, directly or indirectly, on the climatic conditions of the earth. "However, since such a reflector could unfortunately also be of great strategic importance," writes Oberth, "(by its aid military plants could be blown up, hurricanes and thunderstorms created, infantry and their supply trains destroyed, whole cities burned, and in general, great damage could be caused), it is not excluded that in the near future one of the civilized countries will decide to realize this invention, the more so since the large amount of invested capital would be able to yield dividends, even in peacetime." For the construction of such "space mirrors" entire rolling mills (!) would have to be carried aloft. Sodium billets brought to outer space would have to be rolled to a thickness of one five-hundredth of a millimeter (!) and coated on the shadow side with a suitable composition, with the object of maintaining the temperature of the sodium mirror at a level to preserve sufficient elasticity and mechanical strength. By means of hinge systems, the mirror would be assembled on an immense base of sodium wire. The components of the mirror would be remotely oriented by means of electric power. In this case, each hectare of structure, together with the reinforcement and observation chamber, would have to weigh less than 100 kilograms, a weight per unit area about one fifth that of writing paper! The unrealistic nature of this project will be clear from the fact that solar-power engineering has not made much progress in using mirrors hundreds of times heavier on the surface of the earth, where the structure is not menaced by meteors and meteoric dust, as would be the case with space mirrors.

A still more absurd idea has been expressed that artificial satellites, in the form of space mirrors reflecting the rays of the sun in cosmic space, might serve to shield the tropical zones from excessive solar radiation.

The project of utilizing space mirrors for lighting large cities might prove to be more realistic, since in this case, the surface of the mirror could be millions of times smaller than necessary in the above case. It is easy to calculate, for instance, that if the same illumination given by full moon would be considered sufficient, a mirror 30 meters in diameter on a satellite would suffice for lighting a city 20 kilometers in diameter.

Orbit Sections for Various Studies

As demonstrated above, artificial satellites may find the most varied applications. For studying different phenomena, however, it will obviously be necessary to use satellites moving on specially selected orbits. It is clear, for example, that equatorial satellites are unsuitable for studies of the aurora or the ice conditions beyond the Arctic and Antarctic Circles.

Artificial satellites revolving at varying altitudes will find special applications. Such satellites, moving on elliptic orbits, will at times ascend into the more rarefied layers of the ionosphere and at times descend into the denser layers of air. This will allow observations at various levels and will fill the presently existing gaps in our knowledge of solar radiation, dissociation of molecular oxygen and nitrogen at various altitudes, distribution of ozone, magnetic field of the earth, and ionospheric storms, etc. For example, we still do not know, for all altitudes, the shortest wavelengths that can be detected in the solar spectrum, and even less study has been devoted to the altitude distribution of charged particles. (The distribution of these particles at different points of the earth's surface is, in particular, affected by the inclination of the earth's axis to the plane of the ecliptic.)

In the southern hemisphere there is little land and much water. It would therefore be of interest to select the artificial satellite orbit in such a manner that it would remain longer over the northern hemisphere and less long over the southern. This could be accomplished by lengthening the northern part of the orbit and reducing the velocity of the satellite on this segment. In other words, it is necessary for the satellite to have an elliptical orbit with its perigee above the South Pole. In this case, the higher the apogee of the orbit, the shorter the time of flight of the satellite over the southern hemisphere and the longer its flight over the northern.

Prospects

The study of many of the above questions is just beginning, and will demand many years of research. There can be no doubt that artificial satellites will aid in discovering phenomena whose very existence is today completely unsuspected.

The study of all these problems obviously demands many years for its realization. For this reason, the first artificial satellites will be used for studying a more restricted range of questions. More specifically, it is suggested we use the satellites launched during the Third International Geophysical Year for solving questions related to the following schematic program: (a) density of the air at great altitudes; (b) figure of the earth and structure of the earth's crust; (c) measurement of the distance between certain points of the earth's surface; (d) ultraviolet radiation of the sun; (e) cosmic rays; (f) meteoric dust and meteor bodies; (g) temperature of the satellite, especially of its skin, during passage through the dense layers of the atmosphere; (h) the earth's magnetic field; (i) ionization and composition of the atmosphere along the satellite's orbit; (j) propagation of radio waves of various frequencies.

Naturally, an artificial satellite will be used only for special studies that could not be conducted by any other method. With an automatic artificial satellite, it will be possible in several days to collect more data than in decades of launching altitude rockets from various points of the globe.

■ The Artificial Satellite as an Interplanetary Station

Purpose of an Interplanetary Station

From the point of view of astronautics, the use of artificial satellites as interplanetary stations will be of the greatest significance.

To reach Moon, Venus, and Mars, our nearest heavenly neighbors, an interplanetary space ship would have to develop a take-off velocity of $11.1 = 11.6$ kilometers per second, i.e., over 13 times the speed of sound. The construction of such a ship is beyond the capability of present-day technology. To facilitate the solution of this problem, K. E. Tsiolkovskiy proposed utilizing an artificial earth satellite as a peculiar kind of transfer station, thereby dividing a space journey into stages.

Under terrestrial conditions, during stopovers at stations, in ports, and at airfields, ships and locomotives are supplied with coal and water, aircrafts are fueled with gasoline, passengers replenished with provisions. On earth, another locomotive may be hooked onto a train, one aircraft may be replaced by another. For flight into cosmic space, the construction of an interplanetary station will be of analogous significance. Such a station might serve as a starting-off place for further penetration of man into space. Here the cosmonauts will be able to supply themselves with everything necessary for continuing and completing their space journey, fuel that could not be carried by a rocket starting from the earth's surface, equipment, provisions, etc.

Based on an interplanetary station, astronauts will be able, not far from our planet, to acquire varied experience of navigation practice in airless space, as well as to master the art of retarding the cosmic velocity in gliding flight during a descent to the earth.

At an interplanetary station it will also be possible to determine many data necessary for the most rational design of a space ship and space glider.

A space ship, as well as various cargo items necessary for reaching the ultimate objective of the voyage, may be first delivered to such a station in separate parts. This will facilitate the design of the space ship, since for take-off from the platform, the satellite will need a considerably smaller fuel supply than for take-off from the earth.

A major advantage of such an intermediate station is its mobility.

Thanks to this, during landing at such a station, the rocket will maintain its own velocity and will use it in its departure on the next leg of its journey.

In this way, in contrast to people traveling on earth, who make stopovers at intermediate stations, the cosmonauts taking off from an interplanetary station will, as it were, have behind them not only the distance traveled but also the velocity acquired. Thus, to take off from an artificial satellite of the earth for Moon, Venus, or Mars, a rocket will have to develop a velocity of only 3.1 to 3.6 kilometers per second instead of the 11.1 to 11.6 kilometers per second on take-off from the earth's surface, since the station itself already has a velocity of about 8 kilometers per second. This means that a rocket capable of rising from the earth's surface to an altitude of 1000 kilometers could reach Venus or Mars if it started out from an interplanetary station.

Some authors propose the utilization of a stationary artificial satellite as an intermediate station for flight to the moon or planets. Such a satellite, however, has a great disadvantage: it is so far from the earth that excessive take-off and landing speeds[5] would be necessary to reach it (in sum, they would amount to a speed greater than that necessary for circling the moon). But higher speeds also mean more complex rocket design.

An interplanetary station, in contrast to a stationary satellite, should revolve at a low altitude above the earth's surface or, at least, should fly close to the earth on some segment of its orbit. Such a satellite, moving in an elliptical orbit with a distant apogee, could serve as an interplanetary station for more complicated trips than those that could be accomplished by taking off close to the earth from an arti-

---

[5] The speed with which a rocket, moving with engine off, arrives at the artificial satellite will be called the landing speed.

ficial satellite moving in a circular orbit. The point is that, the more distant the apogee, the higher the speed of the satellite in perigee; thus, the departure from an "elliptical" interplanetary station could possibly be effected at the moment of the satellite's maximum velocity, i.e., when it is passing through perigee. To reach a "far-apogee" satellite more powerful rockets would be required on take-off from the earth's surface, but this would be made up by the fact that the design of the ship for the second stage of the flight, i.e., for the departure from the space platform, could be simpler.

However, an interplanetary station moving in a circular orbit at great altitude (thousands of kilometers), as proposed by Von Braun and others, is disadvantageous. To lift an auxiliary rocket, with its cargo, to such an altitude will not only cause additional difficulties in flights from the earth to the satellites but will also demand the development of greater total velocity for ferrying each kilogram of cargo to the moon or the planets. In our opinion, a considerable saving of fuel could be attained by take-off from an interplanetary station revolving around the earth in an elliptic orbit with a perigee as low as possible, since an interplanetary journey with stopover at a high-flying circular-path interplanetary station would demand a greater consumption of fuel than with a stop at a low-flying station.

It has been proposed that astronauts should stop in their path to the moon or the planets at a series of stations located along the path instead of at a single space platform. Thus, in about 1928, Pirquet (Austria) advanced the following project: to place two interplanetary stations in orbit at constant altitudes of about 750 and 5000 kilometers, with respective periods of revolution of 100 and 200 minutes. The third artificial satellite, traveling in an elliptical orbit tangent to the two preceding orbits, would play the role of a kind of coastwise vessel or shuttle for bringing passengers and cargo from the inner interplanetary station to the outer one.

An interplanetary station, however, is not a necessary link in the realization of flight to the moon and planets. A space voyage can also take place without stopping at an interplanetary station. The rocket will take off from the earth's surface and, developing a velocity of about 8 kilometers per second, will convert at an altitude of 200-300 kilometers to a temporary artificial satellite. Gradually, auxiliary rockets will deliver to this rocket-satellite the additional cargo and fuel necessary for the further flight. After receiving "reinforcements," the interplanetary rocket sets out toward its destination. This solution will be of interest since it will decrease the meteor danger, to which the temporary artificial satellite will be exposed only during a short period of time.

According to other proposals (Carter, Great Britain), instead of building interplanetary stations, it will be sufficient to launch fuel tanks, on a circular or elliptic orbit, for refueling the space rockets. This will allow a considerable simplification in the design of the rockets dispatched from the earth into interplanetary space (Fig. XXXI).

We note that the utilization of an artificial satellite as an interplanetary station or, what amounts to the same, the temporary conversion of a space ship into an earth satellite will evidently be applicable only to the initial stage of the development of space travel. The powerful atomic ships of the future will not need to go into circular orbit and receive reinforcements from the earth on their way to the moon or to a planet. It is also possible that the dispatch of small compound guided rockets to the moon and planets will be simpler with a take-off directly from the earth's surface.

Flight from an Artificial Satellite into Space

Most interplanetary flight projects envisage the transfer of the cosmonauts, at an interplanetary station, to a ship assembled in its workshops from parts delivered from the earth. Engines and other parts removed from the rockets arriving at the interplanetary station can be used to equip this space ship.

The conditions of flight from an artificial satellite into interplanetary space differ greatly from the conditions of flight from the earth to the artificial satellite. For this reason, the rockets for such flights will have to be designed differently.

A space ship for flight from the earth to the artificial planet will have to be streamlined, since it must cross the entire thickness of the atmosphere. It will have to be equipped with a powerful engine capable of giving it a velocity of about 8 kilometers per second and thus carry a relatively large fuel supply for the engine. A space ship for flight from the artificial satellite into interplanetary space, however, need not be streamlined since it will not encounter the resistance of a material medium in interplanetary space. In view of this fact, the fuel tanks could be given spherical shapes, which will reduce their weight for a given volume (Fig. XXXII).

Figures XXXIII-XXXVI show the successive stages of construction of the interplanetary station.

In some versions of the space-ship design, the interplanetary station can also be used for the return trip; here the crew would transfer to a space glider, on which it would then land on the earth.

According to some projects, a rocket arriving from the earth at an interplanetary station will itself serve for further flight into cosmic space. At the interplanetary station, the streamlined skin will be removed. The air stabilizers and rudders will also be no longer needed: if the direction of flight must be changed in interplanetary space, a jet of gas in the necessary direction will be ejected from the rocket. After refueling at the interplanetary station, the rocket will proceed further on its trip.

Satellites overflying the poles and convenient for purposes of observation are as a rule unsuitable for interplanetary stations. The reason for this is as follows: an interplanetary station must move, together with the earth, in the plane in which our planet is moving around the sun (what is known as the plane of the ecliptic; all the other planets of our solar system also move approximately in this plane). It is only in this case that the direction of motion of a space ship leaving the interplanetary station can be more or less parallel to the direction of motion of the earth in its orbit. This is a highly important point during departure from the station into cosmic space, since the orbital velocity of the earth will then be compounded with the take-off velocity of the ship, helping it to overcome the attraction of the earth and the sun. However, the earth's axis is inclined at an angle of about 67° to the plane of the ecliptic, so that the planes of the orbits of these two types (polar satellites and satellites with an orbit lying roughly in the plane of the ecliptic) will make a very large angle with each other.

It is clear that the take-off of a space ship from an artificial satellite at an angle to the direction of its orbital velocity would be quite inadvisable, since the velocity of motion of the satellite would be insufficiently utilized (Tsiang, China). Assume, for example, that the take-off takes places at an angle of 45° to the direction of motion of a circular interplanetary station at the given moment (to the direction of the tangent to that trajectory). In this case, a velocity of 7722 meters per second would have to be developed for a flight to the moon on a so-called semielliptic trajectory, whereas on departure in the direction of the tangent to the circular orbit of the satellite (i.e., in the direction of motion at the given moment) a velocity of 3129 meters per second is sufficient. We note, incidentally, that a velocity of 7722 meters per second in the case of departure in a tangential direction would be sufficient to reach Saturn.

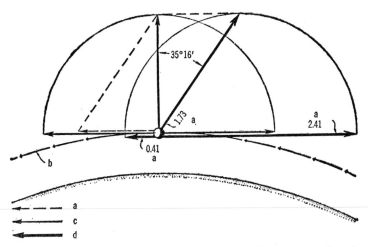

■ FIG. 58.—The Velocities that Must Be Developed by a Rocket Leaving an Interplanetary Station, in Order To Escape from the Attraction of the Earth, Will Vary According to the Direction in which Take-off from the Earth Is Intended. The sketch shows three cases, and the general principle of construction of the parallelogram of forces. (a)—Velocity of satellite; (b)—orbit of satellite; (c)—escape velocity relative to the earth; (d)—velocity imparted by jet engines.

Let us assume, in general, that a rocket is moving, like a satellite, in a circular orbit around some heavenly body (the earth, the sun, the moon, a planet) which is assumed to be isolated in interplanetary space, i.e., is at a distance so great from all other heavenly bodies that their gravitation is entirely insensible. It is clear that the velocity that this rocket must develop to escape completely from the sphere of attraction of that heavenly body will vary according to the direction from which take-off from the earth is planned. In fact, the rocket must develop an additional velocity, which will be compounded with the circular velocity of the rocket according to the parallelogram rule. Thus, in order for a rocket to escape to infinity on a straight line passing through the center of the heavenly body, it would have to be given an additional velocity, as will be easy to calculate, at an angle of 35°16′ to the vertical in a direction opposite to the orbital motion and 1.73 times as great as the circular velocity (Fig. 58). If, however, the rocket is to be given a parabolic velocity in the direction of the orbital motion, then it would be sufficient to give it an additional velocity amounting to 0.41 of the circular velocity. If, however, it is necessary to obtain the parabolic velocity in a direction opposite to the orbital motion, then the rocket would have to develop a velocity 2.41 times as great as the circular velocity, in this direction. The latter two velocities will correspond to the minimum and maximum velocity components of the speed which must be developed to escape the earth's gravitational field in different directions, starting from a circular interplanetary station. In this case the maximum velocity is almost 6 times as great as the minimum velocity.

A rocket capable of developing a velocity of slightly more than 9 kilometers per second in free space will easily be able to fly from the earth to the artificial satellite. The same rocket, on dispatch from the artificial satellite, not only could reach any planet but could also be able to leave our solar system entirely.

The more fuel a rocket departing from the interplanetary station carries with it, the higher will be the final velocity developed by it.[6] In this case, for a take-off from an artificial satellite, rockets of considerably lower power than on take-off from the surface of the earth will be required. Indeed, on starting from the surface of the earth, the thrust must be more than the weight of the rocket, while on take-off from an artificial satellite this condition need not be satisfied. Even at a thrust somewhat smaller than the weight of the rocket on earth, the rocket could gradually gain the necessary velocity. On take-off from the earth, most of the energy of the engine is consumed not only in useful work for overcoming the earth's gravity but also

[6] On take-off from the earth's surface, this is not always so: Whereas, on take-off from an interplanetary station, additional fuel always yields a positive result, the result when starting from the earth itself may be negative because of the gravitational losses (lower velocity and altitude: see Chapter IV).

in compensating so-called gravitational losses. In particular, on stoppage of the engine, the rocket will fall back on the earth. A vehicle leaving an interplanetary station, however, is not menaced by such a danger: even if the rocket engine stops operating, the ship will not fall back on the extraterrestrial station from which it departed, or on the earth. Therefore, the ship is required to carry an incomparably smaller amount of fuel than if it had started from the earth. This is still another reason that makes the utilization of an artificial satellite as an interplanetary station advantageous.

As for the total amount of fuel necessary for flight to the planets, it will prove to be greater in the case of a stopover on an interplanetary station than in the case where the start is made directly from the earth's surface. This results not only from considerations of a practical nature (for example, the necessity of maneuvering during landing on the satellite, etc.) but also from theoretical considerations. Calculation shows that low-flying satellites with circular orbits are more advantageous for flights to the moon and planets than satellites moving at great altitudes, since in the former case a smaller total velocity is necessary for flight from the earth to the satellite and for proceeding, from the satellite, on the further space trip. For a zero artificial satellite, this velocity is equal to 11.19 kilometers per second (this is essentially the zero parabolic velocity, i.e., the parabolic velocity at the earth's surface). If, however, the space rocket must free itself from the earth's gravitational field by developing the local parabolic velocity after stopping at an interplanetary station revolving at an altitude of 637.8 kilometers (0.1 earth radius), then the minimum total velocity that must be imparted to the rocket, in the absence of all losses, will already amount to 11.39 kilometers per second, and for an interplanetary station located at an altitude of 6378 kilometers (the earth's radius), it will increase to 12.01 kilometers per second. The situation will be even worse if the interplanetary station is lifted to an altitude 2 or 3 times as high. But on further increase of the altitude of the space "platform," the total velocity here considered begins to decrease, although it will always remain greater than the zero parabolic velocity.

All above statements will become clearer on studying Table 50, which gives the minimum total velocities, of which we have spoken, for several orbits of gradually increasing dimensions. We note that the minimum total velocity theoretically necessary for a space ship to

escape from the earth's gravitational field (fourth column of the
Table) is equal to the sum of the minimum velocity theoretically
necessary for launching the interplanetary station (second column)
and the escape velocity from the interplanetary station (third column).

■ TABLE 50

**Minimum Total Velocity Theoretically Necessary for the Escape
of a Rocket from the Earth's Gravitational Field in the Case
of an Intermediate "Stopover" on an Interplanetary Station**

Radius of Orbit of Interplanetary Station, in Earth Radii	Minimum Velocity Theoretically Necessary To Launch the Interplanetary Station, in Kilometers Per Second	Escape Velocity from Interplanetary Station, in Kilometers Per Second	Minimum Total Velocity Theoretically Necessary To Liberate a Rocket from the Earth's Gravitational Field, in Kilometers Per Second	Ratio of the Latter Velocity to the Zero Parabolic Velocity, in Per Cent
1	7.912	3.277	11.189	100.0
1.1	8.264	3.125	11.389	101.8
1.3	8.778	2.885	11.663	104.2
1.5	9.136	2.676	11.812	105.6
1.7	9.403	2.514	11.917	106.5
2	9.690	2.317	12.007	107.3
2.5	10.008	2.073	12.081	108.0
4	10.467	1.892	12.106	108.2
7	10.782	1.239	12.021	107.4
10	10.906	1.036	11.942	106.7
30	11.096	0.598	11.694	104.5
50	11.133	0.463	11.596	103.6

We get a different picture if we require the rocket, after taking
off from the interplanetary station, not only to escape from the
earth's gravitational field but also to reach another planet. Now the
rocket will have to develop higher velocities than in the preceding
case. Let us take as an example a flight on a semielliptic trajectory to
Mercury, with a landing on Mercury at the moment when it is at a
distance of 0.37 astronomical unit from the sun. For this, as shown
by calculation, a velocity of 13.70 kilometers per second would have
to be developed at the earth's surface. This is 1.732 times as great as
the zero circular velocity, which is often used in astronautics as the
unit of velocity. (As an example, we intentionally selected an orbit
demanding a higher initial velocity than flights to Venus and Mars,

■ FIG. XXXV.—Assembly of Interplanetary Station (According to A. Shternfeld, Drawing by Artist N. Kolchitskiy).

■ FIG. XXXVI.—An Interplanetary Station (*According to A. Shternfeld, Drawing by Artist N. Kolchitskiy*).

by means of a special installation, it will be used for external purposes (washing, laundry, etc.). The total number of ships participating in the expedition after the start from the interplanetary station is cut to two, one of them being an automatically guided cargo rocket which will not return to earth. Each ship has an initial weight of 1700 tons, of which 1246 tons will be fuel, and is equipped with 12 rocket engines, each with a thrust of 30 tons. Thus the total thrust of the engines (360 tons) is hardly more than a fifth the take-off weight of the rocket so that, at the time of take-off from the interplanetary station, a gravity only one fifth that on the earth's surface will be felt on board the ship. The velocity of the rocket, which at the moment of take-off was equal to the velocity of the interplanetary station itself, i.e., 7.07 kilometers per second, is gradually raised to 9.64 kilometers per second. During this time (the time of engine operation), the rocket's distance from the center of the earth will increase from 1730 to 3170 kilometers. As the fuel is consumed, the gravity felt on board the ship will continuously increase and, on combustion cutoff, will be almost 4/5 of the normal weight on the earth's surface. Subsequently, as far as Mars, the ship will move with engine off, and the astronauts will experience conditions of weightlessness.

On reaching Mars, the space ships will be converted (as in the preceding project) into artificial satellites of that planet. In this case, in view of the fact that on take-off from the earth satellite, the mass of each ship was already substantially smaller because of the high fuel consumption, there will be no need for all 12 engines to operate during the approach to Mars, and it will be sufficient to cut in only 6 engines. After going into circular orbit, the weight of each rocket will be 198 tons. From one of the ships converted into artificial Mars satellites, nine astronauts will land on the surface of the planet by means of a glider, while three will remain on the satellite base. The weight of the glider at the moment of departure from the base is estimated at 161 tons, of which 11 tons will be fuel expended in ejecting the glider from the satellite. This glider, at an altitude of 155 kilometers from the surface of Mars, will dip into its atmosphere. On the surface of Mars and on the above-mentioned circular orbit, the astronauts will leave all housekeeping equipment, research apparatus, and the cargo rocket, and will only take back the scientific materials collected on Mars, of an estimated weight of 5 tons. At the instant of starting on the return trip in a circular orbit around Mars, the ship with the 12 astronauts will weigh 215.4 tons. Of the remaining fuel, 117.3 tons will be utilized for the transition into a semielliptic trajectory, linking Mars with the Earth, while 46.6 tons will be used for transition to a circular orbit around the earth, with the radius of 90,000 kilometers. After final combustion cut off, when all fuel has been consumed, the dry weight[7] of the rocket, including the payload, will amount to about 35 tons. Thus the weight of a rocket passing into circular orbit around the earth will amount to about 2 per cent of the take-off weight of the rocket from the interplanetary station.

■ The Problem of Natural Interplanetary Stations

In the literature on astronautics, assertions will be found to the effect that the moon can be utilized as an interplanetary station. The moon, however, is unsuitable for this purpose: it is too far from the earth's surface. Moreover, since its mass and, consequently, also its attraction are relatively high, a rather large amount of fuel would have to be expended, first for the retardation of the interplanetary ship during descent to its surface and then for the take-off. For instance, let an expedition be dispatched to Mars. Calculations show that, if the artificial satellite used as a transfer station is located at a short distance from the earth, then, during the flight from the earth to the station and from the station to Mars, taken as a whole, the space ship would have to develop a lower total velocity (and, consequently, expend less fuel) than would be required for only a single flight around the moon. The utilization of the moon as an interplanetary station would have a certain significance only if particularly high-grade fuel and building materials were found on the moon.

Thus, as an intermediate planetary station, an artificial satellite has a number of advantages over the moon. In the first place, the satellite could be placed rather close to the earth, which would make the trip far shorter and the fuel consumption smaller. In the second place, the absence of an intrinsic gravitational field for the artificial satellite will save the fuel that would be consumed in landing on the moon followed by subsequent take-off from its surface.

The question might be raised whether there is a second moon or

---

[7] The dry weight of a rocket is the weight of a liquid-fuel rocket without fuel.

even several natural satellites of the earth revolving closer to the earth than its only known satellite, the Moon, which have remained undetected up to now? Some planets actually have several satellites. For example, Jupiter has 12, and Saturn has 9 satellites. Many of the satellites of other planets are very small: the satellites of Mars (Phobos and Deimos) have a diameter of 14 and 8 kilometers, respectively, while the diameters of certain other satellites are so small that they cannot be determined. A second natural satellite of the earth, even if it were exceedingly small, would still be an important step on the path of penetration of man into cosmic space. The discovery of such a satellite (or several such satellites) would considerably facilitate the solution of the problem of flight to the moon and to the planets, and would make the construction of an artificial satellite unnecessary. On a natural satellite it would be relatively easy to set up both a flying observatory and an interplanetary station.

Of course, if such satellites do exist, they would have to be extremely small, and their detection would be exceedingly complicated. Because of the high velocity of such a small satellite, it could not be detected in the ordinary telescope, the more so since it would be located close to the earth. Further than that, if it were near enough to the earth, it might fail to leave any trace on a photographic plate because of the excessively short exposure. In addition, such a satellite, on entering the earth's shadow, would not emit light, and therefore it could be observed only during a short time interval. Astronomers admit the possibility that such a satellite has already been observed at some time or location but might have been taken for a meteor. The methods of radio astronomy, developed in recent years and used for the study of meteors, could be useful for the solution of this problem. Observations along this line are being conducted, for example, by the Meteorite Institute in New Mexico (United States) under the direction of Tombough, who discovered the planet Pluto in 1930.

With this same object of discovering natural satellites of the earth, the sky was "combed" by a special high-sensitivity camera for three years at the Lowell Observatory in the United States. Later, in 1955, this same camera was installed at the city of Quito (Ecuador), which is located almost on the equator, where careful searches are still going on.

The methods and instrumentation recently developed for observation of artificial satellites permit a definitive solution of the problem of the existence of other artificial satellites of the earth.

Obviously, if new moons are in fact discovered, they will be outside the boundaries of the atmosphere. Otherwise, they would long since have fallen on the earth's surface or burned up as a result of the air resistance.

At the conference on questions of rocket engineering and astronautics held at Warsaw in 1957, Gaisler and Pankow (Poland) proposed the transformation of the asteroid Hermes into an earth satellite. Hermes is a small planet moving in an orbit only 29 per cent further away from the sun than the earth and sometimes comes as close as 600,000 kilometers to the earth, which is only 1.5 times the distance to the moon. The authors of this proposal consider that by using thermonuclear energy, a number of asteroids could be made to revolve around the earth, primarily for use as interplanetary stations.

Natural interplanetary stations of other bodies of the solar system are also of great interest for astronautics. For example, a trip to Mars with a descent to its surface would obviously precede exploratory flights around Mars (the situation in a flight to the moon will evidently be analogous). For this purpose, rocket ships will be temporarily converted into artificial satellites of Mars. Indeed, a landing on a planet, followed by take-off, will involve immense difficulties during the initial period, the more so since all the fuel necessary for return will have to be taken along from the earth.

Interplanetary rockets will also be able to descend to the Martian satellites we have already mentioned, Phobos and Deimos, whence it will be possible to conduct prolonged investigations of the surface of Mars. Deimos is 23,000 kilometers from Mars, which is only 1/17 of the distance between the earth and the moon, while Phobos revolves at an altitude of 9000 kilometers above the surface of Mars. Both these satellites move at high speed around the planet: Phobos makes one revolution in about 8 hours and Deimos, one in 30 hours. The dimensions and masses of these heavenly bodies are small, and their gravity is negligible; for this reason, a landing on these satellites followed by a take-off from them will be an easier task than a visit to Mars itself.

The utilization of Phobos and Deimos as natural interplanetary stations, however, carries considerable danger, since their surface is apparently dissected and uneven, and the surface rocks may prove to be very friable (Kenny, Ordway).

■ At the Dawn of the Era of Interplanetary Flight

The dream of the creation of an artificial heavenly body has now been realized.

Relying on the laws of the motion of heavenly bodies and on other laws of nature, utilizing all possibilities of modern science and engineering, Soviet men and women have built and launched the first artificial satellites of the earth. Mankind has now entered the era of interplanetary flight.

The laws of nature favor the development of astronautics. In contrast to aviation, where new altitude records demand increasingly greater efforts and are confined to the boundaries of the atmosphere, in astronautics the ceiling of the rockets is limited by nothing, and equal successive increments of velocity will lift such rockets to ever increasing heights. Thanks to this fact, even from an interplanetary station revolving, for example, at an altitude of only several hundred kilometers, it is sufficient to give a rocket a velocity of 3 to 4 kilometers per second (i.e., less than half the total velocity developed by an orbital rocket) for it to reach the moon and the nearest planets.

For this reason, the dispatch of automatic rockets to the nearest heavenly bodies may be possible even in our own days.

The first artificial satellite has already shown that the meteor danger is not an insuperable obstacle for astronauts. The second one, in all probability, will also demonstrate that the harmful ultraviolet radiation of the sun may be completely absorbed by the skin of the satellite, so that it will not affect the living organism (as for the hazards of cosmic rays for astronauts, this question still remains open).

The experience obtained since the launching of the second satellite also permits the hope that man will be able to travel to an artificial satellite. There is still another matter which will, apparently, prevent us from taking this step for some time to come. Before this step is taken, it would be necessary to be completely sure of the possibility of a safe return of man to earth. But the problem of retarding velocities as high as that which a rocket would have on its return still demand additional research. Specialists of the widely varying branches of science and engineering are today working on the solution of these problems.

The future development of astronautics will constantly unveil new secrets of the universe to mankind.

The construction of artificial satellites also touches a number of international legal and political questions. But there is no doubt that when it finally becomes possible to end the armaments race, when all the energy of mankind, all material and intellectual resources of society are no longer devoted to the creation of weapons of destruction and of war but to the good of mankind, when peaceful collaboration between the nations has become a fact, all the controversial questions in this field will also be amenable to solution. Then magnificent prospects will open for astronautics.

Astronautics can and should become a link in the strengthening of international collaboration.

APPENDIX

■ A. The Dissemination of the Ideas of Astronautics

Astronautical Societies and Their Activity

The ideas of space flight are very popular in all countries of the world. In the U.S.S.R., since 1924, circles and societies have been created with the object of studying the problems of reactive motion and combining the efforts of all those concerned with this field of knowledge. In 1931, at Moscow and Leningrad, groups for the study of jet engines were organized. The activity of these groups was directed toward the solution of questions of the design of rockets and the theoretical development of questions of reactive motion. In the symposia *Reactive Motion* and *Rocket Engineering*, which were published at Moscow from 1935 to 1938, questions of astronautics were also discussed.

In 1954 an astronautic section was formed at the Central Aero Club U.S.S.R. imeni V. P. Chkalov, at Moscow, with the object of encouraging the realization of interplanetary travel for peaceful purposes. In the same year, an interdepartmental commission on interplanetary communications was organized at the Astronomical Council Academy of Sciences U.S.S.R. Many questions, on whose solution the further development of astronautics depends, are also being studied in astronautical circles organized at the higher educational institutions of Moscow, Leningrad, Kiev, Kharkov, and other cities.

The German Society for Space Travel was founded in 1927. For three years, to the end of 1929, the society periodically issued a journal on subjects of interplanetary travel *Die Rakete* (The Rocket). On the Hitlerites advent to power, the society ended its existence. The experimental work of the society ended with the creation of the V-2 military rocket, which afterward also served for scientific research.

A new society under the old name was formed in 1948 in West Germany. In 1956 it already numbered 1000 members. Since 1950 the society has been publishing a quarterly journal *Weltraumfahrt* (*Flight in Cosmic Space*) and symposia on questions of astronautics.

In France an astronautics committee which existed until World War II was organized in 1928, attached to the Astronautical Society. The French Astronautical Society founded after the war has published several numbers of the Journal *L'Astronef* (*The Space Ship*), and has organized astronautical exhibitions, lectures, etc.

The American Interplanetary Society was founded at New York in 1930. In 1934 its name was changed to American Rocket Society. The first flight tests of liquid-fuel rockets built by this society were run in 1933. According to the 1956 data, the society had about 4000 members and is thus the largest in the world. Since 1936 it has been publishing (with interruptions) a journal on rocket engineering and astronautics. The American Rocket Society has a committee on questions of space flight which, incidentally, has played a relatively important part in the organization of the first American work on the project of an artificial earth satellite.

Besides this central society, the United States also has several rocket and astronautical societies which, according to the 1956 data, have several hundred members in all. Some of these societies as for example, the Pennsylvania Society, have available test stands for testing liquid-fuel rockets. Others (for example, the Philadelphia Rocket Society) have rocket fields where experiments with powder rockets are staged.

The Austrian Rocket Society, founded in 1931 at Innsbruck, resumed its activity in 1950 (it had about 150 members in 1956). Earlier, from 1926 to 1930, the Society for Altitude Research existed at Vienna.

The British Interplanetary Society, founded in 1933 at Liverpool, was moved in 1937 to London. During the war, the activity of small British astronautical groups was dispersed and to some extent interrupted. The *Journal of the British Interplanetary Society*, published by the society, became widely known. By 1957, over 70 issues of this journal had been published. In 1956, the society had over 2800 members.

The Polish Astronautical Society, founded at the beginning of 1956, is a scientific society with a membership of 400, which also has a popularization section and four provincial sections. Since 1956, a group of specialists in the system of the Polish Academy of Sciences (*Praczownja Astronautyczna*, Warsaw) has been working on questions of astronautics. Courses on individual fields of astronautics are being given at some higher educational institutions.

Astronautical or rocket societies exist in Japan (768 members), Argentina (600 members), Italy (270 members), Brazil (213 members), The Netherlands (180 members), Yugoslavia (120 members), Spain (120 members), Sweden (108 members), Union of South Africa (99 members), France (72 members), Norway (70 members), Egypt (63 members), Switzerland (63 members), Chile (50 members), and Denmark (45 members),[1] as well as in Australia, Israel, Canada, and Czechoslovakia. In 1956, astronautical societies were just being organized in Greece, Mexico, and Turkey.

International Astronautical Congresses, and the International Astronautical Federation

The first International Astronautical Congress was held at Paris in 1950. The astronautical societies of eight countries (Austria, Great Britain, Argentina, West Germany, Denmark, Spain, France, and Switzerland) participated. A series of lectures was given at the Congress, and the preparatory work for the organization of the International Astronautical Federation was done.

At the Second International Astronautical Congress, held the following year at London, the delegates represented fifteen societies from ten countries, including Italy, the United States, and Sweden, that had not attended the First Congress. The work of the Congress was devoted to scientific problems and to questions of propaganda. The

---

[1] The membership data refer to 1956.

International Astronautical Federation was organized, with its seat at Baden, Switzerland, with an original roster of about 4400 members. E. Sänger was elected the first president of the International Astronautical Federation, and I. Stemmer, its first secretary.

The object of the International Astronautical Federation is to encourage technical and scientific research in the field of astronautics for peaceful purposes; to conduct the exchange of opinions between members of the Federation; to inform the public by means of the press, radio, and moving pictures of the possibilities and prospects of astronautics, and to try to prevent utopian and sensational publications on interplanetary flight.

At the Third International Astronautical Congress held at Stuttgart (West Germany) in 1952, a report of experiments on vertical take-off of a crew on the rocket fighter aircraft *Natter*, reports on sensations under conditions of weightlessness, on radiations in cosmic space, on the chemical, economic, and legal problems of space flight, etc., were read. In all, delegates from fourteen countries read 26 papers.

The Fourth International Astronautical Congress, held in 1953 at Zurich, was marked by the work of committees on the theory of orbits of space ships and methods of control and guidance, on questions of rockets and fuels, on questions of space navigation, and also of a committee on problems of atomic energy. Over 200 scientists from nineteen countries participated in the Congress, and 33 papers were read, devoted to questions of the construction of artificial satellites, questions of the selection of fuels and building materials for space ships, refueling in flight, utilization of solar energy in interplanetary space, interplanetary radar, and instrument building. The members also discussed methods of calculating trajectories, orientation under conditions of weightlessness, methods of recording the track traveled by a ship, questions of the design of computers for astronautical purposes, results of experiments on the effects of the G-force and weightlessness on animals and human subjects, etc. The question of the necessity of coordinating theoretical and practical work in the field of astronautics and rocket engineering was raised at the Congress, with particular reference to questions of collaboration between astronautical and rocket societies.

The Fifth International Astronautical Congress, held at Innsbruck (Austria), in 1954, was attended by representatives of 18 societies with about 8000 members. Brazil, Egypt, and Japan were admitted as members of the International Astronautical Federation.

About 30 papers were read before the Congress: on rocket engines and space ships, on the design of space rockets (especially multistage), on the guidance of rockets in the air and in airless space, on the biology of space flight, on interplanetary law, etc.

It was decided to issue an official organ of the International Astronautical Federation, *Astronautica Acta* (which began publication in 1955), and to publish a series of papers.

The Sixth International Astronautical Congress was held at Copenhagen, Denmark, in 1955. The Congress was devoted primarily to the discussion of questions connected with the creation of an artificial earth satellite. L. I. Sedov and K. F. Ogorodnikov attended the Congress as observers from the U.S.S.R.

The Seventh Congress, held at Rome in 1956, was organized under the auspices of the International Astronautical Federation, by the Italian rocket society. The Congress was attended by 400 delegates, members of astronautical societies, research institutes, as well as representatives of large industrial interests, mainly American.

The sessions were held at the Palazzo dei Congressi, 15 kilometers from Rome, where an Aerobee rocket was shown, among other exhibits. All the papers were simultaneously translated into four languages. Color films on the work of rocket institutes, the behavior of experimental animals in flight, etc., were shown daily. The cockpit of an aircraft with a pilot, during free fall, was also shown on the screen.

The first day of the Congress was devoted to the launching of artificial earth satellites (papers by Robotti and Romani (Italy), and others). Klemperer and Baylor (United States) in their reports, discussed questions of the libration of artificial satellites. De Nike (United States) presented a report on the influence of the oblateness of the earth on the orbit of an artificial satellite. Singer (United States) proposed a method of calculating the equilibrium temperature of an artificial satellite. Several papers were devoted to questions of combustion and of rocket fuels. Simons (New Mexico, United States) reported on the results of many years of research on the action of cosmic rays and weightlessness on small animals taken up on altitude rockets and balloons. Lo Monaco (Italy) also spoke on the physiopathology of rocket flights. Romick (United States) presented a project for a large manned artificial earth satellite. Buchheim (United States) discussed the theory of the artificial satellite of the Moon. Whipple (United States) devoted his speech to the organization of international groups for observation of artificial satellites (this question was subsequently settled by arrangements at New Delhi between the International Astronautical Federation and representatives of the organizers of the International Geophysical Year). Crocco (Italy) presented a paper on the possibility of an annual flight, made without landing, along an elliptical trajectory crossing the orbits of Mars and Venus. Zarankewicz, representing the Polish Astronautical Society, read a paper of mathematical character. Hadomsky, one of the oldest Polish astronomers, presented calendars computed by him for space ships, Moon, Mars, and Venus. Cocca (Argentina) and Haley (United States) reported on legal aspects of astronautics. They emphasized that the law of the air could not be extended to apply to the space above the atmosphere. Forty-five papers in all were read before the Congress. A quarter of them directly related to artificial earth satellites.

The Soviet Union and Poland were admitted to the International Astronautical Association, together with the newly organized (reorganized) French Astronautical Society. Thus the members of the Federation, in 1956, were 24 astronautical societies of 21 countries, with a total of 12,000 members. The president of the British Interplanetary Society, Shepherd, was elected president of the International Astronautical Federation to replace Durant (United States) who had already served two terms as president. The president of the Swiss Astronautical Society, Stemmer, was re-elected general secretary.

The Eighth International Astronautical Congress was held in October 1957 at Barcelona, Spain. It has been decided to hold the Ninth Congress at Amsterdam, Holland, in 1958.

Conventions and Conferences

A substantial role in the development of astronautics is played by the frequent conventions and conferences held in various countries on rocketry, the study of the upper layers of the atmosphere, and on various astronomical and astrophysical problems, with the participation of specialists from many countries. For instance, an international conference on the physics of reactive motion was held at the beginning of 1956 at Freudenstadt, West Germany. In the summer of the same year, an international conference of rocket engineering specialists was held at Rome. A little before that, about 40 papers on the fields of application of artificial satellites were read before the tenth annual conference of the Committee on Rocket Atmospheric Research at Ann Arbor, Michigan (United States). At Oxford, England, under the patronage of the Royal Society of London, a conference on questions of research on the upper layers of the atmosphere, with special reference to the use of artificial satellites, was held. In 1956, at New York, symposia devoted to artificial satellites were organized by the Institute of Radio Engineers and other institutions. In the same year, a symposium on the use of artificial earth satellites for research was held at the Franklin Institute of Philadelphia (United States).

At the end of 1956, an International Congress on Rockets and Guided Missiles was held at Paris. In May 1957 a Conference on Rocket Engineering and Astronautics was held at Warsaw.

In September 1957, the Academy of Sciences U.S.S.R. held a scientific and technical conference at Moscow devoted to the development of the ideas of K. E. Tsiolkovskiy in the field of the theory and practice of reactive motion and the conquest of cosmic space. Ten papers were read before the Conference. They were devoted, among other things, to the flight of animals in rockets into the upper layers of the atmosphere, in the determination of the life of artificial earth satellites, and in the study of the conditions of descent to the earth from an artificial satellite.

■ B. Question of Territorial Rights to the Space Above the Atmosphere

One of the signs of the arriving era of space flights is the appearance of the first "side shoots" of the newest branch of law, that of space law. Numerous papers, books, and dissertations have been devoted to it, and in some foreign countries courses are given on this subject.

A special course, which is a part of the syllabus, is given on this item at the Institute of International Air Law at Montreal University, in Canada. There are jurists who attempt in advance to defend the "rights" of certain circles to interplanetary space, to the moon, or to a neighboring planet. Others, on the contrary, are guided by considerations of the love of peace and humanity. Over a quarter of a century ago, the German author Mandl wrote a book entitled *Space Law*. Legal questions of space flights have been discussed at International Astronautical Congresses by the President of the American Rocket Society, Haley, by the Assistant Secretary General of the United Nations, Schachter, and others. In April 1956, the American International Law Society devoted a special session to questions of the space beyond the atmosphere.

Even tests of superlong-range and altitude rockets already encounter questions of the sovereign rights of various States, under the modern definition of these rights.

The developments of astronautics will naturally again raise the question of the sovereignty of States over the space above their territories.

International air law is based on the fundamental proposition of recognition of the full sovereignty of a State with respect to the air space above the territory subject to its jurisdiction. Many jurists consider that, although this right cannot serve as the fundamental basis for interplanetary space law, it may still be of help in working out the principles of that law.

Certain juridical and political complications, that may arise on the launching of artificial satellites, will become clearer from the following examples:

Let us assume, for instance, that Canada has decided to launch an artificial satellite from Grant Land. Has she the right to do this? If we start out from the air law, she absolutely has that right. But Grant Land is located above the 80th parallel of latitude, and no matter how an artificial satellite is launched from this territory, it must eventually cross the equator and encircle the southern hemisphere, down to Antarctica itself. In this case, any of the countries over which the artificial satellite will fly could consider this fact a "violation of sovereignty." But could that country forbid Canada to launch an artificial satellite from its own territory?

Countries crossed by the equator, such as Indonesia, Brazil, Colombia, and others, could build satellites hovering "motionless" above their territory (stationary artificial satellite).

According to the existing standards of international law no one could prevent, let us say, Ecuador, from launching such a satellite from a point slightly north of Quito, the capital of Ecuador, on the equator. But according to the same international law, such countries as Mexico, Bolivia, Brazil, and certain others, could protest: All of the territory of their countries would be in the field of view of an observer on board such a satellite since it would fly at an altitude of tens of thousands of kilometers!

In this way, the jurist will still encounter insoluble questions. It is therefore not surprising that at the present time the opinions of jurists on the standards of law that should govern questions of the use of cosmic space are in sharp disagreement. Certain foreign experts advance the thesis of "freedom of space" (Meyer, West Germany). Horsford (Great Britain) holds the opinion that, from the legal point of view, the superatmospheric space should be treated like the high seas, on which ships under various flags are allowed to sail. Others urge limitation of the freedom of movement of space vehicles (Cuper, Argentina). Crocco adheres to the view that the sovereignty of a State with respect to air space should be limited to a definite altitude, above which space would be free for cosmic navigation, as the oceans are free for intercontinental travel (the artificial satellites, themselves, will belong to a State, to a group of States or, finally, to the private international enterprise that has created them).

The fundamental difficulty encountered by jurists is the question: To what height above the surface of its territories has a State the right to assert its sovereignty? Although there can be no visible frontiers of demarcation in space, legislative acts governing the upper frontiers of a State may be based on the properties of the earth's gravitational field or of the upper layers of the atmosphere, which are amenable to precise determination.

Criteria being advanced include such points as the blue color of the sky still observable from the orbital altitude of an artificial satellite (Crelle, France), or the "Maximum distance from which a body will still fall on the territory of a given State" (Cooper), which is not defined with adequate clarity by the author himself.

Astronautics, of course, will develop in spite of all these legal difficulties. However, unless suitable measures are taken, its development, together with numberless blessings, may also lead to immense devastation.

The testing of orbital rockets and also of other measures in the field of astronautics, in the opinion of certain jurists, should be subject to international control. The status of the movement of artificial satellites must also be established.

The development of international standards in the field of astronautics and of the testing of superlong-range rockets, in the opinion of Hester, a member of the British Astronomical Society, should be the concern of the United Nations, since discussions through ordinary diplomatic channels could scarcely lead to positive results. Hester brings up the following questions:

(a) Establishment of a United Nations commission to coordinate scientific research in the field of astronautics; (b) exchange of information by scientists and engineers; (c) freedom of international measures and limitation of private initiative in the field of astronautics; (d) control and coordination of tests, including the program of selected routes, velocities, times, take-off, and descent coordinates, etc.; (e) methods of reducing the number of accidents connected with the take-off, flight, and descent of objects (for example, it would be possible to restrict the route of a test flight, from one pole to another, to water space and to definite territories, to employ protective devices against radioactive contamination, to establish launching pads in localities with ice cover, etc.); (f) prohibition of supplying of flight vehicles of any kind with explosive loads; prohibition or at least limitation of the use of astronautical objects for military purposes; (g) adoption of sanctions against States violating an agreement on the peaceful use of astronautics.

It is obvious that all these questions, despite their complexity, can be solved if the contracting parties approach the subject with good will, and under the condition that artificial satellites shall be utilized only for peaceful scientific purposes.

Epilogue, by Willy Ley

■

■

■

At the time of writing of this postscript, the U.S.S.R. had launched two more space rockets—one into an orbit around the earth, the other a man-made "planet" around the sun. I shall comment on these only briefly, because they represent no really new conception or structural scheme beyond what has been discussed in this book.

Perhaps I should say something first about speculations concerning the Soviet launching site. The Russians did not announce where they launched their satellites. It was known that they had a rocket proving ground at Kapustin Yar, north of the Caspian Sea and 50 miles due east of Stalingrad. The orbits of the satellites seemed to be generally consistent with firing from this area, but a Japanese scientist who plotted the orbits carefully decided that the rockets must have been launched at some point considerably east of Kapustin Yar, though at the same latitude. The best Western guess was that the site was in the Kyzyl Kum desert.

The Russians' first two sputniks were shot in quick succession— on October 4 and November 3, 1957. Sputnik I fell back into the atmosphere and burned up in the first week of January, 1958; Sputnik II expired three months later. In the meantime the United States launched its first successful satellites: Explorer I (or 1958 alpha in the terminology of astronomers), Vanguard I (1958 beta) and Explorer III (1958 gamma).

In December of 1957 the Russians announced their intention to fire a third satellite, but Sputnik III did not actually climb into space until May 15, five months later. There was much speculation in the United States about the reasons for this delay, ranging from unsubstantiated stories about dozens of failures to sensible guesses—such as that the Soviet scientists had to wait until they could pry a large rocket loose from the military testing program. It is possible that the actual reason for the delay was that the Russian scientists decided to change the instrumentation of their "bird" in view of a discovery made by the United States satellites. Explorer I brought to light, and Explorer III confirmed, the existence of the shell of intense radiation around the earth which was later named the Van Allen layer. In any event, when Sputnik III (1958 delta) was launched into orbit, it carried instruments designed to detect such radiation.

Sputnik III was a "separated" satellite, meaning that the instrument-bearing cone was separated from the third stage of the rocket engine that propelled it into orbit—thus the third rocket stage also became a satellite. The weight of Sputnik III was given as 2965 pounds. The Russians did not announce the weight of the rocket third stage, but Western observers decided it must be somewhere between 7000 and 9000 pounds. On launching, Sputnik III had a period of 106 minutes around the earth; its apogee was 1160 miles from the earth's surface and its perigee was 123 miles. The big cone, 11 feet 8 inches tall and 5 feet 8 inches in diameter at its base, was destroyed by air resistance within a year; its still larger third-stage rocket had burned up before that.

On January 2, 1959, the Russians launched a new series with a shot toward the moon. This rocket was first called "Lunik" (from *rakyeta na luna*—"rocket to the moon"), but the Russians soon changed its name to *metchtá*, a word which is best translated as "daydream." The rocket actually missed the moon by 4660 miles and went into orbit around the sun. The total weight of this object now orbiting the sun was given as about 4030 pounds, of which 797 pounds are instruments, batteries, etc.

When Metchta was fired, the earth was near its closest to the sun—91.5 million miles. The perihelion of Metchta's orbit around the sun must be at about the same distance; in other words, it will never approach the sun appreciably closer than the earth does. Metchta's aphelion, expected to be reached in September, 1959, is about 122 million miles from the sun—between the orbits of the earth and Mars.

The orbital period of the rocket in its first trip around the sun was thought to be 447 days. Naturally none of these figures is definite, but they ought to be about the right order of magnitude. After five years, when the earth has completed five full revolutions around the sun, Metchta will have completed four full revolutions. Therefore, early in January, 1964, the rocket and the planet earth should come close to each other. That the rocket will run into the earth and suffer burn-up is possible, but not very likely. It is more likely that it will come close enough to the earth to be thrown into a new orbit by the earth's gravitational field.

CONVERSION TABLES

MEASURES OF LENGTH

1 millimeter (mm.)	0.03937 inch
1 centimeter (cm.)	0.3937 inch
1 meter (m.)	39.37 inch
1 kilometer (km.)	0.62137 mile

MEASURES OF SURFACE

1 square millimeter (mm^2)	1.55	square inches
1 square centimeter	15.5	square inches
1 square meter	1,550	square inches
1 square kilometer	.3861	square mile

MEASURES OF CAPACITY

1 centiliter	0.338	fluid ounces
1 deciliter	6.1025	cubic inches
1 liter	1.0567	liquid quarts
1 kiloliter	264.18	gallons

MEASURES OF WEIGHT

1 centogram	0.1543	grain
1 decigram	1.5432	grains
1 gram (gm.)	15.432	grains
1 kilogram (kg.)	2.2046	pounds

MEASURES OF VOLUME

1 cubic centimeter (cm^3)	.0061	cubic inch
1 cubic decimeter	61.025	cubic inches
1 cubic meter	1,308	cubic yards

0°C. (Centigrade) is equivalent to 32°F. (Fahrenheit)

one micron unit is equivalent to 0.000039 inch

Index

astronauts, 285, 320, 322, 330; descent of to atmosphere, 261; expedition to Mars by, 330–332; food and respiration requirements of, 184–185; training of for orbital flight, 186–189 (*see also* man in space; space medicine; space stations)
astronomical observations, from artificial satellite, 304–309
Astrophysical Institute, Kazakh S.S.R., 239
Atlantic Ocean, measurement of, 294
atmosphere, characteristics of, xvii; crossing of, in launching, 117–119, 136; crosswind velocity of, 30; danger of pure or almost pure oxygen microatmospheres, 206; effect of on artificial satellite, 25, 30, 258; effect of on carrier rocket, 33–35; heating effects of, xv, 118, 210, 259; influence of on motion of satellites, xv; investigation of by satellites and rockets, 295–300; ionization of, 300; principal layers of, xv; re-entry of space glider into, 268–269; retardation of satellite in, 30, 258; solar radiation and, 212; temperature fluctuation in, xvi; territorial rights to space above, 343–346; U.S. research in, 80; upper layers of, xiv, 296–297
atmospheric pressure, 205; measurement of, 296
atomic fuel, 87, 90–91
atomic rocket, 90–91
atomic weapons, testing of, 313
atoms, ionized, in upper atmosphere, xviii
attraction, spheres of, for planes, 278–279
aurora displays, 297, 300, 304, 318
Austrian Rocket Society, 338
automatic controls, 145–147
autopilot, 145–146

ballistic elliptical arc, launching on, 106–109
balloon, stratosphere, 123; weather, 295
barometer, aneroid, 223
batteries, various types for satellite power, 213–215
beryllium, 306
beta-disintegration, 214
biological research, by artificial satellite, 312–313
"biosatellite," 209 (*see also* manned artificial satellite)
black-body temperature, 210
bolides, 266
bolometers, on U.S. satellites, 219
bombing, from artificial satellites, 314
braking, by rocket engines, 151
British Astronomical Society, 346
British Interplanetary Society, 338, 342
British rocket engine, 86
Bumper rocket, U.S., 79–80, 143

camera, rotating-shutter type, 238 (*see also* photography)

cargo rockets, 161; orbital, 158; for space station, 158
carrier rocket, Sputnik I, 31–35, 255
cartography, precision, 292
catalpa, heliophilic, 159
ceiling, of artificial satellites, 10
celestial sphere, apparent motion of satellite in, 58–63, 199
Central Aero Club, U.S.S.R., 337
centrifugal force, compensation for by gravity, 6; G-force and, 165 (*see also* G-force)
charged-particle counter, 306
Cherenkov counters, 306
chlorella (microscopic alga), 159
chloric acid, 87
circular orbit, 26; angular velocity for artificial satellite in, 57; characteristics of, 68
circular velocity, 5, 7, 14, 16, 97, 124, 326; of planetary satellites, 276–277; zero (*see* zero circular velocity; *see also* velocity)
clocks, for satellite use, 224
clouds, aerial surveys and, 293; formation of, xv; motion of, 299; noctilucent, 301
color photography, 147–148
combustion, weightlessness and, 174
combustion chamber, materials used for, 82–83; optimum pressure in, 83
comets, artificial satellites of, 281–283; structure, life and death of, 281–282
Committee on Rocket Atmospheric Research, 343
computers, automatic, 149
Conference on Rocket Engineering and Astronautics, 343
Congress of American Military Specialists, Second, 314
constellations, as seen from artificial satellite, 198
continental shift, confirmation of, 294
control, accuracy of, in space rocket, 176
control equipment and instruments, 215–226
conventions and conferences, in development of astronautics, 342–343
conversion tables, c.g.s. to i.p.s., 347
corrosion inhibitors, 90
cosmic dust, study of, 301–304
cosmic radio relay communication, 244–246
cosmic rays, xiv, 335; danger of, to human organism, 177–179; earth's shielding effect against, 221–222; effect of, on photographic plates, 293; instrumentation for, in Sputnik II, 216; intensity studies of, 301, 306; variation in, 306
cosmic trips, on artificial satellites and planets, 289
"cosmic wind," 30
cosmology, 304
"cosmonauts," 185, 189, 261, 272, 320, 323